MECHANICS OF
ENGINEERING STRUCTURES

MECHANICS OF

ENGINEERING STRUCTURES

Grover L. Rogers, Sc.D.
Professor of Engineering Science
The Florida State University

M. Lander Causey, Sc.M.
Associate Professor of Civil Engineering
The Citadel

JOHN WILEY AND SONS, INC., NEW YORK · LONDON

PREFACE

This book has been written with the goal of presenting a work on the mechanics of engineering structures that is truly in tune with the times. It is directed toward those students who study problems of stresses and strains in bar-type structures whether they be enrolled in curricula of aeronautical engineering, civil engineering, or engineering mechanics.

When viewed in the light of our rapidly expanding engineering technology, the average undergraduate structures courses often appear to be completely insensitive to the changes being wrought in the engineering profession. It is not unusual to find textbooks being widely used that have not been appreciably revised since their first publication twenty, even forty, years ago. But modern engineering structures are not the same as structures of a quarter of a century, even a decade, ago. Structural forms are constantly changing. The ancient and honorable pin-jointed plane truss is becoming a true rarity, yet its analysis and design still monopolize many valuable hours of student time. The structure composed of curved as well as straight elements in an integrated spatial arrangement is more typically the structure of our time, and attention to some of its fundamental features should be a characteristic of the earliest undergraduate courses. The study of bar-type structures, especially, can be well handled at this level, thus leaving the more difficult problems of sheet and shell-type structures for the advanced student.

Our understanding of the capabilities of building materials is constantly improving. We no longer are forced to assume that all materials are subjected to stresses that vary linearly with strain in order to prepare an analysis. Design techniques based on inelastic behavior are now well advanced and are becoming stock-in-trade for handling simple and complex configurations. The philosophy of their use now becomes an important part of the education of the undergraduate.

The loads on structures can no longer be counted on to be strictly static in nature. We are required, sometimes by law, to design for earthquake effects and air pressure. The fundamental concepts of dynamic behavior thus become important parts of the early education of the engineer. Also, methods of analysis are being constantly improved as are the means of making engineering computations. A modern first course in structural mechanics should reflect these changes. Long forgotten methods may assume renewed importance as more recently developed methods may already be fading into disuse.

We have attempted in this work to present many fundamental problems in the mechanics of engineering structures in such a way as to serve as a minimum coverage for the general practitioner while at the same time serving as a firm building block for the embryo structures specialist. We have attempted to present an integrated approach to statically determinate and statically indeterminate structures; to elastic and elastoplastic structures; to straight and curved members; to planar and spatial con- figurations; and to static and dynamic loads. In short, we have not been content to treat only those problems (with their many special cases) that have to do with the single province of straight, elastic, plane structures under static load.

The first chapter deals with statically determinate stress resultants. In years gone by this material was considered to be of sufficient importance to require an entire semester for its coverage. Although we have curtailed it drastically, we have managed to cover the most important classical problems including the well-loved graphical method of Maxwell for finding bar stresses in trusses. This brevity is considered to be admissable in view of the continually improving courses in engineering statics given at most schools and the generally decreased interest in the methods of graphic statics.

In Chapter 2 we deal with the relations between stress resultants and stress intensities. To some extent this is a repetition of material given in courses on the mechanics of materials (although presented in a different fashion). The treatment of such subjects as elastoplastic behavior and the column analogy in later chapters are best handled, however, when this material is present in the same volume. It may be covered quickly or omitted completely depending on the background of the students.

Chapter 3 covers displacements in elastic members. The absence of any discussion of elastoplastic displacements is no serious omission since in an actual design situation we would use the elastoplastic analysis for com- puting collapse loads and then check displacements elastically using the design loading. The Williot-Mohr graphical method for trusses is pre- sented since it is still by far the best way of finding many joint deflections simultaneously. The conjugate beam is presented as a tool to be used over and over again throughout the book. It also enjoys the special distinction of being the first example of the use of a mathematical analogy in structural analysis.

Chapter 4 presents energy methods from a unified point of view. Students have too long failed to see the relationships between these methods and have thought of them as being so many different ways of solving the same basic problems. The sections on influence diagrams are special examples of the use of the energy principles. Thoughts on inelastic behavior add variety to the presentation.

The problems of indeterminate beams and the calculation of collapse loads are the subject matter for Chapter 5. The methods of analysis given in Chapters 3 and 4 are put to extensive use.

Curved structures are treated in Chapter 6. The equations of Bresse, so widely seen in European textbooks but so rarely displayed in American books, are given in all their generality. The column analogy, which can be deduced from the equations of Bresse, completes the chapter.

Chapter 7 treats the slope-deflection equations and their derivative form: moment distribution. These methods are useful in computer programming and in the design office alike.

Methods of matrix analysis so widely used in treating very complicated structures are introduced in Chapter 8. These are destined to enjoy wider and wider use in the future. The aeronautical structures engineer, especially, will find them to be an invaluable tool.

The terminal chapter deals with some problems in the dynamics of engineering structures. It is designed as a bridge between this book, which is essentially a work on structural statics, and more advanced books dealing exclusively with structural dynamics.

The material in this book may be covered in a single semester when topics are judiciously omitted and when working with advanced students. It is primarily designed, however, for a two-semester course given at the junior-senior level. A more leisurely course of three semesters is easily planned by treating three chapters each term.

It is now our pleasure to acknowledge some of the people who have contributed directly or indirectly to the preparation of this work. The students at the Virginia Polytechnic Institute where the first class notes were used over a period of five years as well as the students at the Florida State University and the Citadel, where certain chapters were used, have been of much assistance. Mrs. Beth Causey was constant and faithful in assisting with the preparation of the final draft, and Mrs. Louise Ward was a meticulous editor and typist in preparing the final copy. To all these we extend our warmest thanks.

October, 1961 GROVER L. ROGERS
Tallahassee, Florida M. LANDER CAUSEY
Charleston, South Carolina

CONTENTS

▌ EQUILIBRIUM ANALYSIS OF STRUCTURES

1.1 Definitions

In this work we shall confine ourselves exclusively to the study of structures composed of members whose lengths are much greater than their lateral dimensions. These members, sometimes called bars, may be straight or curved and may have constant or variable cross sections. We call such structures *framed structures* or *bar structures*. For the most part, we shall deal with loads whose magnitudes remain constant with time. Our principal topic is thus *structural statics*. Dynamic problems* are briefly considered only in the last chapter.

The exact terms used to describe specific members of a framed structure vary from one industry to another as well as from one country to another. A long, slender, straight bar subjected only to axially applied compressive forces is usually called, in the United States, a *column* in the building industry and a *strut* in the aircraft industry, but is called a *stanchion* in Great Britain. Short, straight members subjected to axial compression are called *posts*. Straight members subjected to axial tension are called *ties*, or simply *tension members*. Members subjected to bending may be called *beams*, *joists*, or *girders*. They may be of a single span or of many spans, in which case they are called *continuous beams*.

Members subjected to axial compression as well as bending are called *beam-columns*. This combination of axial compression and flexure occurs in many important practical structures. The effects of the bending are sometimes much less significant than the effects of the axial compression,

* For an extended treatment of problems in structural dynamics see Grover L. Rogers, *An Introduction to the Dynamics of Framed Structures*, John Wiley and Sons, 1959.

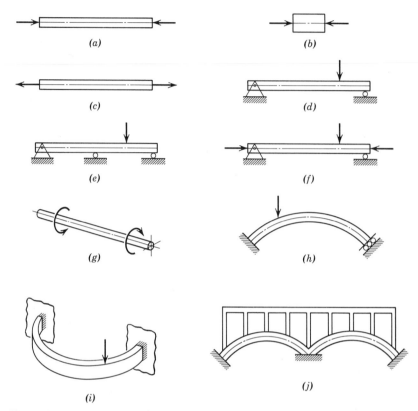

Figure 1.1 (*a*) Column, (*b*) post, (*c*) tie, (*d*) beam, (*e*) continuous beam, (*f*) beam-column, (*g*) shaft, (*h*) arch, (*i*) balcony beam, (*j*) multiple arch.

hence the bending is neglected; at other times the effects of the axial stresses are much less significant than the effects of the bending and the axial compression is neglected. An example of the first is a lower story interior column of a typical building frame, whereas an example of the latter is a column of a rigid frame.

Straight members subjected to twisting are called *shafts*. These, like the beams, may be of a single span or continuous over several supports.

Curved members subjected to bending are called *curved beams*. When the applied loads are in the plane of the member we speak of the structure as an *arch*, but when the applied loads are not in the plane of the member we have a *balcony beam* or a *bow girder*. Arches may occur singly or in a series; the latter are called *multiple arches*.

Illustrations of these types of structural members are shown in Figure 1.1.

Individual members may be connected in several ways. *Pins, welds, rivets*, and *bolts* are the most common connecting devices for structures today. When a frictionless pin is used, the angle between connected members may change appreciably as the structure is loaded, since the pinned joint offers no resistance to relative rotation of the members connected. Since such a joint behaves as a hinge, we speak of the pin connected structure as one with *hinged joints*. When there is total resistance to relative rotation of the connected members, the structure is said to have *rigid joints*. The modern welded connection best illustrates this construction. Joints that offer some resistance to relative rotation of connected members but not total resistance are called *semirigid*. The riveted and bolted connections are good examples of such jointing. Typical connections are shown in Figure 1.2.

Structures having nothing but hinged joints will, in this book, be called *trusses*. In the analysis of these structures we shall assume that the loads are applied only at the joints. Consequently, only end forces will act on a free body of any member of the truss, and these forces will pass through the centroids of the end cross sections, giving no bending moments at the hinged ends. Furthermore, because only two forces are present on the free body, equilibrium requires that these two be equal, opposite, and collinear. Hence, in a truss loaded at the joints, all members are subjected to axial compression or axial tension. There will be no bending in any member. This is only an idealization since there will usually be some transverse loads (such as dead weight) to cause some bending in the members and there will be some resistance to relative rotation at the joints giving rise to some

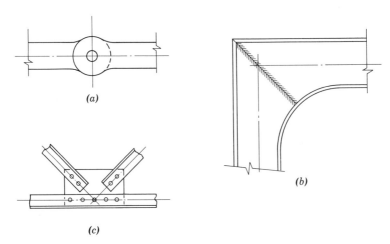

Figure I.2   (*a*) Pinned connection, (*b*) welded connection, (*c*) riveted or bolted connection.

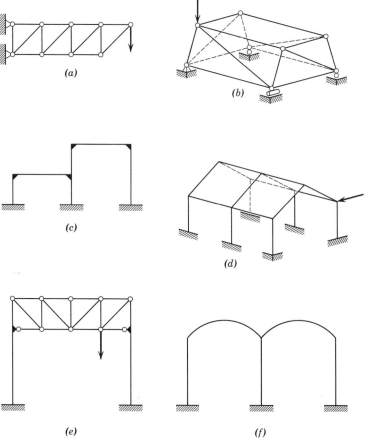

Figure 1.3 (*a*) Plane truss, (*b*) space truss, (*c*) plane bent, (*d*) space bent, (*e*) trussed bent, (*f*) arched bent.

bending in the members. Bending due to either cause is often small, however, so that our assumption of a hinged structure with all loads applied at the joints is indeed satisfactory. When the applied loads and all the truss members are in the same plane, the structure is called a *plane truss*. When the members do not lie in the same plane we have a *space truss*. The television tower is a good example of a space truss.

Structures having all joints rigid are called *bents* in this book. This is a more general use of this term than is normally found in the literature but it will be seen to lend clarity to our discussions. In general, a bent experiences bending and axial forces in its members with the effects of bending being far more significant than the effects of the axial forces. When the applied loads and all the members of the bent are in the same plane we have a *plane bent*. When all of the members do not lie in a single plane or when all the members do lie in the same plane with loads applied out of the plane, the structure is called a *space bent*. The three dimensional skeleton of a modern building taken as a whole illustrates very well the space bent.

The *arch*, *truss*, and *bent* are the principal types of framed structures. Combinations of these yield hybrid structures of less general use. The trussed bent which combines interior joints that are hinged and fixed illustrates one hybrid type. Figure 1.3 shows a variety of structural systems.

1.2 Equations of Equilibrium

Static equilibrium can be assured for any body provided that the sum of all forces (or their components) acting in any possible direction is zero and if the sum of all moments of forces about any axis is zero. Since force and moment are vector quantities, it must follow that resultant force and resultant moment will be zero if and only if their components are zero. Choosing the x, y, and z axes as a set of mutually perpendicular directions, this statement is equivalent to the following six mathematical conditions for static equilibrium.

$$\begin{aligned} \sum F_x = 0 && \sum M_x = 0 \\ \sum F_y = 0 && \sum M_y = 0 \\ \sum F_z = 0 && \sum M_z = 0 \end{aligned} \tag{1}$$

where F_x, for example, is the component of any force F in the x direction, and M_x, for example, is the moment of any force F about the x axis.

If all the forces present lie in the same plane, and hence are *coplanar*, and if the x and y axes are taken in that plane, it follows that $\sum F_z = 0$ and $\sum M_x = \sum M_y = 0$, by definition, and the six equations of static equilibrium reduce to the three equations

$$\begin{aligned} \sum F_x = 0 \\ \sum F_y = 0 \\ \sum M_z = 0 \end{aligned} \tag{2}$$

The preceding equations of equilibrium must be satisfied for any body whether it be a complete structure acted upon by applied loads and reactions or whether it be but a portion of a structure acted upon by applied loads and internal forces.

Several special propositions may be drawn from the foregoing discussion.

(1) When two and only two forces act on a body, equilibrium is possible if and only if these two forces are equal, opposite, and collinear. This

guarantees that the vector sum of forces and vector sum of moments each equals zero.

(2) When three coplanar forces act on a body, equilibrium is possible if and only if the three forces are concurrent. This insures that the vector sum of moments equals zero. We must further require that the vector sum of forces equal zero.

(3) When a set of coplanar forces acts on a body, equilibrium is guaranteed if and only if there is no resultant moment or resultant force.

(4) A single set of coplanar forces not in equilibrium can always be reduced to a single resultant force *or* a single resultant moment.

When the number of unknown reaction components is exactly equal to the number of independent equations of statics, the structure is said to be *statically determinate externally.* When there is an excess of reaction components the structure is said to be *statically indeterminate.* Thus, in Figure 1.4 we have three unknown reaction components and three equations of statics and the structure is thus statically determinate. A quick calculation shows that by setting the sum of forces in the horizontal direction equal to zero we find $H_L = 0$; by setting the sum of moments about the left support equal to zero we find $V_R = P/2$; and by setting the sum of forces in the vertical direction equal to zero we find $V_L = V_R = P/2$. The left end of the beam in Figure 1.4 has a hinged support; that is, there is no resistance to rotation at that support (hence there can be no reactive couple there), but there is complete resistance to translation (hence two components of reactive force may be present). The right end of the beam has a roller support, which indicates no resistance to rotation and no resistance to translation along the roller bed. Hence, the only reaction possible is a force acting normal to the roller bed. In all our discussions the roller symbol will be used to suggest only a reactive force normal to the

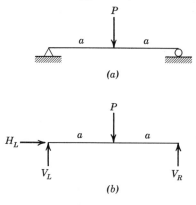

(a)

(b)

Figure 1.4

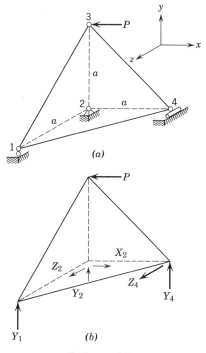

Figure 1.5

roller bed. It is understood that this force may have either sense normal to the roller bed.

In space, a hinged support represents no resistance to rotation about any axis and total resistance to translation in every direction as illustrated in joint 2 of Figure 1.5. A spherical roller, in space, indicates no resistance to rotation about any axis and total resistance to translation only in the direction normal to the plane roller bed as illustrated at joint 1 of Figure 1.5. A cylindrical roller, in space, indicates no resistance to rotation about any axis and resistance to translation in two directions. One direction is perpendicular to the plane on which the cylinder rests and the other is parallel to the axis of the cylinder as illustrated at joint 4 of Figure 1.5. For the structure of Figure 1.5 we have six unknown reaction forces and six equations of statics and the structure will be seen to be statically determinate externally. By summing moments about the axis through joints 1 and 2 we find $Y_4 = -P$. By summing forces in the direction of X_2 we find $X_2 = +P$. By summing moments about an axis through joints 2 and 4 we find $Y_1 = 0$, and by summing forces in the y direction we find $Y_2 = -Y_4 = +P$. By summing moments about an axis passing through

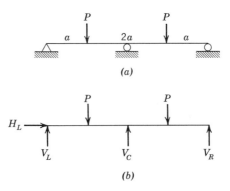

Figure 1.6

joints 2 and 3 we find $Z_4 = 0$. Finally, we sum forces in the z direction to find $Z_2 = -Z_4 = 0$.

Sometimes there is other valuable information at hand in addition to the equations of equilibrium; namely, *equations of condition.* One such equation of condition arises whenever we have symmetry of loading and design. In the beam of Figure 1.4, for example, it is evident from the symmetry of the problem that reaction V_L must equal reaction V_R once it has been established that $H_L = 0$. In Figure 1.6 reaction V_L equals reaction V_R only if symmetry of structure is present to accompany the symmetry of loading. For example, if the left span is of the same cross-sectional size and shape as the right span but is made of a different material, the structure will not be symmetric, and even though the loading is symmetric V_L will not necessarily equal V_R. Or, if the spans are of the same material but one has a different size and shape of cross section than the other, the reactions will not necessarily be equal.* Assuming symmetry of structure to be present for the two structures in Figures 1.7 and 1.8 we note that, by inspection, $V_L = V_R$, $H_L = H_R$, and $M_L = M_R$.

When an equation of condition is available, the degree of indeterminacy may be reduced. Thus we find the structure of Figure 1.7 to be indeterminate to the second degree, whereas it would be indeterminate to the third degree if the symmetry were not present. In Figure 1.6, however, the structure is still indeterminate to the first degree even after symmetry is considered, since the symmetry condition gives the same information as the equilibrium condition; that is, the sum of moments about the center support must equal zero.

Other equations of condition follow when particular construction devices are present. For example, in Figure 1.9a we have a device which we shall

---

* It is shown later that the symmetry of structure conditions can be liberalized to mean symmetry of *relative stiffness* of the two spans.

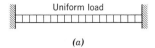

(a)

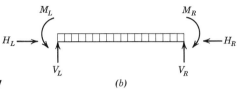

M_L M_R

H_L →   ← H_R

V_L V_R

Figure 1.7   (b)

call a *hinge*. It permits relative rotation of the two pieces connected but is nevertheless capable of resisting relative translation of the joined pieces. In Figure 1.10a, on the other hand, we have what we shall call a *shear connector*. It makes possible a relative translation perpendicular to the axis of the structure but prevents relative rotation of the joined pieces. In drawing line diagrams we shall use the symbols of Figure 1.9b and 1.10b to illustrate these two connections. The sum of moments to *either* side of a hinge is equal to zero. This should not be confused with the general equilibrium requirement that the sum of moments *around* any point equals zero. The sum of moments to either side of a section of a

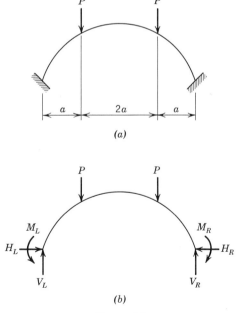

(a)

(b)

Figure 1.8

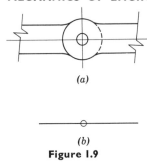

(a)

(b)

Figure 1.9

member is defined as the *bending moment* at that section; hence the bending moment at a hinge always equals zero. The sum of forces taken to either side of a shear connector in the direction perpendicular to the member is equal to zero. The sum of forces to one side of a section of a member and perpendicular to the axis of the member is defined as the *shear force* at that section; hence, the shear force at a shear connector is always equal to zero.

In Figure 1.11 we have a continuous beam with a hinge in the right span. There are four unknown reaction components, three independent equations of statics, and one equation of condition (the sum of moments to either side of the hinge equals zero) and thus the reactions are determinate since the number of unknowns equals the number of available equations. Specifically, $H_L = 0$, $V_R = 0$, $V_L = V_C = P/2$.

In Figure 1.12 we have the identical situation as in 1.11 since the hinge action of the two joined trusses is the same as for the two joined beams.

Figure 1.13 shows a shear connector and $V_R = P$, $V_L = -V_C = P/4$.

Figure 1.14 shows four reaction components and one interior hinge. Since the sum of moments to the left of the hinge must be zero, the line of action of the resultant of the components H_L and V_L must pass through the hinge along the dotted line. Further the components H_R and V_R may be combined to yield a single resultant force at the right support. We

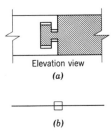

Elevation view

(a)

(b)

Figure 1.10

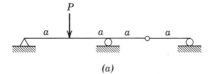

(a)

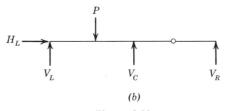

(b)

Figure 1.11

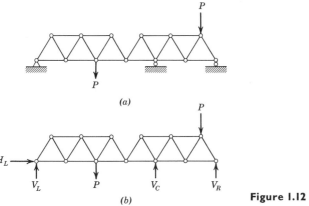

(a)

(b)

Figure 1.12

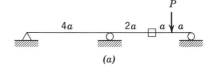

(a)

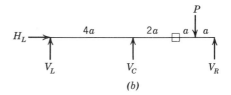

(b)

Figure 1.13

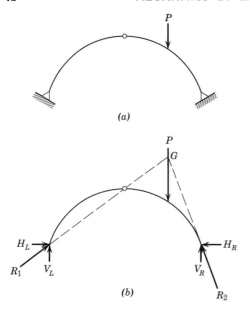

(a)

(b)   Figure 1.14

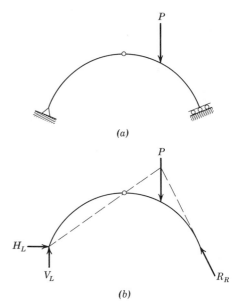

(a)

Figure 1.15   (b)

thus have three forces in equilibrium and by proposition 2, page 6, we note that these three forces must be concurrent. The point of intersection G of the left reaction and the load is known. The right reaction must also pass through G along the dotted line, in order that the forces be concurrent. We now take the sum of moments about the left reaction to find the relation between H_R and V_R. We get another relation by summing moments to the right of the hinge. We then solve these two equations for H_R and V_R. Finally, $H_L = H_R$ and $V_L = P - V_R$.*

The reactions of the arch in Figure 1.15 may be found following the method described for the arch of Figure 1.14. The reader will observe that only one slope of the roller bed is possible for a given position of the load. For any other slope, there is no concurrent force system and the structure is declared *unstable*.

1.3 Stability of Trusses

The *truss* was defined in § 1.1 as a structure consisting of members joined by frictionless pins and supporting loads applied only at the joints. Such a structure is shown in Figure 1.16. The truss may be supported externally by three hinged supports as shown in that figure. Taking the reaction components at any support as positive in the directions shown in Figure 1.16b and denoting them by X, Y, and Z, with a subscript to indicate the support location, we have for the structure shown, nine components of reaction represented on the plan and elevation views of the structure in Figures 1.16c and 1.16d.

In this structure there are nine components of reaction and six equations of statics, which makes the structure statically indeterminate to the third degree. If all support were removed at joint C six reaction components would remain, as shown in Figure 1.17, and we would be tempted to conclude that with the six equations of statics, the structure would be statically determinate. This, however, would not be so, for it is clear that on removal of all support from C the structure would be capable of rotating as a rigid body about an axis passing through joints A and B. Hence, under these circumstances the structure must be judged to be *unstable*.†

---

* The reactions can also be found graphically as discussed in the usual course in engineering mechanics by noting that the forces in equilibrium must form a closed polygon.

† A structure is said to be unstable when any possible system of loads will cause it to rotate or translate as a rigid body. There may be certain special loading patterns for which the structure will actually be stable. For example, the truss under discussion would be stable with the support removed from C provided the load applied at D were in the plane ABD.

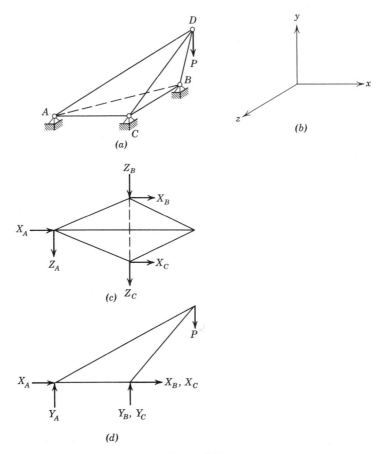

Figure 1.16

If the support C were a spherical roller acting on the place ABC and if support B were a cylindrical roller free to move in the x direction, the reaction components would be as shown in Figure 1.18. Here again we have six reaction components and six equations of statics. Furthermore, the structure is now stable and must be considered to be statically determinate.

If all supports were on cylindrical rollers resting on the plane ABC and free to move only in the direction x, the reaction components would be as shown in Figure 1.19. Here there are six components and six equations of statics, which suggests that the structure may be statically determinate; but closer observation indicates that the structure is free to move as a rigid body in the x direction and must therefore be judged unstable.

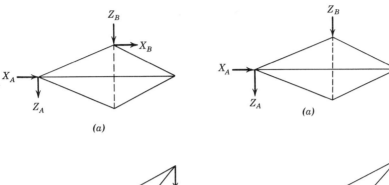

(a)

(a)

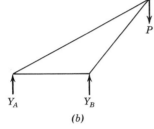

(b)

Figure 1.17

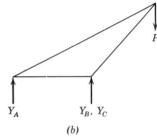

(b)

Figure 1.18

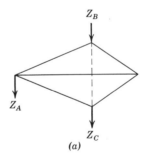

(a)

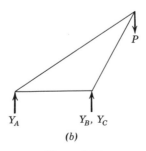

(b)

Figure 1.19

Finally, if the number of reaction components is reduced in any way so as to be less than six, the structure will surely be unstable for a general loading.

Now let r be the number of independent reaction components and n be the total number of equations available. We conclude that if $r < n$ the structure will be unstable, and that if $r = n$ the structure may either be unstable or stable and statically determinate, and that if $r > n$ the structure may either be unstable or stable and statically indeterminate.

When certain equations of condition are present, these must be added to the equations of statics in order to give n the total number of equations available. This is easily shown for the plane structure of Figure 1.20. By the nature of this structure the reactions at the base must be in the directions of the bars joining the base in accordance with proposition 1, page 5. For example, the direction of the reaction at B must make an angle of α

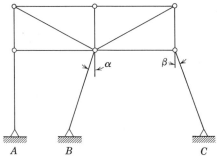

Figure 1.20

with the vertical. We have here three unknown reactions (with directions specified) or five unknown reaction components (with two equations of condition giving the ratios that must exist between the horizontal and vertical reaction components at B and C). However, this structure will always be statically indeterminate if it is also stable.

When $\alpha = \beta = 0$ the structure is unstable since the entire top section could suffer a rigid body translation to the right or left. If β and α are so chosen that the lines of action of the three reactions are concurrent, as shown in Figure 1.21, the structure will again be unstable for it can rotate about the point E as an instantaneous center. For all other values of α and β the structure will be stable and statically determinate as far as reactions are concerned.

We define a statically determinate truss as a truss whose reactions and internal *bar forces** can be determined by using only the equations of

---

* The term *bar force* is used in this work to denote the total axial force carried by a bar of a truss. When divided by the cross sectional area of the bar we obtain the *stress* in the bar.

static equilibrium and such equations of condition as are available. When the external reaction can be found directly (making no reference to the bar forces) the structure is said to be *statically determinate externally* as previously discussed. When all reactions are prescribed and the bar forces can be determined the structure is said to be *statically determinate internally*.

Generally the number of unknowns will be $r + b$ where r is the number of unknown independent reaction components and b is the number of bars in the truss. To solve for these unknowns we may consider the structure joint by joint, writing as many as three (for the *space truss*) equations of static equilibrium for each joint. Thus, if the truss has n joints, we can say that when $r + b = 3n$ the structure, if stable, will be statically determinate. And when $r + b > 3n$ the structure, if stable, will be statically indeterminate.

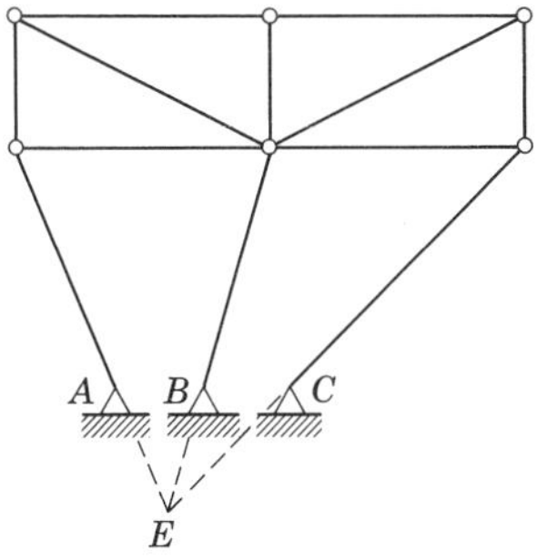

Figure 1.21

If the reactions are found directly, we use six of the equations of equilibrium and note that when $b = 3n - 6$ the structure, if stable, is statically determinate internally, and if $b > 3n - 6$ the structure, if stable, will be statically indeterminate internally. When $b < 3n - 6$ the structure will surely be unstable internally.

For the *plane truss*, we may write two equations of equilibrium for each joint and conclude that when $r + b = 2n$ the structure, if stable, is statically determinate. When $r + b > 2n$ the structure, if stable, is statically indeterminate. When $r + b < 2n$ the structure is unstable. Similarly, when the reactions are found directly three equations of equilibrium will have been used and we note that for $b = 2n - 3$ the structure, if stable, will be statically determinate. When $b > 2n - 3$ the structure, if stable, will be statically indeterminate. When $b < 2n - 3$ the structure will be unstable.

As far as the arrangement of bars required to produce an internally stable structure is concerned, it suffices to say that in any plane a triangulation of bars will guarantee a stable configuration. In Figure 1.22a, for

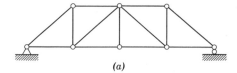

(a)

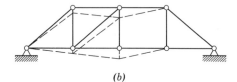

(b)

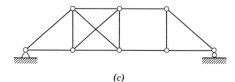

(c)

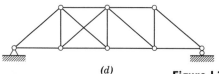

(d)   **Figure 1.22**

example, we have an internally stable plane truss since there is a complete triangulation of members. Furthermore, there are 8 joints, 13 bars, and 3 reactions. Thus $r + b = 16$ and $n = 8$. We have $r + b = 2n$ indicating that the structure is statically determinate. In Figure 1.22b we have $r = 4$, $b = 12$, and $n = 8$. Thus $r + b = 2n$ but here the structure is stable and statically indeterminate to the first degree externally and unstable internally (since relative rigid body rotation of the two sides of the rectangular panel is possible), and we must conclude that, taken as a whole, the structure is unstable. This emphasizes that satisfying the condition $r + b = 2n$ does not guarantee the stability of the structure. The open panel of Figure 1.22b will be observed to act as a shear connector in a beam. In Figure 1.22c the structure again satisfies the equation that $r + b = 2n$ but again due to the arrangement of bars the structure taken as a whole is unstable. Finally, in Figure 1.22d we have a structure that is statically determinate externally and statically indeterminate internally. Taken as a whole the structure must be judged stable and statically indeterminate.

In general, we may say that a structure is unstable when the number of independent equations of equilibrium and condition exceeds the number of unknown forces (whether bar forces or reaction components). Thus, the set of equations will not possess a unique solution. Conversely, we may say that a structure is unstable if we can establish that more than one solution exists for the set of equations. This leads us to a useful method of studying the stability of trusses known as the *zero-load test*. We reason that if a structure is stable, the bar forces will all be zero in magnitude when there are no external loads applied. If we can show that a set of nonzero bar forces exists that is compatible with zero external loads, we will have shown that two sets of bar forces can be found that are compatible with the same zero external load. The solution to the governing equations will then not be unique; hence, the configuration is unstable. Figures 1.23 and 1.24 show configurations that are unstable and stable, respectively.

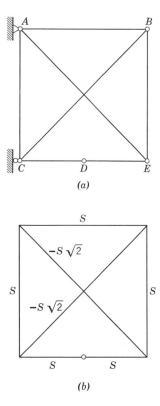

(a)

(b)

Figure 1.23

To apply the zero load test we note first that the reaction components must be zero when external loads are zero. Next we assume that a tensile force of $+S$ exists in bar AB. For the truss of Figure 1.23a, the set of bar forces shown in 1.23b is compatible with zero reactions and hence with the zero load. Since zero forces in all members must also be compatible with the zero load, we conclude that the structure is unstable. For the truss in Figure 1.24a it is impossible to find a set of bar forces other than zero that will satisfy the equations of equilibrium at the various joints. Hence, that configuration is stable.

From physical considerations we can see that the truss of Figure 1.23a is unstable under the action of a vertical force applied to joint D since appreciable displacements can be realized without causing members to be stressed. This is not so for the truss of Figure 1.24.

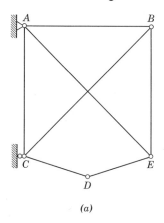

(a)

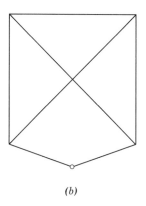

(b)

Figure 1.24

In general, unstable structures such as those previously treated that are stable will show $r + b = 2n$. The unstable configuration is often called a *critical form*.

1.4 Equilibrium of Statically Determinate Trusses

As mentioned in § 1.3, one method of determining the bar forces in a truss once the external reactions are known is to consider the equilibrium of the joints successively. We begin at a joint where the number of unknown forces is equal to the number of equilibrium equations available (two for plane trusses and three for space trusses). We solve for the unknown forces and then move to the next joint where the number of unknown forces equals the number of equilibrium equations available. We continue this until we have found all of the bar forces for the structure. This is the *method of joints.**

For a typical joint of a truss we begin by assuming that all unknown forces are tensile and take as our sign convention forces positive in the direction of the positive x, y, and z axes as given in Figure 1.16b. In Figure 1.25, for example, we have a joint composed of an external force P and three unknown bar forces F_1, F_2, and F_3. Summing forces in the three directions we have

$$P_x + F_{1x} - F_{2x} - F_{3x} = 0$$
$$-P_y + F_{1y} - F_{2y} - F_{3y} = 0 \qquad (1)$$
$$0 - F_{1z} + 0 + F_{3z} = 0$$

The force components of a given member are related in the same way as the three geometric projections of the length of that member. Let θ_{1x} be the angle formed by the member 1 and its x projection. Then,

$$\frac{F_{1x}}{F_1} = \cos \theta_{1x} = \frac{L_{1x}}{L_1} \qquad (2)$$

where L_1 is the length of member 1 and L_{1x} is its x projection. We use 1.4.2 to rewrite 1.4.1 in the form

$$P_x + \left(\frac{F_1}{L_1}\right)L_{1x} - \left(\frac{F_2}{L_2}\right)L_{2x} - \left(\frac{F_3}{L_3}\right)L_{3x} = 0$$

$$-P_y + \left(\frac{F_1}{L_1}\right)L_{1y} - \left(\frac{F_2}{L_2}\right)L_{2y} - \left(\frac{F_3}{L_3}\right)L_{3y} = 0 \qquad (3)$$

$$0 - \left(\frac{F_1}{L_1}\right)L_{1z} + 0 + \left(\frac{F_3}{L_3}\right)L_{3z} = 0$$

---

* The first widespread use of the truss occurred in the United States in the mid-nineteenth century, and it was the American engineer Squire Whipple (1804–1888) who first contributed to its rational analysis through the development of the method of joints.

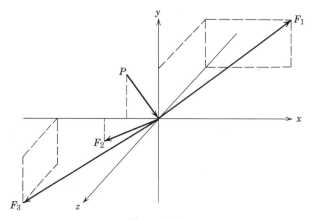

Figure 1.25

For convenience we introduce the symbols $F_1/L_1 = T_1$, $F_2/L_2 = T_2$, and $F_3/L_3 = T_3$, defined as *tension coefficients* to simplify the foregoing set of equations.

$$P_x + T_1 L_{1x} - T_2 L_{2x} - T_3 L_{3x} = 0$$

$$-P_y + T_1 L_{1y} - T_2 L_{2y} - T_3 L_{3y} = 0 \qquad (4)$$

$$0 - T_1 L_{1z} + 0 + T_3 L_{3z} = 0$$

Note that there are but three unknowns in this set of equations: T_1, T_2, and T_3. We solve the set simultaneously to find their values. Upon finding the values of T we multiply each by the associated length to find the bar force.

The great advantage of the *method of tension coefficients* lies in the ease with which we can write the equations of equilibrium. Equation 1.4.4 may be written directly with little thought. This ease is appreciable especially for space trusses and also in the general case of plane trusses. Also, the possible sources of numerical error are reduced in number, as will be seen in the following examples.

Example 1.4.1 Determine all bar forces for the space truss of Figure 1.26. Inspection shows this structure to be stable, internally and externally. If the horizontal component of the reaction at C were in the direction of bar BC instead of the z direction, it would be unstable, since the structure could move as a rigid body in the horizontal plane with support B as a center of rotation. The number of bars is 6, the number of reaction components is 6, and the number of joints is 4. Therefore, $r + b = 3n$. The structure is statically determinate.

There are several approaches that we might follow in analyzing this structure. We could first find the reactions directly, then find the bar forces at joints A,

B, and C, and check our work using joint D. Or we could begin by finding the bar forces at joint D, then find reactions and bar forces at A, B, and C, and check our work by finding the reaction directly. We will use the first method. We sum moments about an axis along member 4 to find $Y_C = -0.5$ kips. We sum moments about a vertical axis through joint B to find $Z_C = -0.25$ kips. We sum forces in the x direction to find $X_B = 1.0$ kips. We sum forces in the z direction to find $Z_B = 0.25$ kips. We sum moments about an x axis through B to find $Y_A = 0.25$ kips. We sum forces in the y direction to find $Y_B = 0.25$ kips. Next we write the equilibrium equations in the x, y, and z directions (in that order) for joint A using the method of tension coefficients.

$$5T_3 + 10T_6 = 0$$

$$10T_3 + Y_A = 0 \qquad (5)$$

$$-10T_4 - 5T_3 - 5T_6 = 0$$

From the second we find $T_3 = -Y_A/10 = -0.025$ kips. From the first we find $T_6 = -0.5T_3 = 0.0125$ kips. From the third we find $T_4 = -0.5T_3 - 0.5T_6 = 0.00625$ kips. Now at joint B we sum forces in the x and y directions to obtain

$$X_B + 20T_5 + 10T_1 = 0$$
$$\qquad (6)$$
$$Y_B + 10T_1 = 0$$

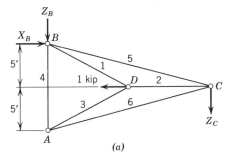

(a)

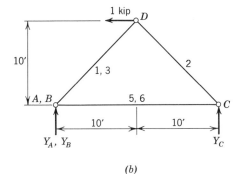

(b)

Figure 1.26

From the second of these we find $T_1 = -0.025$ kips. From the first $T_5 = -0.0375$ kips. From joint C we sum forces in the y direction to get

$$Y_C + 10T_2 = 0$$

or

$$T_2 = 0.05 \text{ kips} \tag{7}$$

We now check joint D by summing forces in the x, y, and z directions.

$$\begin{aligned} -1 + 10T_2 - 10T_1 - 10T_3 &= 0 \\ -10T_1 - 10T_2 - 10T_3 &= 0 \\ -5T_1 + 5T_3 &= 0 \end{aligned} \tag{8}$$

Using the values just found we obtain

$$\begin{aligned} -1 + 0.50 + 0.25 + 0.25 &= 0 \\ 0.25 - 0.50 + 0.25 &= 0 \\ +0.125 - 0.125 &= 0 \end{aligned} \tag{9}$$

The lengths of the various members are found to be $L_1 = 15$ ft., $L_2 = 14.14$ ft., $L_3 = 15$ ft., $L_4 = 10$ ft., $L_5 = 20.65$ ft., and $L_6 = 20.65$ ft. The actual bar forces are given by the products of lengths and tension coefficients. Thus, $F_1 = -0.375$ kips, $F_2 = 0.707$ kips, $F_3 = -0.375$ kips, $F_4 = 0.0625$ kips, $F_5 = -0.7744$ kips, and $F_6 = 0.2581$ kips where the positive value indicates that we assumed the correct direction for the bar forces. Since we assumed all forces to be in tension we have positive values for tension and negative for compression.

Example 1.4.2 Find all bar forces for the plane truss of Figure 1.27. We begin by finding the reactions to be $H_L = 0$, $V_L = V_R = 1.5$ kips. Using tension coefficients, we begin at the joint A and set the sum of forces in the horizontal x and vertical y directions to be zero.

$$\begin{aligned} H_L + 10T_2 + 10T_1 &= 0 \quad \text{or} \quad T_1 = -T_2 \\ V_L + 10T_2 &= 0 \quad \text{or} \quad T_2 = -0.15 \text{ kips} = -T_1 \end{aligned} \tag{10}$$

From joint F we find that

$$\begin{aligned} -10T_1 + 10T_3 &= 0 \quad \text{or} \quad T_3 = 0.15 \text{ kips} \\ 10T_4 - 1 &= 0 \quad \text{or} \quad T_4 = 0.1 \text{ kips} \end{aligned} \tag{11}$$

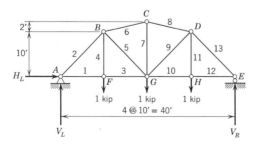

Figure I.27

From joint B we find the sums of forces in the horizontal and vertical directions to be

$$-10T_2 + 10T_6 + 10T_5 = 0$$
$$-10T_2 - 10T_4 - 10T_5 + 2T_6 = 0 \tag{12}$$
$$T_5 = 0.0167 \text{ kips} \quad \text{and} \quad T_6 = -0.1667 \text{ kips}$$

From joint G and by making use of the symmetry of the structure we get the sum of forces in the vertical direction

$$12T_7 + 10T_5 + 10T_9 - 1 = 0 \tag{13}$$

Thus, $T_7 = 0.0555$ kips. The bar lengths are $L_1 = L_3 = L_4 = 10$ ft., $L_2 = L_5 = 14.14$ ft., $L_7 = 12$ ft., and $L_6 = 10.2$ ft. The bar forces, finally, are $F_1 = 1.5$ kips, $F_2 = -2.121$ kips, $F_3 = 1.5$ kips, $F_4 = 1.0$ kips, $F_5 = 0.236$ kips, $F_6 = -1.7$ kips, and $F_7 = 0.667$ kips.

For plane trusses with parallel chords (i.e., BC and CD horizontal in Figure 1.27 the economy of thought found in using the method of tension coefficients is not nearly as great as for structures such as the one solved.

When all the bar forces of a given truss are desired, the method of joints is a satisfactory and systematic scheme for finding them. Also, the method of joints is useful in quickly identifying bars that carry no load. Such rapid identification is possible as a consequence of propositions 1 and 2, § 1.2. A joint is isolated as a free body such that the forces acting are the internal bar forces associated with bars meeting at that joint and the external force applied to the joint. From these propositions we may state the following:

(1a) When two and only two forces act at a joint, the two forces must be equal, opposite, and collinear. Also, if two and only two bars are present at the joint and if no external force is applied, the two bar forces are zero unless the bars are collinear.

(1b) When all forces lie in the same plane but one, then that one force must be zero.

Example 1.4.3   Identity by inspection the zero bar forces in the pedestal of Figure 1.28 which carries a single vertical load P at joint A. Let all base supports be fixed against translation. At joint C, members 5, 10, and 16 lie in a common plane. Bar force F_4 at that joint is the only force not lying in that same plane. Hence by proposition 1b it must be zero. By a similar argument, at joint B we find $F_5 = 0$; and at joint E, we find $F_2 = 0$; and at joint D, we find $F_3 = 0$. At each joint C, E, D there remain two unknown forces. By proposition 1a these must be zero since the bars are not collinear. Thus we find $F_{10} = F_{16} = F_{20} = F_9 = F_{19} = F_8 = 0$. We see, by inspection, that the load P is carried only by members shown as solid lines in Figure 1.29. If desired we could now complete the analysis of this pedestal by using the method of joints.

When only a single bar force or but a few bar forces are desired, the method of joints is likely to be too tedious in that many other bar forces

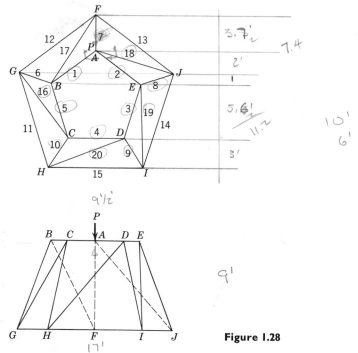

Figure 1.28

might have to be found prior to finding those required. Finding F_6, for example, in Figure 1.27 would require also the finding of F_1, F_2, F_3, F_4, and F_5. However, a much more useful approach is found in the *method of sections*,* which leads to a direct calculation of the desired force. In this method we take as a free body diagram a portion of the structure larger than a single joint. We cut the structure in such a way as to bring into the picture a number of unknown bar forces equal to or less than the number of equations of equilibrium available for solving them.

Example 1.4.4   Find the forces F_3, F_5, and F_6 in the truss of Figure 1.27. We pass a section through members 3, 5, and 6 as shown to get the free body in Figure 1.30. Assuming that the reaction components are known, we have three unknown bar forces, F_3, F_5, and F_6, and three equations of statics for finding them. If we sum moments about joint G it is evident that the only unknown appearing in the equation will be F_6. This may be broken into components at joint C as shown. We may write

$$20V_L - (1)(10) + F_{6x}(12) = 0 \tag{14}$$

Since $V_L = 1.5$ kips, this yields $F_{6x} = -1.67$ kips and $F_6 = -1.7$ kips. Similarly, we may find F_3 by taking moments about B and find F_5 by taking moments about the point of intersection of lines 3 and 6 at K as indicated on

* The method of sections or "method of moments," as it is sometimes called, was developed by the German engineer, August Ritter.

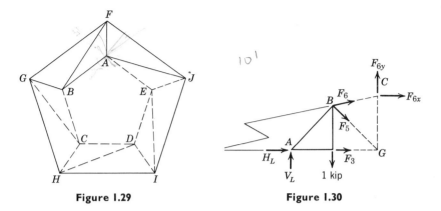

Figure 1.29   **Figure 1.30**

Figure 1.30. Here, we might wish to break F_5 into its horizontal and vertical components at G.

In applying the method of sections to space trusses, we may not have more than six unknown bar forces in the free body since we have but six equilibrium equations available.

1.5 General Method of Analyzing Trusses

As has been mentioned, a truss can be statically determinate only if the number of unknown forces (bars and reactions) equals twice the number of joints in a plane structure or three times the number of joints in a space structure. In using the method of joints for analyzing trusses, we try to find all the forces at a single joint before investigating the next joint in sequence. This is not always possible as illustrated in Figure 1.31. A possible approach to the problem would be to write all of the equations of equilibrium for the five joints as a set of fifteen simultaneous equations in the fifteen unknowns (eight bar forces and seven reaction components) and use some systematic scheme for solving them. One such scheme is the *method of elimination*, which we shall now illustrate with a set of four equations before applying it to the larger set associated with the structure in Figure 1.31.

Let the following set of equations govern the unknowns T_1, T_2, T_3, and T_4 of some fictitious structure.

$$10T_1 + 20T_2 + 30T_3 + 40T_4 = 50$$
$$T_1 - 10T_2 - 45T_3 + 16T_4 = 29$$
$$2T_1 - 10T_2 + 20T_3 - 6T_4 = -18 \tag{1}$$
$$3T_2 - 6T_3 + 9T_4 = -15$$

To save work let us now just write the following five columns where the first four are associated with the coefficients on the left hand side of 1.5.1 and the fifth is associated with the right hand terms. Thus,

$$
\begin{array}{rrrrr}
10 & 20 & 30 & 40 & 50 \\
1 & -10 & -45 & 16 & 29 \\
2 & -10 & 20 & -6 & -18 \\
0 & 3 & -6 & 9 & -15
\end{array}
\tag{2}
$$

We begin by dividing each row of 1.5.2 through by its leading nonzero constant, giving

$$
\begin{array}{rrrrr}
1 & 2 & 3 & 4 & 5 \\
1 & -10 & -45 & 16 & 29 \\
1 & -5 & 10 & -3 & -9 \\
0 & 1 & -2 & 3 & -5
\end{array}
\tag{3}
$$

Keep the first row of this array of numbers and subtract the elements of

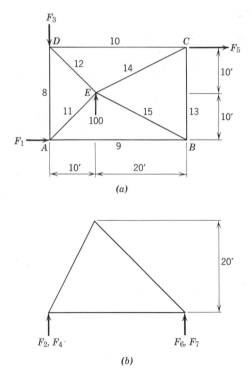

(a)

(b)   **Figure 1.31**

each of the remaining rows, not starting with a zero element, from the elements of the first row to give

$$
\begin{array}{ccccc}
1 & 2 & 3 & 4 & 5 \\
0 & +12 & +48 & -12 & -24 \\
0 & +7 & -7 & +7 & +14 \\
0 & 1 & -2 & 3 & -5
\end{array}
\tag{4}
$$

Next divide each of the last three rows by the leading nonzero number to get

$$
\begin{array}{ccccc}
1 & 2 & 3 & 4 & 5 \\
0 & 1 & 4 & -1 & -2 \\
0 & 1 & -1 & 1 & 2 \\
0 & 1 & -2 & 3 & -5
\end{array}
\tag{5}
$$

Repeat the process followed in the last three steps using the second row to get

$$
\begin{array}{ccccc}
1 & 2 & 3 & 4 & 5 \\
0 & 1 & 4 & -1 & -2 \\
0 & 0 & +5 & -2 & -4 \\
0 & 0 & +6 & -4 & +3
\end{array}
\tag{6}
$$

and

$$
\begin{array}{ccccc}
1 & 2 & 3 & 4 & 5 \\
0 & 1 & 4 & -1 & -2 \\
0 & 0 & 1 & -0.4 & -0.8 \\
0 & 0 & 1 & -0.67 & +0.5
\end{array}
\tag{7}
$$

and now using the third row we find

$$
\begin{array}{ccccc}
1 & 2 & 3 & 4 & 5 \\
0 & 1 & 4 & -1 & -2 \\
0 & 0 & 1 & -0.4 & -0.8 \\
0 & 0 & 0 & +0.27 & -1.3
\end{array}
\tag{8}
$$

These correspond to the equations

$$
\begin{aligned}
T_1 + 2T_2 + 3T_3 + 4T_4 &= 5 \\
T_2 + 4T_3 - T_4 &= -2 \\
T_3 - 0.4T_4 &= -0.8 \\
+0.27T_4 &= -1.3
\end{aligned}
\tag{9}
$$

We find $T_4 = -4.81$ from the last, $T_3 = -2.724$ from the third equation; then $T_2 = 4.086$ from the second and $T_1 = 24.24$ from the first. This method is especially good when a desk calculator is available. For large scale computers the matrix method introduced in a later chapter is useful.

Example 1.5.1 Find the bar forces in the structure of Figure 1.31. We write the following set of equations in terms of the relevant tension coefficients. These equations represent the sum of forces in the x, y and z directions at joints A, B, C, D, and E in that order.

$$F_1 + 30T_9 + 10T_{11} = 0 \qquad F_6 \qquad\qquad + 20T_{14} = 0$$
$$F_2 \qquad + 20T_{11} = 0 \qquad\qquad + 20T_{13} + 10T_{14} = 0$$
$$- 20T_8 - 10T_{11} = 0 \qquad\qquad + 30T_{10} + 10T_{12} = 0$$
$$- 30T_9 - 20T_{15} = 0 \qquad F_4 \qquad\qquad + 20T_{12} = 0$$
$$F_7 \qquad + 20T_{15} = 0 \qquad F_3 + 20T_8 + 10T_{12} = 0 \qquad (10)$$
$$- 20T_{13} - 10T_{15} = 0 \qquad\qquad - 10T_{11} - 10T_{12} + 20T_{14} + 20T_{15} = 0$$
$$F_5 - 30T_{10} - 20T_{14} = 0 \qquad\qquad - 20T_{11} - 20T_{12} - 20T_{14} - 20T_{15} = 0$$
$$\qquad\qquad\qquad\qquad\qquad - 10T_{12} - 10T_{14} + 10T_{11} + 10T_{15} = 100$$

These equations are now rearranged and given the tabular form:

F_1	F_2	F_3	F_4	F_5	F_6	F_7	T_8	T_9	T_{10}	T_{11}	T_{12}	T_{13}	T_{14}	T_{15}	Load
1	0	0	0	0	0	0	0	30	0	10	0	0	0	0	0
	1	0	0	0	0	0	0	0	0	20	0	0	0	0	0
		1	0	0	0	0	20	0	0	0	10	0	0	0	0
			1	0	0	0	0	0	0	0	20	0	0	0	0
				1	0	0	0	0	-30	0	0	0	-20	0	0
					1	0	0	0	0	0	0	0	20	0	0
						1	0	0	0	0	0	0	0	20	0
							-20	0	0	-10	0	0	0	0	0
								-30	0	0	0	0	0	-20	0
									30	0	10	0	0	0	0
										-10	-10	0	20	20	0
										10	-10	0	-10	10	100
												-20	0	-10	0
										-20	-20	0	-20	-20	0
												20	10	0	0

(11)

With this particular choice of numbers for the members of the truss we have reduced considerably the work required to solve the set of equations. By using the elimination method this reduced to:

F_1	F_2	F_3	F_4	F_5	F_6	F_7	T_8	T_9	T_{10}	T_{11}	T_{12}	T_{13}	T_{14}	T_{15}	Load
1	0	0	0	0	0	0	0	30	0	10	0	0	0	0	0
	1	0	0	0	0	0	0	0	0	20	0	0	0	0	0
		1	0	0	0	0	20	0	0	0	10	0	0	0	0
			1	0	0	0	0	0	0	0	20	0	0	0	0
				1	0	0	0	0	-30	0	0	0	-20	0	0
					1	0	0	0	0	0	0	0	20	0	0
						1	0	0	0	0	0	0	0	20	0
							1	0	0	0.5	0	0	0	0	0
								1	0	0	0	0	0	0.67	0
									1	0	0.33	0	0	0	0
										1	1	0	-2	-2	0
											1	0	-0.5	-1.5	-5
												1	0	0.5	0
													1	1	0
														1	0

(12)

We obtain finally the values:

Bar	T	L	F	Bar	T	L	F	Reaction	F
15	0	30	0	9	0	30	0	7	0
14	0	30	0	8	$-\frac{5}{2}$	20	-50	6	0
13	0	20	0					5	$+50$
12	-5	22.49	-112.5					4	$+100$
11	$+5$	22.49	$+112.5$					3	$+100$
10	$+\frac{5}{3}$	30	$+50$					2	-100
								1	-50

$$(13)$$

A refinement of the elimination method that is ideally suited for desk calculators has been developed by P. D. Crout* and has the special advantage that each calculation can be made with a continuous sequence of machine operations. Associated with each set of n simultaneous equations is an array of numbers arranged in n rows and $n + 1$ columns. An example of four simultaneous equations given by Crout is the following:

$$
\begin{aligned}
12.1719w + 27.3941x + 1.9827y + 7.3757z &= 6.6355 \\
8.1163w + 23.3385x + 9.8397y + 4.9474z &= 6.1304 \\
3.0706w + 13.5434x + 15.5973y + 7.5172z &= 4.6921 \\
3.0581w + 3.1510x + 6.9841y + 13.1984z &= 2.5393
\end{aligned}
$$

$$(14)$$

The associated array (a 4 × 5 matrix) is:

$$
\begin{bmatrix}
12.1719 & 27.3941 & 1.9827 & 7.3757 & 6.6355 \\
8.1163 & 23.3385 & 9.8397 & 4.9474 & 6.1304 \\
3.0706 & 13.5434 & 15.5973 & 7.5172 & 4.6921 \\
3.0581 & 3.1510 & 6.9841 & 13.1984 & 2.5393
\end{bmatrix}
$$

$$(15)$$

The key to the Crout method lies in the finding of an *auxiliary matrix* also having n rows and $n + 1$ columns. The elements of this matrix are determined in the following order: elements of the first column, elements of the first row to the right of the first column, elements of the second column (not already found), elements of the second row to the right of the second column, and so forth until we find elements of the nth column (not already found), and finally elements of the nth row to the right of the nth column. This order is shown schematically in Figure 1.32. The elements 1 are identical to the elements of the first column of the given matrix.

---

* For a more detailed discussion of the Crout method and other methods of solving sets of linear equations see F. B. Hildebrand, *Methods of Applied Mathematics*, Prentice-Hall, Englewood Cliffs, N.J., 1952.

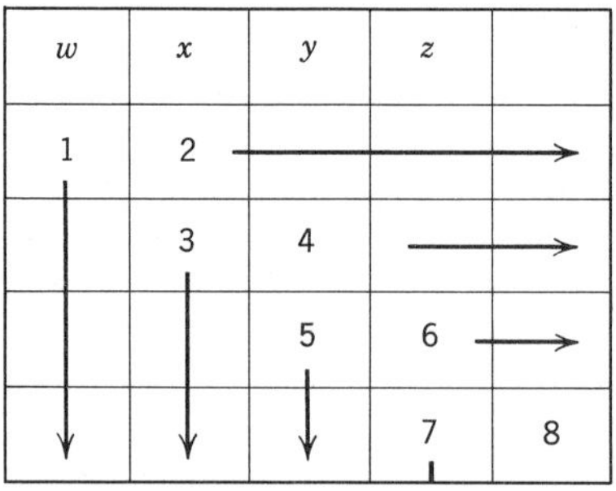

w	x	y	z	
1	2			
	3	4		
		5	6	
			7	8

Figure I.32

The elements 2 are found by dividing corresponding elements of the given matrix by the first element of that row. Elements lying on the diagonal beginning at the upper left hand element and passing through the nth element in the nth row are called *principal diagonal* elements. Each element on or below the principal diagonal is equal to the corresponding element of the given matrix minus the sum of products of elements in its row and corresponding elements in its column (in the auxiliary matrix) that contain only previously computed elements. Each element to the right of the principal diagonal is found in the same way prescribed for elements below the principal diagonal with the single modification that the result is finally divided by the principal diagonal element in its row of the auxiliary matrix.

The complete auxiliary matrix is found to be:

$$\begin{bmatrix} 12.1719 & 2.2506 & 0.16289 & 0.60596 & 0.54515 \\ 8.1163 & 5.0720 & 1.6793 & 0.00057629 & 0.33632 \\ 3.0706 & 6.6327 & 3.9585 & 1.4193 & 0.19891 \\ 3.0581 & -3.7316 & 12.7526 & -6.7332 & 0.060806 \end{bmatrix} \quad (16)$$

A *final single column matrix* gives the solutions. The last element, z, is found first, then the next to last, y, and so on until the first element, w, is found. The last element is equal to the corresponding element in the last column of the auxiliary matrix. Every other element is equal to the corresponding element of the last column of the auxiliary matrix minus the sum of products of elements in its row of the auxiliary matrix and corresponding elements in its column of the *final* matrix that contain only previously computed elements. The solution to the set of equations given above is found to be:

$$\begin{Bmatrix} w \\ x \\ y \\ z \end{Bmatrix} = \begin{Bmatrix} 0.1594 \\ 0.1469 \\ 0.1126 \\ 0.0608 \end{Bmatrix} \quad (17)$$

It will be observed that a distinct advantage of the Crout method is the fact that the first n columns of the auxiliary matrix are not affected by a change in the $n + 1$st column of the given matrix. Hence, in a structures problem many different load combinations can be studied with little extra work.

1.6 Maxwell Force Diagram

A fast and accurate means of finding bar forces in a plane truss is by use of the graphical construction* associated with Clerk Maxwell. It is based on the single theorem of mechanics, which states that the vector sum of a group of concurrent forces in equilibrium must be zero. Graphically, this means that the vector diagram associated with these forces will form a closed polygon. The Maxwell method is to prepare vector diagrams for all joints in the order in which bar forces would be found by using the method of joints and then by combining these in such a way as to give a single simple construction.

To illustrate this method, consider the truss of Figure 1.33. We isolate joint A and draw the associated vector polygon as shown in Figure 1.34a. Beginning with the known force P which is laid off to scale we encircle the joint in a clockwise manner, drawing in bar force F_1 parallel to member 1 and then bar force F_2 parallel to member 2 to complete the polygon. Bar forces F_1 and F_2, if desired, can now be read off to scale from the figure. Considering the action on the joint we read F_1 as tension and F_2 as compression. The directions of the force vectors correspond to the forces in

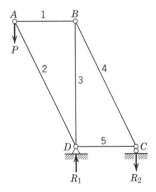

Figure 1.33

---

* Graphical methods have played an important role in the history of structural engineering science. The force diagram was developed by the great English physicist James Clerk Maxwell (1831–1879) but is sometimes called the Maxwell-Cremona force diagram to jointly honor Maxwell and the Italian engineer L. Cremona who improved it.

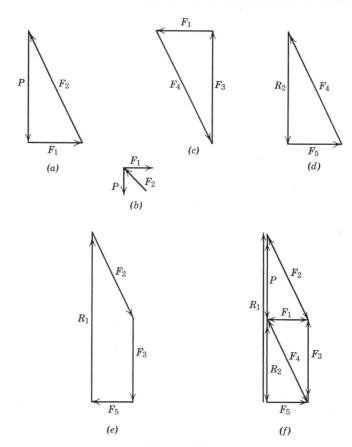

Figure 1.34

the free body diagram of the joint as shown in Figure 1.34b. Similarly, we can draw the diagram for joint B since F_1 is known to be tensile and only two unknowns, F_3 and F_4, remain to be found at that joint. Again we start with the known force and encircle the joint in a clockwise manner in order to draw the polygon shown in Figure 1.34c. For joint C we get the diagram shown in Figure 1.34d. For joint D we will know F_2, F_3, F_5 and draw the diagram shown in Figure 1.34e to find R_1. Finally, we can see that if we combine these diagrams so that like forces are placed over one another we get a single diagram as shown in Figure 1.34f. In effect we draw the diagram a and upon it draw c, then d, and e to give the entire picture of all bar forces in the truss.

Example 1.6.1 Use the Maxwell diagram to find the bar forces in the truss of Figure 1.35. The left reaction is $0.25P$ and the right reaction is $0.75P$. We

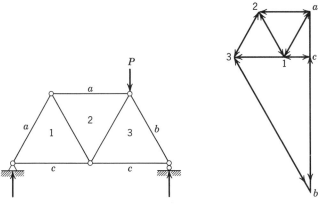

Figure 1.35   **Figure 1.36**

designate each member by the letters given to the spaces separated by the member. For example, the left diagonal is $a1$, the right reaction is bc, and the load is ab. We now draw the Maxwell diagram shown in Figure 1.36 starting with the joint $ca1$ (note that we always name in a clockwise sense and start with the known force, in this case the reaction ca.) We locate position 1 and note that bar $a1$ is in compression and bar $1c$ is in tension. These are read from the diagram as if they were acting on the joint in question. We next, in order, add lines corresponding to the remaining members of the truss, always naming in a clockwise sense. We read off the magnitude of all members using the scale set initially for the given load P. Tension or compression is indicated by moving clockwise around the diagram in accordance with the members present at a joint, giving, for example, at the loaded joint the free body diagram of Figure 1.37.

1.7 Equilibrium of Straight Beams

In this section we shall consider straight members subjected to bending about a principal axis of inertia of the cross section.

Let a differential length dx be cut from a beam as shown in Figure 1.38.

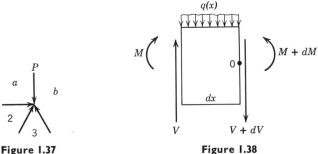

Figure 1.37   **Figure 1.38**

Let the bending moment acting on the left face of the free body be denoted by M and the bending moment acting on the right face be denoted by $M + dM$ where increasing moment is taken in the same direction as increasing x so that we shall have no trouble with signs. Bending will be considered positive as shown. Let the shear force that acts normal to the axis of the beam be taken as V on the left face and $V + dV$ on the right face, being positive as shown. Let the vertical load be positive when acting downward and given by $q(x)$, representing any arbitrary function of x and having the dimensions of force per unit length of beam. Since the element is of differential length dx, the load function regardless of its variation may be considered as uniform over that short length, giving a total vertical load on the element of $q(x)\, dx$. Equilibrium of the element requires that the sum of all forces acting be equal to zero. Hence we write:

$$V - q(x)\, dx - (V + dV) = 0$$

or

$$\frac{dV}{dx} = -q(x) \tag{1}$$

This elementary differential equation may be solved by separating variables and integrating. Thus

$$V = \int dV = -\int q(x)\, dx + C \tag{2}$$

where C is the constant of integration. When the load over a length of a beam is zero, we have $q(x) = 0$ over that length and

$$V = C \tag{3}$$

which indicates that *the shear force is constant over an unloaded length of beam.* A plot of the shear force along the length of the beam would show a curve having constant ordinate over the unloaded length. When the loading is uniform over a given length we have $q(x) = q_0$, some constant, over that length and

$$V = -q_0 x + C \tag{4}$$

This is the equation of a straight line of slope $-q_0$. The shear force diagram will vary linearly with a slope equal to $-q_0$ over a length of beam supporting a uniformly distributed load q_0.

Equilibrium also requires that the sum of moments must be equal to zero about any point in Figure 1.38. Let the point 0 serve as a moment center and write

$$M - q(x)\, dx \left(\frac{dx}{2}\right) + V\, dx - (M + dM) = 0$$

The second term of this expression is a higher order differential than the others since it contains a differential squared. We may neglect it and deduce that

$$\frac{dM}{dx} = V \tag{5}$$

This is exactly the same kind of equation as 1.7.1. We may draw similar conclusions. If the shear force is constant along a length of a beam, the bending moment will vary linearly with a slope V. Since the bending moment is a maximum when the bending moment diagram has a zero slope, we conclude that *maximum bending moment must be accompanied by zero shear force.*

We now combine equations 1.7.1 and 1.7.5 to obtain

$$\frac{d^2M}{dx^2} = -q(x) \tag{6}$$

which relates bending moment and load directly. Equation 1.7.6 is the *basic equation of equilibrium* for a beam. Note that thus far we have made no restrictions on our beam. It may be uniform or not, it may be of any material whatsoever. We may separate variables in 1.7.6 as before and on integrating twice obtain

$$M = -\int\int q(x)\, dx\, dx + C_1 x + C_2 \tag{7}$$

This shows that when $q(x) = q_0$ we have

$$M = \frac{-q_0 x^2}{2} + C_1 x + C_2 \tag{8}$$

which indicates that the bending moment diagram is parabolic in shape when the loading is uniform and a straight line when $q_0 = 0$.

Example 1.7.1 Find the equations for bending moment and shear force for the beam in Figure 1.39 by using the integration approach as well as a direct application of the laws of equilibrium. The equation for bending moment is given by 1.7.8. We find the constants C_1 and C_2 by applying the known conditions that the bending moment is zero at the two supports. Thus, $M = 0$ at $x = 0$ and

$$0 = -\frac{q_0}{2}(0)^2 + C_1(0) + C_2$$

or

$$C_2 = 0$$

and $M = 0$ at $x = L$ and

$$0 = -\frac{q_0 L^2}{2} + C_1 L$$

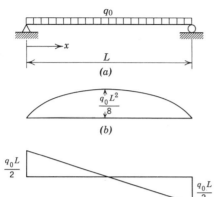

(a)

(b)

(c)   **Figure 1.39**

or

$$C_1 = \frac{q_0 L}{2}$$

Finally

$$M = \frac{q_0 L x}{2} - \frac{q_0 x^2}{2} \tag{9}$$

The shear force is given by the derivative of M with respect to x according to equation 1.7.5. Thus

$$V = \frac{q_0 L}{2} - q_0 x \tag{10}$$

We now check our results by the direct application of the equations of equilibrium. We begin by finding the reactions to be equal to $q_0 L/2$. We next make a free body diagram for the portion of the beam between the left support and some distance x to the right as shown in Figure 1.40. By summing forces in the vertical direction, we have

$$\Sigma F = \frac{-q_0 L}{2} + q_0 x + V = 0$$

or

$$V = \frac{q_0 L}{2} - q_0 x \tag{10}$$

as given previously. We sum moments about the cut section to find

$$\Sigma M = \frac{q_0 L}{2} x - \frac{q_0 x^2}{2} - M = 0$$

$$M = \frac{q_0 L x}{2} - \frac{q_0 x^2}{2} \tag{9}$$

as also given previously. Note that again $dM/dx = V$ and that $dV/dx = -q_0$ in accordance with equation 1.7.1. In using the free body method we

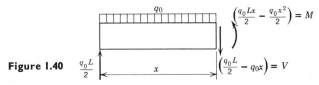

Figure 1.40

always assume the unknown stress resultants (in this case V and M) to be positive so that a negative result indicates a negative stress resultant. This second method of solution is sometimes referred to as the *free body method*. The bending moment and shear force diagrams are shown in Figures 1.39b and 1.39c.

For the beam of Figure 1.41 we find from direct application of the laws of statics that at the support we will have a negative bending moment of $-Pa$ and since the bending moment is zero to the right of the load and must be linear where there is no load, the resulting diagram must be as shown. The shear force diagram is also shown. From the deflected structure given in Figure 1.41a, we note that *the bending moment diagram is drawn on the side of the beam having fibers in compression*. Furthermore, where the bending moment diagram is zero, there is no compression or tension in the fibers of the beam, hence the deflection curve is a straight line.

We now consider beams that are statically determinate and contain interior hinges and shear connectors. Such a beam is shown in Figure 1.42.

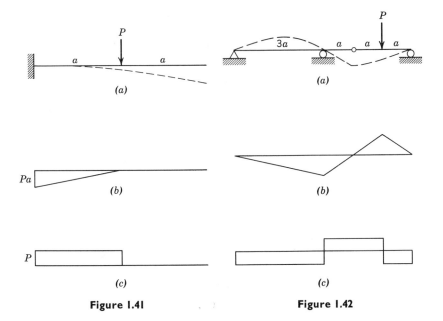

Figure 1.41   **Figure 1.42**

To get the shape of the bending moment diagram we note that $M = 0$ at the two exterior supports and at the interior hinge. Furthermore, the moment diagram is a straight line over an unloaded portion of a beam (the interior support provides an upward vertical load) and we must expect straight lines between the load and the right support, between the two left supports, and between the interior support and the load. These three lines will not necessarily have the same slopes. We noted in Figures 1.39b and 1.41b that the bending moment diagram is plotted on the side of the beam with fibers in compression. Hence, we expect the moment diagram to take the shape given in Figure 1.42b. The shape of the shear force diagram is shown in Figure 1.42c. It is positive when the bending moment diagram has a positive slope; it is constant when the moment diagram is linear; it suffers an abrupt change in magnitude at any concentrated force such as a reaction or applied load. It is a valuable exercise for the student to sketch the shapes of moment and shear diagrams without making any reference to the numerical calculations.

When the interior hinge of Figure 1.42 is replaced by an interior shear connector, the shapes of moment and shear diagrams are as shown in Figure 1.43. Note that the bending moment is a maximum when the shear force is zero. Also the moment diagram must be a horizontal line between the center support and the load, hence the shape shown. Furthermore, in drawing the shear diagram we recall that a zero slope of the moment

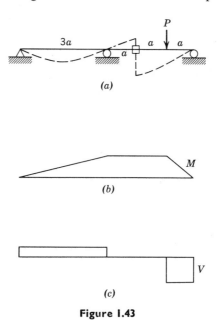

(a)

(b)

(c)

Figure I.43

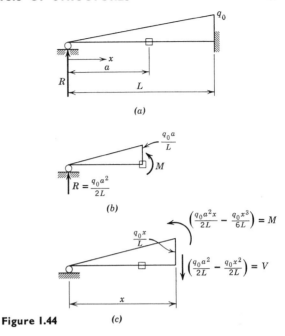

Figure 1.44

diagram demands zero shear. The actual numerical values are readily found from statics.

Example 1.7.2 Find the bending moment and shear force equations for the structure in Figure 1.44. The governing differential equation is given by 1.7.6. The equation for the load is

$$q(x) = \frac{q_0 x}{L} \tag{11}$$

The solution to the differential equation is

$$M = -\frac{q_0 x^3}{6L} + C_1 x + C_2 \tag{12}$$

We know that $M = 0$ at $x = 0$ and $V = dM/dx = 0$ at $x = a$. Using the first of these, we find

$$0 = -\frac{q_0}{6L}(0)^3 + C_1(0) + C_2$$

or

$$C_2 = 0$$

Applying the second, we have

$$V = \frac{dM}{dx} = -\frac{q_0 x^2}{2L} + C_1$$

and

$$0 = -\frac{q_0 a^2}{2L} + C_1$$

or

$$C_1 = \frac{q_0 a^2}{2L}$$

Thus

$$M = \frac{q_0 a^2 x}{2L} - \frac{q_0 x^3}{6L} \tag{13}$$

and

$$V = \frac{q_0 a^2}{2L} - \frac{q_0 x^2}{2L} \tag{14}$$

The free body solution to this problem follows in the usual fashion. We first make a free body diagram of the portion of the beam from the left support to the interior shear connector showing bending moment at the connector but no shear force. We sum vertical forces on the free body to find the left reaction R. See Figures 1.44b and 1.44c.

$$R - \left(\frac{q_0 a}{L}\right)\left(\frac{a}{2}\right) = 0$$

$$R = \frac{q_0 a^2}{2L} \tag{15}$$

A free body of a portion of the beam from the left support to any distance x to the right (whether it includes the shear connector or not) is now taken and forces are summed in the vertical direction to give

$$R - \left(\frac{q_0 x}{L}\right)\left(\frac{x}{2}\right) - V = 0$$

or

$$V = \frac{q_0 a^2}{2L} - \frac{q_0 x^2}{2L} \tag{14}$$

Summing moments about the cut section we find

$$Rx - \left(\frac{q_0 x}{L}\right)\left(\frac{x}{2}\right)\left(\frac{x}{3}\right) - M = 0$$

$$M = \frac{q_0 a^2 x}{2L} - \frac{q_0 x^3}{6L} \tag{13}$$

as found previously by the differential equation.

In the cases treated thus far we have been able to write a single equation representing the variation in bending moment over the entire length of the beam. This is not always possible.

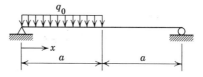

Figure 1.45

Example 1.7.3 Find bending moment and shear force equations for the structure shown in Figure 1.45, where the load is given by $q(x) = q_0$ when $0 \le x \le a$ and by $q(x) = 0$ when $a \le x \le 2a$. Two equations for the load will invariably lead to two separate bending moment equations. For the left half we find

$$M = -\frac{q_0 x^2}{2} + C_1 x + C_2 \tag{16}$$

For the right half we find

$$M = C_3 x + C_4 \tag{17}$$

We now apply the conditions that $M = 0$ at $x = 0$ and also at $x = 2a$ to find

$$0 = -\frac{q_0}{2}(0) + C_1(0) + C_2$$

or

$$C_2 = 0$$

and

$$0 = C_3(2a) + C_4$$

or

$$C_4 = -2aC_3 \tag{18}$$

Furthermore, the bending moment at an infinitesimally small distance to the left of midspan must equal the bending moment at an infinitesimally small distance to the right of midspan, since there is nothing to cause an abrupt change in moment at that location. Hence we write

$$-\frac{q_0(a)^2}{2} + C_1 a = C_3 a - 2aC_3$$

or

$$C_3 = \frac{q_0 a}{2} - C_1 \tag{19}$$

Also, the shear force must be the same at each side of the midspan point.

$$V = -q_0 x + C_1 \tag{20}$$

for the left half and

$$V = C_3 \tag{21}$$

for the right half. Thus

$$C_3 = -q_0 a + C_1 \tag{22}$$

Combining 1.7.22 and 1.7.19 we get

$$-q_0 a + C_1 = \frac{q_0 a}{2} - C_1$$

or

$$C_1 = \frac{3q_0 a}{4} \tag{23}$$

and finally,

$$M = -\frac{q_0 x^2}{2} + \frac{3q_0 a x}{4} \tag{24}$$

for the left half and

$$M = -\frac{q_0 a x}{4} + \frac{q_0 a^2}{2} \tag{25}$$

for the right half. In this problem there are two differential equations with two arbitrary constants in each of the two solutions. Four conditions, therefore, are required to evaluate them. These are furnished by the two conditions of bending moment at the supports and the two conditions of moment and shear equality at midspan.

The free body solution to this problem is very direct. We first set the sum of moments about the right support to zero and find the left reaction to be $(3q_0a)/(4)$ acting upward. At any section $x < a$ we draw a free body diagram and apply the equations of static equilibrium to find

$$V = \frac{3q_0a}{4} - q_0x \tag{20}$$

$$M = \frac{3q_0ax}{4} - \frac{q_0x^2}{2} \tag{24}$$

We now cut the section at $x > a$ to obtain

$$V = \frac{3q_0a}{4} - q_0a = \frac{q_0a}{4} \tag{22}$$

$$M = \frac{3q_0ax}{4} - (q_0a)\left(x - \frac{a}{2}\right) = \frac{q_0a^2}{2} - \frac{q_0ax}{4} \tag{25}$$

The foregoing examples indicate quite clearly that the free body method of solution is to be preferred over the differential equation method when the loading consists of uniformly distributed, linearly varying, and concentrated loads. For more irregular loading the differential equation may be preferred.

Example 1.7.4 Find the bending moment and shear force equations for the structure in Figure 1.46. We have a simply supported beam loaded with the sinusoidal load

$$q(x) = q_0 \sin \frac{\pi x}{L} \tag{26}$$

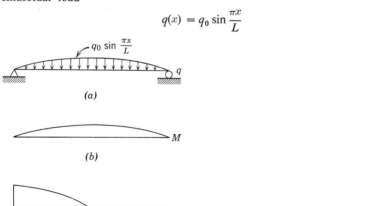

(a)

(b)

(c) **Figure 1.46**

From 1.7.7 we find

$$M = \frac{q_0 L^2}{\pi^2} \sin \frac{\pi x}{L} + C_1 x + C_2 \tag{27}$$

Applying the conditions of zero bending moment at $x = 0$ and $x = L$, we find

$$0 = \frac{q_0 L^2}{\pi^2} (0) + C_1(0) + C_2$$

or

$$C_2 = 0 \tag{28}$$

and

$$0 = \frac{q_0 L^2}{\pi^2} (0) + C_1 L + 0$$

or

$$C_1 = 0 \tag{29}$$

Thus

$$M = \frac{q_0 L^2}{\pi^2} \sin \frac{\pi x}{L} \tag{30}$$

Now using 1.7.5, we obtain

$$V = \frac{q_0 L}{\pi} \cos \frac{\pi x}{L} \tag{31}$$

The bending moment and shear force diagrams are also shown in Figure 1.46. It is left to the reader to demonstrate that using the free body approach to this problem would be extraordinarily tedious. It would also be a tedious approach whenever the load function $q(x)$ can be easily expressed in equation form across the entire length of the beam.

1.8 Equilibrium of Beams with Irregular Loading

In many practical problems we must deal with a very irregular distribution of load. Exact solutions for the bending moment equation are, in such circumstances, laborious and impractical to determine. We content ourselves with approximate solutions.

The basis for the method to be described in this section is the equilibrium equation 1.7.6 and the mathematical *theory of finite differences*. Consider the beam as being divided into a number of segments of equal length λ as illustrated in Figure 1.47. We shall call the ends of the segments "stations" and denote the bending moment at station i by M_i and at the next station to the right M_{i+1} and the next left M_{i-1}. The slope of the moment diagram at station $i + \frac{1}{2}$ is given approximately by

$$\left[\frac{dM}{dx} \right]_{i+\frac{1}{2}} = \frac{M_{i+1} - M_i}{\lambda} \tag{1}$$

At a station $i - \frac{1}{2}$ we have

$$\left[\frac{dM}{dx} \right]_{i-\frac{1}{2}} = \frac{M_i - M_{i-1}}{\lambda} \tag{2}$$

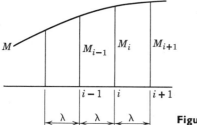

Figure 1.47

The second derivative of the bending moment at station i represents the rate of change of dM/dx at that station. This is given approximately by

$$\left[\frac{d^2M}{dx^2}\right]_i = \frac{\left[\dfrac{dM}{dx}\right]_{i+\frac{1}{2}} - \left[\dfrac{dM}{dx}\right]_{i-\frac{1}{2}}}{\lambda} = \frac{M_{i+1} - 2M_i + M_{i-1}}{\lambda^2} \tag{3}$$

An approximate expression for 1.7.6 is now seen to be

$$\frac{M_{i+1} - 2M_i + M_{i-1}}{\lambda^2} = -q_i(x) \tag{4}$$

or

$$M_{i-1} - 2M_i + M_{i+1} = -q_i(x)\lambda^2 \tag{5}$$

where $q_i(x)$ is the intensity of load in units of force per unit of length at station i. When concentrated forces are present we use $q_i(x)\lambda$ to represent an approximation to the concentrated force over the length of beam λ. We shall speak of equation 1.8.5 as the *equilibrium difference equation*.

Example 1.8.1 Find the bending moment at the quarter points of the structure in Figure 1.48. We break the span into four equal lengths so that $\lambda = L/4$ and number the stations zero to four. The end conditions are $M_0 = M_4 = 0$. We now write equation 1.8.5 for each station.

$$-2M_1 + M_2 = -\frac{q_0L^2}{16}$$

$$M_1 - 2M_2 + M_3 = -\frac{q_0L^2}{16}$$

$$M_2 - 2M_3 = -\frac{q_0L^2}{16} \tag{6}$$

The symmetry here indicates that $M_1 = M_3$ or

$$-2M_1 + M_2 = -\frac{q_0L^2}{16}$$

$$2M_1 - 2M_2 = -\frac{q_0L^2}{16} \tag{7}$$

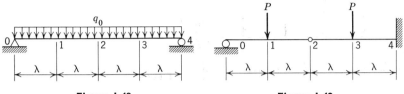

Figure 1.48   Figure 1.49

We add these to find

$$M_2 = \frac{q_0 L^2}{8} \tag{8}$$

and then find

$$M_1 = \frac{3q_0 L^2}{32} \tag{9}$$

Comparing these with the exact values gotten from equation 1.7.9 we find

$$M_2 = \frac{q_0 L^2}{8} \quad \text{and} \quad M_1 = \frac{3q_0 L^2}{32} \tag{10}$$

Here, the results from our approximate method are seen to be identical to those from the exact equation, but this will not always be so.

Example 1.8.2 Find the bending moment at the quarter points in the structure shown in Figure 1.49. The concentrated loads at stations 1 and 3 will be treated as $q_1(x)\lambda = P$ and $q_3(x)\lambda = P$. Thus

$$M_0 - 2M_1 + M_2 = -P\lambda$$
$$M_1 - 2M_2 + M_3 = 0 \tag{11}$$
$$M_2 - 2M_3 + M_4 = -P\lambda$$

Thus, $M = 0$ at stations 0 and 2. Hence from equations 1.8.11 we find

$$M_1 = \frac{P\lambda}{2} = \frac{PL}{8}$$

$$M_3 = M_1 = \frac{PL}{8} \tag{12}$$

Again, these agree exactly with the known solution.

Example 1.8.3 Find the bending moment at the quarter points of the structure in Figure 1.50. In this example we have a known shear force and bending moment for we know that $V = M = 0$. at station 0. If we proceed as before, we get the equations

$$M_0 - 2M_1 + M_2 = -P\lambda$$
$$M_1 - 2M_2 + M_3 = -P\lambda \tag{13}$$
$$M_2 - 2M_3 + M_4 = -P\lambda$$

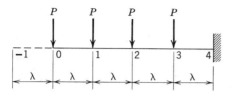

Figure 1.50

Since we know only M_0, we are faced with three equations in four unknowns. In previous problems we were given one additional value of bending moment. To overcome this difficulty we imagine that our beam is extended an additional distance at its free end as shown by the dotted line in the figure. This in no way changes the prescribed conditions of $V = M = 0$ just to the left of the first load P. However, we do get the additional information, $M_{-1} = 0$. Writing the equilibrium equation for station 0, we have

$$M_{-1} - 2M_0 + M_1 = P\lambda \tag{14}$$

and since $M_{-1} = M_0 = 0$, this gives

$$M_1 = -P\lambda \tag{15}$$

Equation 1.8.13 plus 1.8.15 now leads to the solutions

$$M_1 = -\frac{PL}{4}, \quad M_2 = -\frac{3PL}{4}, \quad M_3 = -\frac{3PL}{2}, \quad M_4 = -\frac{5PL}{2} \tag{16}$$

Example 1.8.4 Find the bending moment at the quarter points of the structure in Figure 1.51. In this structure we know that $M = 0$ at station 0 and $V = 0$ at station 2, the shear connector. To make use of the information about V we note that

$$V = \frac{dM}{dx}, \quad V_2 = \frac{M_3 - M_1}{2\lambda} \tag{17}$$

which gives, for $V_2 = 0$,

$$M_1 = +M_3 \tag{18}$$

Our set of equations in this structure is now

$$-2M_1 + M_2 = -P\lambda$$
$$2M_1 - 2M_2 = 0$$

which yields

$$M_1 = M_2 = M_3 = P\lambda = \frac{PL}{4} \tag{19}$$

and

$$M_2 - 2M_3 + M_4 = -P\lambda$$

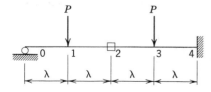

Figure 1.51

or
$$P\lambda - 2P\lambda + M_4 = -P\lambda$$
or
$$M_4 = 0 \tag{20}$$

Example 1.8.5 Find the bending moment at the quarter points of the structure in Figure 1.52a. Using $\lambda = L/4$ as shown, we must find a satisfactory method of interpreting the expression $q_i(x)\lambda^2$ in our basic equation. We consider $q_i(x)\lambda$ to represent an equivalent concentrated load at station i. We thus must approximate the loading of Figure 1.52a by a series of concentrated loads applied only at the station points. To do this we consider the loading between adjacent station points to be equivalent to concentrated loads at the station points equal to the reactions of a simply supported beam of length λ and loaded with the given load. For example, the uniform load from stations 0 to 1 would become equal concentrated loads of $(10)(12/2) = 60$ kips at these two stations. The load of 90 kips would reduce to concentrated loads of 60 kips at station 2 and 30 kips at station 3, as shown in Figure 1.52b. The associated set of equations is now given by the following:

$$-2M_1 + M_2 = -60(12)$$
$$M_1 - 2M_2 + M_3 = -60(12) \tag{21}$$
$$M_2 - 2M_3 = -30(12)$$

We solve these by elimination to find

$$M_1 = 990 \text{ ft-kips}, \qquad M_2 = 1260 \text{ ft-kips}, \qquad M_3 = 810 \text{ ft-kips} \tag{22}$$

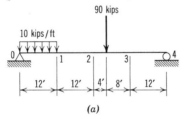

(a)

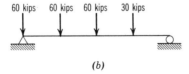

(b)

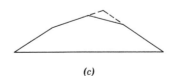

(c)

Figure 1.52

Exact results would be the same. However, the moment diagrams would have different shapes as shown in Figure 1.52c where dotted lines represent the exact bending moment diagram.

More accurate results can always be obtained by dividing the beam into a large number of segments, and the resulting set of simultaneous equations may be solved by the methods discussed in § 1.5.

1.9 Analysis of Other Statically Determinate Structures

In previous sections we have concerned ourselves exclusively with the equilibrium analysis of trusses and beams. In this section we shall consider other statically determinate structures through the use of several illustrative examples.

Example 1.9.1 Analyze the structure in Figure 1.53a. In this example the structure is subjected to axial force as well as bending moment and shear force. We first find the reaction components recognizing that the upper support can supply only a vertical reaction. By summing moments about the lower support we find $R_B = -38.5$ kips, $R_A = 38.5$ kips, $H_A = 0$. The forces normal and tangential to the beam axis are shown in Figure 1.53b. A plot of the variation

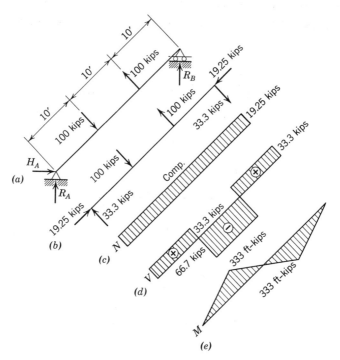

Figure 1.53

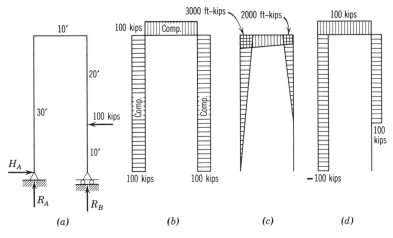

Figure 1.54

in axial force is shown in Figure 1.53c, shear force in 1.53d and bending moment in 1.53e.

Example 1.9.2   Analyze the structure in Figure 1.54a. We first note that the structure is statically determinate, then solve for the reaction components to find $H_A = 100$ kips, $R_A = 100$ kips, and $R_B = -100$ kips. Axial force, bending moment, and shear force diagrams are shown in Figures 1.54b, c, and d.

Example 1.9.3   Analyze the curved structure in Figure 1.55a. We can write equations for the various forces and moments acting on any cross section of the member by a direct consideration of the equilibrium of that portion to the left of the section in question. The radius of the axis of this member is given by a and the angular distance of any cross section from the vertical is given by θ. To make the problem as clear as possible, two free body diagrams are shown for the typical section. One shows only the forces acting and the other shows only the couples acting. The symbol $\odot$ indicates a vector pointing out of the paper and $\otimes$ indicates a vector directed into the paper. A single headed arrow will be used to represent a vector force and a double headed arrow will be used to represent a vector couple. Since force and couple are both vector quantities we use these symbols in both figures. In Figure 1.55b we show a horizontal shear force P balancing the applied load P and a vertical force Q balancing the applied load Q. The radically directed shear force at any location is given by

$$V = Q \cos \theta \qquad (1)$$

and the normal force on any cross section is given by

$$N = Q \sin \theta \qquad (2)$$

See Figure 1.55d. In Figure 1.55c we show the couples acting. By taking moments about an axis perpendicular to the plane of the structure we obtain bending moment shown by the vector $Qa \sin \theta$. By taking moments about a vertical axis we get the vector $Pa \sin \theta$. By taking moments about a horizontal axis we get

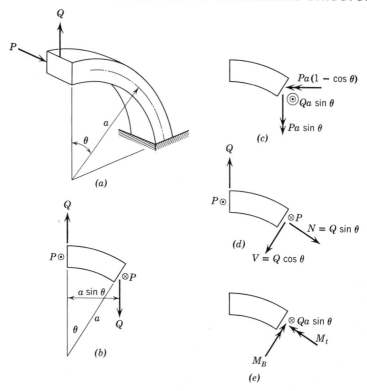

Figure 1.55

the vector $Pa(1 - \cos \theta)$. These may be broken into a bending moment (given by a vector tangent to the section) and a twisting moment (given by a vector normal to the section) as shown in Figure 1.55c. These are seen to be

$$M_t = Pa \sin^2 \theta - Pa(1 - \cos \theta) \cos \theta \qquad (3)$$

$$M_B = Pa \sin \theta \cos \theta + Pa(1 - \cos \theta) \sin \theta \qquad (4)$$

Problems

1.1.1 The plane truss underwent a period of continuous development during the building of the American railroads. Use whatever library resources available to you to sketch the trusses associated with the names of (*a*) Pratt, (*b*) Petit, (*c*) Howe, (*d*) Warren, (*e*) Whipple, and (*f*) Parker.

1.1.2 The plane truss has been widely used in the building industry. Use your library resources to sketch the (*a*) compound Fink, (*b*) Belgian, (*c*) bowstring, (*d*) scissors, (*e*) hammer beam, and (*f*) saw tooth.

1.1.3 Use your library resources to identify a major building in your geographical location which is designed with (*a*) riveted connections, (*b*) welded connections, (*c*) bolted connections.

1.2.1   Find the reactions of the following trusses.

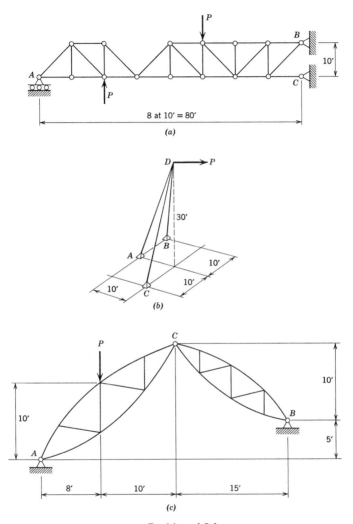

(a)

(b)

(c)

Problem 1.2.1

1.2.2 Find the reactions of the following beams.

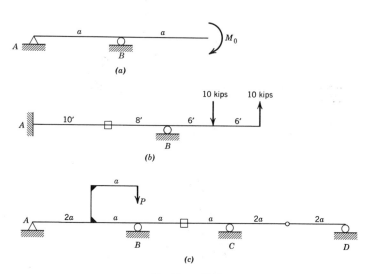

(a)

(b)

(c)

Problem 1.2.2

1.2.3 Find the reactions of the following beams.

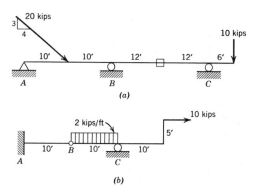

(a)

(b)

Problem 1.2.3

1.2.4 Find the reactions of the following curved structures.

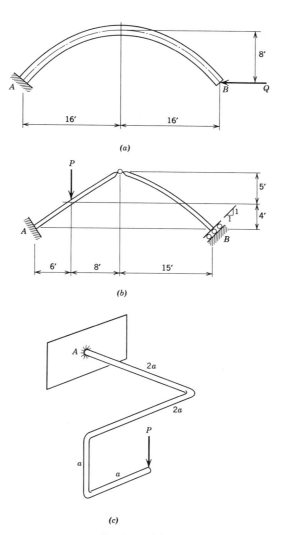

(a)

(b)

(c)

Problem 1.2.4

1.2.5 Find the reactions of the following bents.

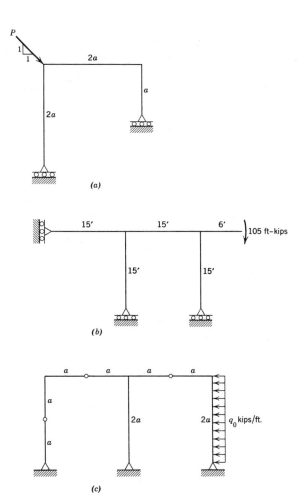

Problem 1.2.5

1.3.1 Determine whether or not the following trusses are stable. If stable, are they statically determinate or statically indeterminate externally? Give reasons to support all conclusions.

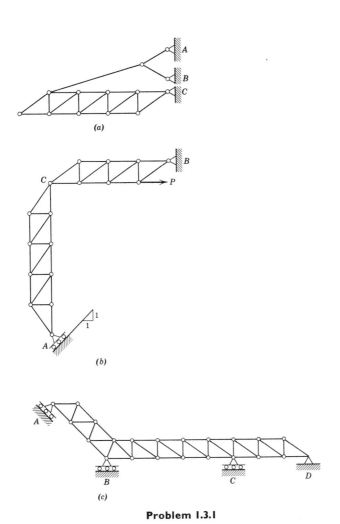

(a)

(b)

(c)

Problem 1.3.1

1.3.2 Determine whether or not the following trusses are stable. If stable, are they statically determinate or statically indeterminate internally? Give reasons to support all conclusions.

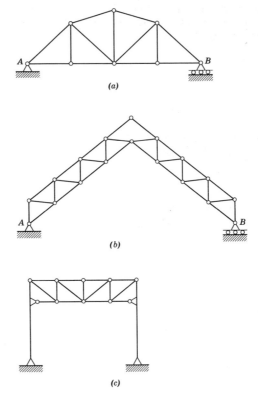

Problem 1.3.2

1.3.3 Determine whether or not the following trusses are stable. If stable, are they statically determinate or indeterminate when all bars and reactions are considered together?

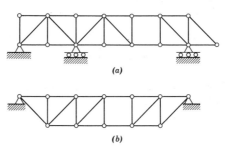

Problem 1.3.3

1.4.1 Using tension coefficients and the method of joints, find the forces in all of the bars of the following trusses.

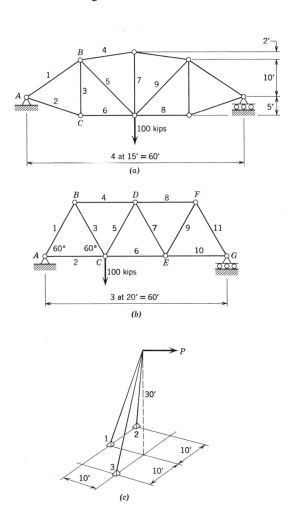

Problem I.4.I

1.4.2 Using the method of sections, find the bar forces X, Y, and Z in the following trusses.

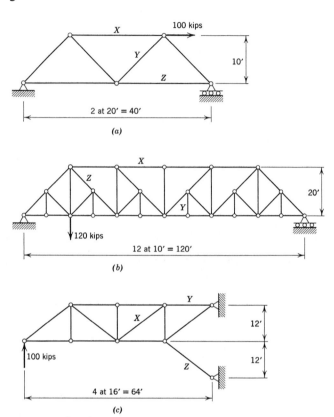

(a)

(b)

(c)

Problem 1.4.2

1.4.3 Indicate on a sketch of the following trusses, which members carry zero bar force. Do this by inspection.

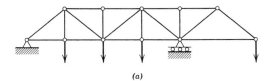

(a)

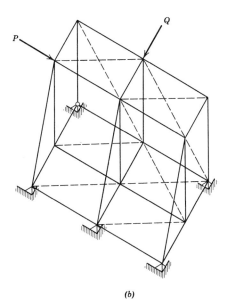

(b)

Problem 1.4.3

1.5.1   Find the reactions of the following trusses using statics, and then use influence coefficients and the elimination method of solving simultaneous equations to find all bar forces.

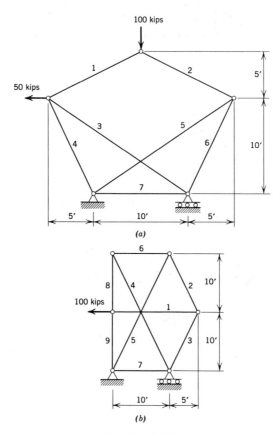

(a)

(b)

Problem 1.5.1

1.5.2 Check the stability of the following trusses using the zero load test.

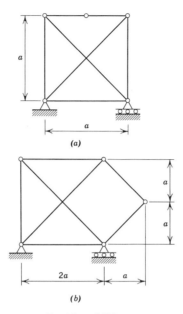

(a)

(b)

Problem 1.5.2

1.6.1 Solve for the reactions for the trusses in Problem 1.4.1 algebraically and then determine all bar forces using the Maxwell force diagram.

1.7.1 Write the equations for the bending moment and then the shear force using the method of integration for each of the following beams. Draw the bending moment and shear force diagrams.

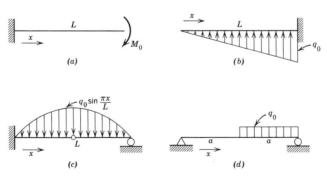

(a)

(b)

(c)

(d)

Problem 1.7.1

1.7.2 Write the bending moment and shear force equations for the beams given in Problems 1.7.1(a, b, and d) using the free body method.

1.7.3   Under what circumstances can there be an abrupt change in slope in the bending moment diagram? What does this imply for the bending moment diagram at mid-span of the beam in Problem 1.7.1(d)?

1.8.1   Write and solve the set of difference equations for the bending moments for the following beams. Divide the total length of each beam into six equal parts.

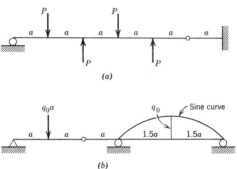

(a)

(b)

Problem 1.8.1

1.9.1   Analyze the structures shown. Draw axial force, shear force, and bending moment diagrams.

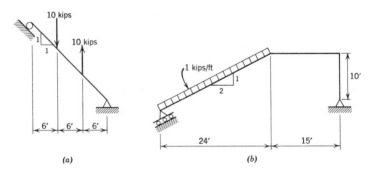

(a)   (b)

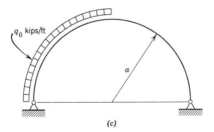

(c)

Problem 1.9.1

2 STRESS RESULTANTS AND STRESS INTENSITIES

2.1 Basic Relations

When a free-body diagram is to be made of only a portion of a structure, it becomes necessary to cut certain members and show at the cut sections forces and couples equivalent to the internal action in the uncut structure. In the most general case we may have a resulting force and a resulting couple acting on the cut section. Choosing a set of axes as shown in Figure 2.1a where the x axis is normal to the section and positive to the right, we may express both the resultant force and the resultant couple in terms of three component forces in the directions of the axes and three component couples about the three axes. Since force is a vector quantity, we show the components as vectors in Figure 2.1b where the normal force is N, the shear force in the y direction is V_y, and the shear force in the z direction is V_z. The directions chosen suggest our sign convention. By taking an element of length dx of the bar, we see that equilibrium requires forces as shown in Figure 2.1c. Positive shear V_y on an element is given by an upwardly directed vertical force on the left and a downwardly directed vertical force on the right. Positive normal force N is given by a tensile force on each face. The symbols $\bigcirc$ and $\otimes$ represent vectors coming out of and going into the page.

Similarly, Figure 2.1d shows the vector representation of the three components of the couple. The normal vector represents the twisting moment T on the section, and M_y and M_z represent the bending moments on the section. The sign convention on the couples is best understood by taking an element of length as shown in Figure 2.1e. Note that moment vectors are represented with a double-headed arrow.

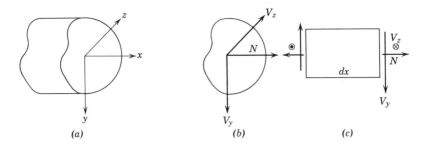

(a)   (b)   (c)

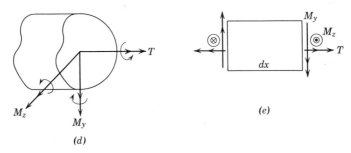

(d)

(e)

Figure 2.1

If an element of area, dA, of the cross section in Figure 2.2 is acted on by a normal stress intensity of s_n and shear stress s_{xy} and s_{xz} in the y and z directions,* we may say that the total normal force on that elemental area is $s_n\,dA$ and the total shear forces are $s_{xy}\,dA$ and $s_{xz}\,dA$. If we sum all such forces over the entire cross section we obtain the forces N, V_y and V_z as follows:

$$N = \int_A s_n\,dA$$

$$V_y = \int_A s_{xy}\,dA \qquad (1)$$

$$V_z = \int_A s_{xz}\,dA$$

* Normal stress is frequently represented by the Greek letter σ and shear stress by the Greek letter τ in the technical literature. However, the authors feel that the notation employed throughout this book is the most acceptable to students and the most easily extended in advanced courses when tensor notation might be used.

Now if we sum moments of elemental forces about the three axes we get the couples M_y, M_z, and T.

$$M_y = \int_A s_n z \, dA$$

$$M_z = \int_A s_n y \, dA \tag{2}$$

$$T = \int_A s_{xz} y \, dA - \int_A s_{xy} z \, dA = \int_A (s_{xz} y - s_{xy} z) \, dA$$

These then are the basic expressions representing the relations between the *stress intensities* s_n, s_{xy}, and s_{xz}, and the *stress resultants* N, V_y, V_z, T, M_y, and M_z. An interesting feature of these expressions is that terms containing the normal stresses do not contain the shear stresses. Therefore, we may consider the distribution of normal stress as separate and distinct from our consideration of shearing stresses. Those expressions depending on normal stress only are

$$N = \int_A s_n \, dA$$

$$M_y = \int_A s_n z \, dA \tag{3}$$

$$M_z = \int_A s_n y \, dA$$

and those depending on the shear stress only are

$$V_y = \int_A s_{xy} \, dA$$

$$V_z = \int_A s_{xz} \, dA \tag{4}$$

$$T = \int_A (s_{xz} y - s_{xy} z) \, dA$$

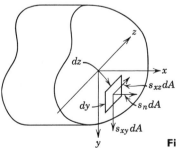

Figure 2.2

2.2 Normal Stress in Straight, Elastic Bars

The best and simplest physical approach to the analysis of normal stress distribution over the cross section of a bar is that based on an hypothesis due to Navier;* namely, *a section that is plane and perpendicular to the axis of a bar before bending remains plane and perpendicular to the axis of the bar after bending.* A more concise expression is that "plane sections remain plane." This is a condition on the displacements in the x direction.

Consider an element of bar length as given in Figure 2.3. Before any deformation occurs, the element is defined by the rectangle $ABCD$. Due to bending of the member from which it was cut the upper fibers are compressed and the lower fibers are extended as indicated by the deformed figure $FGHK$. The plane cross sections represented by AB and CD now become the plane sections represented by FG and HK. Let the displacement of any point on the cross section AB in the x direction be denoted by u and at a similarly located point in the cross section CD be denoted by $u + du$ as shown. These displacements will be functions of y and z, giving $u = -BG$ and $u + du = -BC$ at certain top fibers and $u = +AF$ and $u + du = +DK$ at certain bottom fibers. Since the plane sections AB and CD remain plane, we must have a linear variation of u and $u + du$ over the cross sections. Such a planar distribution of u may be described mathematically by the equation

$$u = a' + b'y + c'z \tag{1}$$

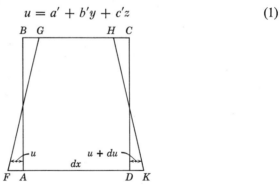

Figure 2.3

* Louis Marie Henri Navier (1785–1836), a French engineer and mathematician and the author of the first great textbook on structural engineering science, presented the first complete treatment of stresses in beams using the theory of plane sections, and it is in accordance with long-standing use among the French that we use the expression *Navier's hypothesis.* However, the Swiss mathematician James Bernoulli (1654–1705) first employed this hypothesis but presented an unacceptable theory since he erroneously concluded that the position of the neutral axis is immaterial.

where a', b', and c' are unspecified constants. Similarly $u + du$ may be described by the equation

$$u + du = a'' + b''y + c''z \qquad (2)$$

The change in length ΔL of any fiber of the element of length dx is given by

$$\Delta L = (u + du) - (u) = (a'' - a') + (b'' - b')y + (c'' - c')z \qquad (3)$$

The normal strain ϵ_n of any fiber is the *change in length divided by the original length.* Thus,

$$\epsilon_n = \frac{\Delta L}{L} = \frac{(a'' - a') + (b'' - b')y + (c'' - c')z}{dx} \qquad (4)$$

If we are dealing with an elastic material we have the simple relationship between normal stress and normal strain given by Hooke;* namely,

$$s_n = E\epsilon_n \qquad (5)$$

where E is *Young's modulus of elasticity.*† Substituting 2.2.4 into 2.2.5 we obtain

$$s_n = \frac{E(a'' - a')}{dx} + \frac{E(b'' - b')y}{dx} + \frac{E(c'' - c')z}{dx} \qquad (6)$$

Since E, a', b', c', a'', b'', c'', and dx are constant for all of the positions (y, z) due to the bar's being a straight member, we shall introduce the new constants a, b, and c and write

$$s_n = a + by + cz \qquad (7)$$

This indicates a linear relation between normal stress and position. Thus Navier's hypothesis for a straight elastic bar is equivalent to the statement that the *distribution of normal stress is linear* over the cross section of the member. We now must find some means of determining the constants a, b, and c in 2.2.7.

Since the stress resultants N, M_y, and M_z depend on the normal stress s_n,

---

* The English geometrician Robert Hooke (1635–1703) discovered this law in working with spiral watch springs which he was preparing to introduce as a substitute for the older pendulum. In order to protect his invention until a patent could be obtained and also to establish his famous law, he published the law in latin in the form of an anagram, *ceiiinosssttuv*, meaning "ut tensio sic vis" and proceeded to interpret it after the patent was secured. Rendered into English it stated that the resistance of any spring was proportional to the extension. The first person to apply this law directly to the fibers of a beam, however, was E. Mariotte (1620–1684), the French scientist.

† The English physicist Thomas Young (1773–1829) is credited with the discovery of the proportionality constant E and also the shearing strain ϵ_s discussed in §2.8.

we should be able to solve for the constants a, b, and c in terms of N, M_y, and M_z by substituting 2.2.7 into 2.1.3. Attempting this we find

$$N = \int_A a \, dA + \int_A by \, dA + \int_A cz \, dA$$

$$M_y = \int_A az \, dA + \int_A byz \, dA + \int_A cz^2 \, dA \qquad (8)$$

$$M_z = \int_A ay \, dA + \int_A by^2 \, dA + \int_A czy \, dA$$

The constants a, b, and c may be taken out of the integral signs. Furthermore, if we choose the y and z axes as *centroidal axes* for the cross section, we have

$$\int_A y \, dA = \int_A z \, dA = 0 \qquad (9)$$

and the remaining integrals are the following well-known expressions for area A, moment of inertia about the y-axis I_y, moment of inertia about the z-axis I_z, and the product of inertia I_{yz}.

$$\int_A dA = A$$

$$\int_A y^2 \, dA = I_z$$

$$\int_A z^2 \, dA = I_y \qquad (10)$$

$$\int_A yz \, dA = I_{yz}$$

Substituting 2.2.9 and 2.2.10 into 2.2.8, we get

$$N = aA$$
$$M_y = bI_{yz} + cI_y \qquad (11)$$
$$M_z = bI_z + cI_{yz}$$

Solving these for a, b, and c, we get

$$a = \frac{N}{A}$$

$$b = \frac{M_z I_y - M_y I_{yz}}{I_y I_z - I_{yz}^2} \qquad (12)$$

$$c = \frac{M_y I_z - M_z I_{yz}}{I_y I_z - I_{yz}^2}$$

Finally we rewrite 2.2.7 as

$$s_n = \frac{N}{A} + \frac{M_z I_y - M_y I_{yz}}{I_y I_z - I_{yz}^{2}} y + \frac{M_y I_z - M_z I_{yz}}{I_y I_z - I_{yz}^{2}} z \qquad (13)$$

When the stress resultants N, M_y, and M_z are given, the normal stress s_n at any point (y, z) of the cross section may be found directly from equation 2.2.13.

In a given situation, we begin by finding the purely geometric properties of the cross section, A, I_y, I_z, and I_{yz}. We then determine the coordinates y and z of the point at which the normal stress is desired. Finally, we substitute these values with the known values of the stress resultants N, M_y, and M_z to get the normal stress s_n.

When the centroidal axes are also *principal axes of inertia* for the cross section we have

$$I_{yz} = 0 \qquad (14)$$

and 2.2.13 reduces to

$$s_n = \frac{N}{A} + \frac{M_z}{I_z} y + \frac{M_y}{I_y} z \qquad (15)$$

The stress resultants may be reduced to a single force N applied eccentrically at some location (y_k, z_k), using

$$M_y = N z_k, \qquad M_z = N y_k \qquad (16)$$

When the only stress resultant is a normal force acting at the centroid of the cross section we have $z_k = y_k = 0$ and obtain the uniform distribution of normal stress given by

$$s_n = \frac{N}{A} \qquad (17)$$

When the only stress resultant is a bending moment about the z axis, the distribution of normal stress is given by

$$s_n = \frac{M_z}{I_z} y \qquad (18)$$

The following examples are designed to illustrate as many facets of the general equation 2.2.13 as possible.

Example 2.2.1 Find the equation for normal stress at any point on the cross section of Figure 2.4 due to the stress resultants shown. We begin by finding the geometric properties of the cross section. The vertical axis is an axis of symmetry; hence, it is a principal axis of inertia. The other principal axis of inertia is normal to it passing through the centroid of the cross section as shown. The positive directions of y and z are taken according to the convention of

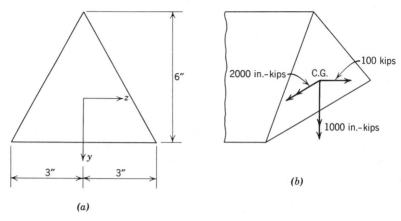

(a)

(b)

Figure 2.4

Figure 2.1*a*. The value of I_{yz} is zero for these principal axes. $I_z = \frac{1}{36}(6)(6)^3 = 36$ in.^{4}, $I_y = \frac{2}{12}(6)(3)^3 = 27$ in.^{4}, and $A = \frac{1}{2}(6)(6) = 18$ in.^{2}. With principal axes we may use the reduced form of the general equation given by 2.2.15. Using the prescribed sign convention on the stress resultants we have $N = 100$ kips, $M_y = 1000$ in.-kips, $M_z = 2000$ in.-kips. The normal stress equation is now given by

$$s_n = \frac{100}{18} + \frac{2000}{36}y + \frac{1000}{27}z = 5.55 + 55.55y + 37.02z \qquad (19)$$

Example 2.2.2   Find the maximum compressive stress on the cross section shown in Figure 2.5 due to a single compressive force of 100 kips acting at point *A*.

We begin by choosing temporary axes y' and z' as shown and using them to find the centroid of the area.

$$A = (3)(3) \quad\quad + \tfrac{1}{2}(3)(3) \quad\quad\quad\quad = 13.5 \text{ in.}^2$$
$$y' = [(3)(3)(1.5) + \tfrac{1}{2}(3)(3)(1)] \div 13.5 = 1.33 \text{ in.} \qquad (20)$$
$$z' = [(3)(3)(1.5) - \tfrac{1}{2}(3)(3)(1)] \div 13.5 = 0.67 \text{ in.}$$

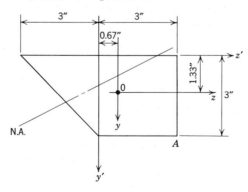

Figure 2.5

We now choose our y, z axes as shown passing through the centroid. Using these centroidal axes, we now find

$$I_y = (\tfrac{1}{12})(3)(3)^3 + (3)(3)(1.50 - 0.67)^2 + (\tfrac{1}{36})(3)(3)^3$$
$$+ (\tfrac{1}{2})(3)(3)(1.00 + 0.67)^2 = 27.75 \text{ in.}^4$$

$$I_z = (\tfrac{1}{12})(3)(3)^3 + (3)(3)(1.50 - 1.33)^2 + (\tfrac{1}{36})(3)(3)^3$$
$$+ (\tfrac{1}{2})(3)(3)(1.33 - 1.00)^2 = 9.75 \text{ in.}^4 \tag{21}$$

$$I_{yz} = (3)(3)(1.50 - 1.33)(1.50 - 0.67) + (\tfrac{1}{72})(3)^2(3)^2$$
$$+ (\tfrac{1}{2})(3)(3)(1.00 + 0.67)(1.33 - 1.00) = 4.875 \text{ in.}^4$$

Since we are not using principal axes we must employ the general equation 2.2.13. The bending moments are given by 2.2.16 since we have a single eccentrically applied normal resultant force. We have $z_k = (3.00 - 0.67) = 2.33$ in. and $y_k = (3.00 - 1.33) = 1.67$ in., and $N = -100$ kips, $M_z = -(100)(1.67) = -167$ in.-kips, $M_y = -(100)(2.33) = -233$ in.-kips. At any position, the normal stress is given by

$$s_n = -\frac{100}{13.5} + \frac{(-167)(27.75) - (-233)(4.875)}{(27.75)(9.75) - (4.875)^2}y$$
$$+ \frac{(-233)(9.75) - (-167)(4.875)}{(27.75)(9.75) - (4.875)^2}z \tag{22}$$

or

$$s_n = -7.41 - 14.18y - 5.91z \tag{23}$$

Now the *neutral axis* is given by this equation when we set $s_n = 0$ or

$$7.41 + 14.18y + 5.91z = 0 \tag{24}$$

This is shown plotted on Figure 2.5. Since the normal stress variation is linear over the cross section, we will find compressive stress on that side of the neutral axis on which the compressive force N is applied and tensile stress on the other side. The maximum compressive stress will occur at the point on the cross section that is the most distant from the neutral axis on the compressive side or in this figure, at point A, the load point. The coordinates of this point are $y = 1.67$ in., $z = 2.33$ in. Substituting these into 2.2.23 we find $s_n = -44.86$ ksi, the answer.*

Example 2.2.3 Determine the maximum normal stress in the beam of Figure 2.6a. The bending moment about the z axis is given in 2.6c. The bending moment about the y-axis is zero everywhere and the axial force is $N = -100$ kips over the left half as shown in 2.6d. Normal stress depends only on N and M_z here. Both of these stress resultants are a maximum at the center. The maximum stress is compressive and occurs at the top fibers just to the left of midspan and equals

$$s_n = -\frac{100}{54} + \frac{(5000)(-4.5)}{364.5} = -63.56 \text{ ksi} \tag{25}$$

* There are those who would prefer finding the principal axes of inertia for the given cross section and solving the problem using equation 2.2.15. The authors feel that there is less chance for error and that a more rapid solution is found using the longer equation 2.2.13 since the quantities present in that equation are much more readily found than the quantities in 2.2.15.

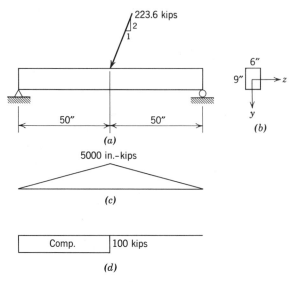

Figure 2.6

whereas the maximum tensile stress occurs at the bottom fibers just to the right of midspan and equals

$$s_n = \frac{(5000)(4.5)}{364.5} = 61.7 \text{ ksi} \qquad (26)$$

When the normal force and bending moments do not reach their maximum values at the same cross section, it may be necessary to try several sections before finding the absolute maximum normal stress.

Example 2.2.4   Select a beam cross section capable of supporting the single stress resultant $\bar{M}_z$ in such a way that the normal stress will never exceed the value $\bar{s}_n$. Here we make use of 2.2.18 and write

$$s_n = \frac{M_z y}{I_z} \qquad (27)$$

Since s_n and M_z are given as $\bar{s}_n$ and $\bar{M}_z$ and normal stress reaches its maximum value at the outer fiber at $y = c$, we find from 2.2.27

$$\frac{I_z}{c} = \frac{\bar{M}_z}{\bar{s}_n} \qquad (28)$$

We introduce the new symbol Z, called the *section modulus*

$$Z = \frac{I_z}{c} = \frac{\bar{M}_z}{\bar{s}_n} \qquad (29)$$

and say that the beam cross section must have a section modulus equal to $\bar{M}_z/\bar{s}_n$. Tables are available that give the section moduli for many structural shapes.

Example 2.2.5 Find the location of a single resultant normal force on Figure 2.5 such that the equation for the neutral axis will be $z = -0.074$ in. For this problem, we shall introduce 2.2.16 into 2.2.13 and write

$$s_n = N \left[\frac{1}{A} + \frac{y_k I_y - z_k I_{yz}}{I_y I_z - I_{yz}^2} y + \frac{z_k I_z - y_k I_{yz}}{I_y I_z - I_{yz}^2} z \right] \tag{30}$$

At the neutral axis the quantity in the brackets must be zero and in the present example must reduce to $0 = z + 0.074$. Or

$$0 = +0.074 + z = \frac{1}{A} + \frac{y_k I_y - z_k I_{yz}}{I_y I_z - I_{yz}^2} y + \frac{z_k I_z - y_k I_{yz}}{I_y I_z - I_{yz}^2} z \tag{31}$$

Using the geometric properties found earlier, we match terms on the left-hand side of 2.2.31 with terms on the right side to give

$$\frac{1}{A} = 0.074$$

$$\frac{y_k I_y - z_k I_{yz}}{I_y I_z - I_{yz}^2} = 0 \tag{32}$$

$$\frac{z_k I_z - y_k I_{yz}}{I_y I_z - I_{yz}^2} = 1$$

From 2.2.32 we confirm that $A = 13.5$ in.^{2} and find

$$y_k = \left[\frac{I_{yz}}{I_y} \right] z_k = \frac{4.875}{27.75} z_k = 0.176 \, z_k \tag{33}$$

We substitute this into the third of 2.2.32 to find $z_k = 27.75$ in., and from 2.2.33. we then obtain $y_k = 4.88$ in., which gives the coordinates of the load position required.

2.3 Normal Stresses in Curved Elastic Members

We now apply Navier's hypothesis to the curved, elastic beam in order to find a relation between normal stress and the stress resultants N, M_v, and M_w where v and w are centroidal axes in the plane of the cross section as shown in Figure 2.7. The radius of curvature of the centroidal axis is given by r. The length of an elemental fiber located at the centroid is given by ds, and the fiber a distance w from the centroid is given by ds_w. The radius of curvature of the fiber of length ds_w is $(r - w)$ since w is taken as positive toward the center of curvature. From similar triangles we find $(ds_w)/(r - w) = ds/r$, or

$$ds_w = \frac{r - w}{r} \, ds \tag{1}$$

Following the procedure employed in §2.2, when Navier's hypothesis was

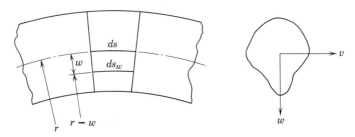

Figure 2.7

applied to straight members we have the strain at any location (v, w) given by

$$N = \frac{(a'' - a') + (b'' - b')v + (c'' - c')w}{ds_w} \tag{2}$$

and the normal stress for the elastic material is given by

$$s_n = \frac{E}{ds}\left[(a'' - a') + (b'' - b')v + (c'' - c')w\right]\frac{r}{r - w} \tag{3}$$

Since v and w are the only variables in 2.3.3 we may introduce new constants a, b, c to read

$$s_n = (a + bv + cw)\frac{r}{r - w} \tag{4}$$

We rewrite the fraction as

$$\frac{r}{r - w} = \frac{1}{1 - \left(\dfrac{w}{r}\right)} \tag{5}$$

so as to be able to see more clearly that only as the ratio w/r approaches zero (or as r approaches ∞) does the expression for normal stress in 2.3.4 become linear as prescribed in 2.2.7 for straight elastic members. Thus, *only for straight members does the assumption that plane sections remain plane lead to a linear distribution of stress* over the cross section.

We now substitute 2.3.4 into 2.1.3, changing y to w and z to v,

$$N = a\int_A \frac{r\,dA}{r - w} + b\int_A \frac{rv\,dA}{r - w} + c\int_A \frac{rw\,dA}{r - w}$$

$$M_v = a\int_A \frac{rw\,dA}{r - w} + b\int_A \frac{rvw\,dA}{r - w} + c\int_A \frac{rw^2\,dA}{r - w} \tag{6}$$

$$M_w = a\int_A \frac{rv\,dA}{r - w} + b\int_A \frac{rv^2\,dA}{r - w} + c\int_A \frac{rwv\,dA}{r - w}$$

If we introduce the symbols

$$J_v = \int_A \frac{rw^2 \, dA}{r - w}$$

$$J_w = \int_A \frac{rv^2 \, dA}{r - w} \tag{7}$$

$$J_{vw} = \int_A \frac{rvw \, dA}{r - w}$$

we note that as $r \to \infty$ (using 2.3.5), $w \to y$ and $v \to z$ and J_v, J_w, and J_{vw} reduce to I_z, I_y, and I_{yz}, respectively.

Using the following relations obtained from direct division, we find

$$\frac{r}{r - w} = 1 + \frac{w}{r} + \frac{w^2}{r(r - w)}$$

$$\frac{rv}{r - w} = v + \frac{vw}{r - w} \tag{8}$$

$$\frac{rw}{r - w} = w + \frac{w^2}{r - w}$$

We rewrite the integrals appearing in 2.3.6 as

$$\int_A \frac{r \, dA}{r - w} = A + \int_A \frac{w \, dA}{r} + \frac{J_v}{r^2}$$

$$\int_A \frac{rv \, dA}{r - w} = \int_A v \, dA + \frac{J_{vw}}{r} \tag{9}$$

$$\int_A \frac{rw \, dA}{r - w} = \int_A w \, dA + \frac{J_v}{r}$$

We chose v and w as centroidal axes, thus

$$\int_A v \, dA = \int_A w \, dA = 0 \tag{10}$$

Equations 2.3.6 are rewritten as

$$N = a \left[A + \frac{J_v}{r^2} \right] + b \frac{J_{vw}}{r} + c \frac{J_v}{r}$$

$$M_v = a \frac{J_v}{r} + b J_{vw} + c J_v \tag{11}$$

$$M_w = a \frac{J_{vw}}{r} + b J_w + c J_{vw}$$

We solve these simultaneously for a, b, and c to find

$$a = \frac{N}{A} - \frac{M_v}{Ar}$$

$$b = \frac{M_w J_v - M_v J_{vw}}{J_v J_w - J_{vw}^2} \tag{12}$$

$$c = \frac{M_v J_w - M_w J_{vw}}{J_v J_w - J_{vw}^2} - \frac{N}{Ar} + \frac{M_v}{Ar^2}$$

Finally we combine terms to write 2.3.4 in its final form

$$s_n = \frac{N}{A} - \frac{M_v}{Ar} + \frac{M_w J_v - M_v J_{vw}}{J_v J_w - J_{vw}^2}\left(\frac{vr}{r-w}\right)$$

$$+ \frac{M_v J_w - M_w J_{vw}}{J_v J_w - J_{vw}^2}\left(\frac{wr}{r-w}\right) \tag{13}$$

When $J_{vw} = 0$, we get the reduced form

$$s_n = \frac{N}{A} - \frac{M_v}{Ar} + \frac{M_w}{J_w}\left(\frac{rv}{r-w}\right) + \frac{M_v}{J_v}\left(\frac{rw}{r-w}\right) \tag{14}$$

The value of J_{vw} is always zero when the w axis is an axis of symmetry. This is easily seen if we consider a pair of elemental areas taken equidistant from the symmetry axis. For each, the value of $r/(r - w)$ is the same. The product vw for one of the elements is equal in magnitude but opposite in sign to the product vw for the other. Thus the sum of the $(rvw \, dA)/(r - w)$ must be zero when taken over the entire area.

In many practical problems we find $M_w = 0$ and 2.3.14 becomes

$$s_n = \frac{N}{A} - \frac{M_v}{Ar} + \frac{M_v}{J_v}\left(\frac{rw}{r-w}\right) \tag{15}$$

It should be noted that expressions 2.3.13, 2.3.14, and 2.3.15 reduce to those for straight members when r becomes infinitely large.

A very useful value of J_v in 2.3.15 is that for the rectangular area of width b and depth h in Figure 2.8a.*

$$J_v = -r^2bh - r^3b \ln\left(\frac{2r - h}{2r + h}\right) \tag{16}$$

Another convenient value of J_v is that of a circular section of radius R and radius of curvature r shown in Figure 2.8b. It is given by

$$J_v = \pi r^2(2r^2 + 2r\sqrt{r^2 - R^2} - R^2) \tag{17}$$

* When $r > 4h$, seven-place logarithm tables must be used for accurate results.

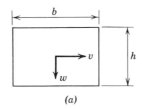

(a)

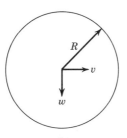

(b)   **Figure 2.8**

Example 2.3.1   Find the normal stresses at points A and B in the structure shown in Figure 2.9a. For this structure we find $J_{vw} = 0$, $A = 18$ in.^{2} and

$$J_v = -(9)^2(3)(6) - (9)^3(3) \ln \left(\frac{18 - 6}{18 + 6} \right) = 57.92 \text{ in.}^4 \qquad (18)$$

At points A and B we have

$$N = -70.7 \text{ kips} \qquad M_v = -636.3 \text{ in.-kips} \qquad M_w = 0 \qquad (19)$$

Substituting into 2.3.15 we obtain

$$s_n = -\frac{70.7}{18} + \frac{636.3}{(18)(9)} - \frac{(636.3)(9)}{57.92} \left(\frac{w}{9 - w} \right) \qquad (20)$$

$$[s_n]_A = 24.72 \text{ ksi}, \qquad [s_n]_B = -49.44 \text{ ksi}$$

If the formula 2.2.15 derived for straight beams were used instead of 2.3.15 we would have

$$s_n = -\frac{70.7}{18} - \frac{636.3w}{54} \qquad (21)$$

giving $$[s_n]_A = 31.42 \text{ ksi}, \qquad [s_n]_B = -39.28 \text{ ksi} \qquad (22)$$

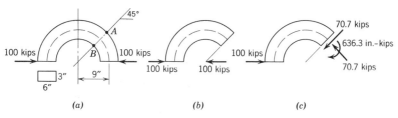

(a)   (b)   (c)

Figure 2.9

The error introduced by using the straight beam formula is seen to be very great here; however, it diminishes as the ratio w/r decreases. For large structures such as arch bridges it may be assumed to be zero without introducing appreciable error. Only then will the assumption that plane sections remain plane be consistent with a linear variation in stress.

2.4 Normal Stresses in Elastoplastic Members—Axial Forces*

The assumption that the material of a member obeys Hooke's law is usually a good assumption as long as the maximum strain on any fiber is small. For large strains, the assumption is not valid. In this and the next few sections we shall relate our discussion to one particular material; namely, mild steel.

A stress-strain plot for a typical structural grade of steel obtained from a uniaxial tension test is as shown in Figure 2.10. We note that as long as the strain is less than the proportional limit, ϵ_0, the relationship between stress and strain is linear, following Hooke's law. For strains greater than ϵ_0 the relationship is decidedly nonlinear. As a conservative approximation for this material we choose the idealized curve shown in Figure 2.11 so that our computations will be as simple as possible. The yield strain, ϵ_0, is taken equal to the proportional limit. For an A-7 steel we shall have ϵ_0, given by 0.0011 in./in. at a stress level of $s_0 = 33$ ksi. We shall use this value and the curve of Figure 2.11 for our future investigations. It will be noted that the chosen values of the yield strain and the yield stress indicate that within the elastic range the value of Young's modulus of elasticity is 30,000 ksi. For a perfectly elastic material, the curve in Figure 2.11 would continue upward as shown by the dashed line. We speak of our idealized curve as

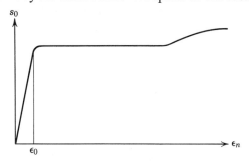

Figure 2.10

---

* The plasticity of bars was first studied systematically by the great French scientist, Barré de Saint-Venant (1797–1886), who solved a number of basic problems including the pure bending of a prismatic bar and the twisting of a right circular cylindrical bar. Consideration of plastic deformation in practical problems did not occur, however, until relatively recent years.

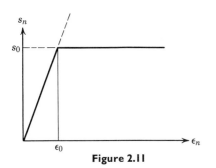

Figure 2.11

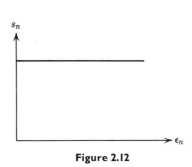

Figure 2.12

representing the behavior of a perfect *elastoplastic* material. When there is no elastic portion present, we have the curve of Figure 2.12, which represents the behavior of a *perfect plastic* material. In structural problems the elastoplastic material is the most realistic.

We now assume that plane sections remain plane just as for an elastic bar. The strain is the same as for the elastic bar and may be described mathematically by

$$\epsilon = a + bx + cy \tag{1}$$

For simplicity we shall investigate the special case: $b = c = 0$. We find that the distribution of normal stress, s, is uniform. We may write

$$s = a \tag{2}$$

We have dropped the n subscript from ϵ and s since only normal stresses and strains are considered and no confusion arises in using this simpler notation. The stress resultants associated with this distribution of stress are

$$N = \int_A a \, dA$$

$$M_y = \int_A az \, dA \tag{3}$$

$$M_z = \int_A ay \, dA$$

By using centroidal axes these equations reduce to $N = aA$, $M_y = 0$, and $M_z = 0$. Equation 2.4.2 thus is written

$$s = \frac{N}{A} \tag{4}$$

as for perfect elasticity. We now reverse our argument and say that a single concentrated normal force acting at the centroid of the area of an elastoplastic bar gives rise to a uniform distribution of normal stress. The strain associated with this stress may either be less than or greater than the yield strain for the material.

As the axial force N on a perfectly elastoplastic bar is increased, the normal stress also increases until it reaches the yield stress s_0. Upon reaching this stress, the strain (and consequently, the deformation) continues to increase beyond the yield strain without limit. In an actual material, as opposed to an idealized material, the increasing strain will usually be associated with some increase in stress.

We note that a statically determinate and stable truss made from our elastoplastic material is able to carry any load less than that causing the most highly stressed bar to reach the yield stress. When this yield load is reached the bar in question is stressed to its limit and the structure taken as a whole is unable to carry additional load without collapsing. We speak of the load causing the first bar to reach its yield stress as the *yield load*, and the load necessary to cause collapse of the structure as the *collapse load*. These are the same in the statically determinate structure, since the structure becomes unstable and collapses as soon as one of its members is incapable of supporting additional force.

For an indeterminate elasto-plastic truss, as Chapter 5 shows in detail, there is a reserve of strength associated with the fact that the collapse load is greater than the yield load. With but one redundant bar in the truss, for example, the structure reaches its yield load when the most highly stressed bar reaches its yield stress, but the structure does not fail, since by virtue of being indeterminate to the first degree this first bar may not be necessary to preserve the stability of the structure.* Only when a second bar that is necessary to stability reaches its yield stress will the truss collapse.

2.5 Normal Stresses in Elastoplastic Beams—Bending

The nonlinear nature of the stress-strain curve for the elasto-plastic material leads to such complexities in analysis that we cannot give a completely general discussion as was possible for the elastic material. Rather, we can treat only special problems of practical importance. Bending about a principal axis in the absence of axial force is such a problem.

Again using Navier's hypothesis regarding plane sections, we find, as before, that for a straight bar the strain will vary linearly over the cross section of the bar. In this section we shall assume furthermore, that the y and z axes are principal axes, and that bending occurs only about the

* When the first bar to yield is a bar that is necessary to the stability of the structure, collapse occurs immediately.

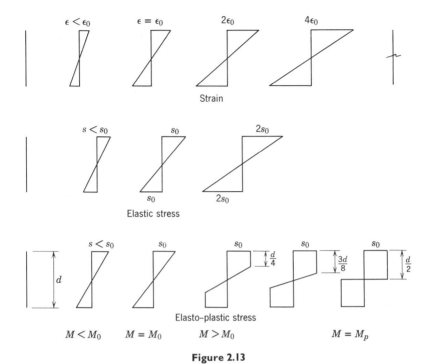

Figure 2.13

z axis. The bending moment and moment of inertia about the z-axis is denoted simply by M and I.

With a linear variation of strain, we can expect the maximum values to occur at the fibers the most distant from the z-axis. As long as the moment is small, the maximum strains are less than the yield strain and all points in the cross section are strained elastically. Such a distribution of strain is associated with a linear distribution of stress according to Hooke's law.

As the moment is increased, the extreme fiber strain reaches the yield strain ϵ_0, signaling first yielding of the cross section. The moment causing first yielding is denoted by M_0 and called the *yield moment*. For moments larger than M_0 the distribution of strain remains linear according to Navier's hypothesis, and the extreme fiber strain exceeds ϵ_0. The portion of the cross section having strains less than ϵ_0 is deforming elastically, and over that portion the normal stress continues to vary in linear fashion. At the fibers having strains equal to or greater than the yield strain we find from Figure 2.11 that the normal stress is constant and equal to s_0. Plots of strain and stress distributions over a cross section for various bending moments are given in Figure 2.13. Plots of normal stress for elastic as well as elasto-plastic materials are shown.

Figures 2.13a and 2.13b show the distributions for $\epsilon < \epsilon_0$ and $\epsilon = \epsilon_0$. In each the fibers are deformed elastically and normal stress variations are linear. In Figure 2.13c the maximum strain is equal to $2\epsilon_0$. If the material were elastic, the stress distribution would remain linear with the maximum stress being $2s_0$. The fibers having a strain equal to the yield strain of a rectangular cross section are one-half the distance between the centroid and the outer edges. At these locations we also find the normal stress equal to the yield stress. Between these fibers and the edges, fibers are strained beyond the yield strain and from Figure 2.11 we see that they must be stressed the constant amount s_0 as shown in Figure 2.13c.

When $\epsilon = 4\epsilon_0$ at the outer fibers, the elastic core for the elasto-plastic material still has a linear variation of stress. The fibers with $\epsilon = \epsilon_0$ now occur at points three-eighths the depth from the edges. Between these points there is again a core of elastic deformation. Between either of these points and the nearest outer edge there is a region of plastification. The stress distributions are shown in Figure 2.13d.

Clearly, as the bending moment continues to increase, the strain distribution continues to remain linear by Navier's hypothesis, the stress distribution for elastic materials remains linear by Hooke's law, and the stress distribution for elasto-plastic materials approaches as a limit that shown in Figure 2.13e. It is equally clear that it can only approach this state as a limit since to actually reach it would mean infinite strains at the edges of the cross section. The moment necessary to cause this limiting condition is designated as the *fully plastic moment* and given the symbol M_p.

We shall now compute the values of the bending moments necessary to cause the stress distributions of Figure 2.13 by using a rectangular section of width b and depth d. This is easily done by summing the moments of the stress diagrams about the neutral axes. For 2.13a we have the resulting forces shown in Figure 2.14 acting at the centers of pressure of the stress areas. This gives

$$M = \frac{sbd^2}{6} \tag{1}$$

For Figure 2.13b we find similarly that

$$M = M_0 = \frac{s_0bd^2}{6} \tag{2}$$

Each of these could be predicted by the elastic analysis of §2.2 since the stress variation is completely linear. For such a calculation we find the section modulus to be

$$Z = \frac{I}{c} = \frac{(\frac{1}{12})(b)(d)^3}{(d/2)} = \frac{bd^2}{6} \tag{3}$$

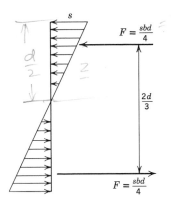

Figure 2.14

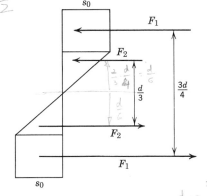

Figure 2.15

and from 2.2.29

$$M = sZ = \frac{sbd^2}{6} \tag{4}$$

For the distribution of Figure 2.13c we find the moment using Figure 2.15. We have

$$F_1 = \frac{s_0bd}{4} \qquad F_2 = \frac{s_0bd}{8} \tag{5}$$

and

$$M = \left(\frac{s_0bd}{4}\right)\left(\frac{3d}{4}\right) + \left(\frac{s_0bd}{8}\right)\left(\frac{d}{3}\right) = \frac{11s_0bd^2}{48} \tag{6}$$

For full plastification we use Figure 2.16 to find

$$F = \frac{s_0bd}{2} \qquad M = M_p = \frac{s_0bd^2}{4} \tag{7}$$

We defined Z as the section modulus for the elastic beam and indicated

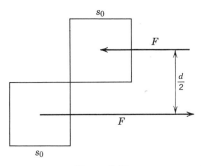

Figure 2.16

that it is equal to the bending moment divided by the extreme fiber stress. We similarly define Z_p as the *plastic section modulus* and let it equal the value of the plastic moment, M_p, divided by the yield stress, s_0. Thus for the rectangular section we have

$$Z_p = \frac{bd^2}{4} \tag{8}$$

The difference between the value of M_0, the yield moment, and M_p, the plastic moment, represents the reserve strength that the beam has available for carrying moment beyond that necessary to cause first yielding. A good measure of this reserve is given by

$$\frac{M_p}{M_0} = \frac{s_0 Z_p}{s_0 Z} = \frac{Z_p}{Z} = \alpha \tag{9}$$

where the ratio of plastic section modulus to elastic section modulus is given the special symbol, α, called the *plastic shape factor* for the cross section. We see that for the rectangular section we have

$$\alpha = \left(\frac{bd^2}{4}\right)\left(\frac{6}{bd^2}\right) = 1.5 \tag{10}$$

This states that the moment necessary to cause full plastification of the cross section is 50% greater than the moment necessary to cause first yielding.

For the more general case of a cross section having a single axis of symmetry as shown in Figure 2.17, we note that the positive and negative stress solids have equal volumes (thus forming a couple as a resultant) only if the neutral axis occurs at a location such that it divides the total area in half. Letting the distances from the neutral axis to the centroids of these two partial areas be designated by $\bar{y}_1$ and $\bar{y}_2$ as shown in Figure 2.17, we find

$$Z_p = \frac{M_p}{s_0} = \frac{s_0}{s_0}\left(\frac{A}{2}\right)(\bar{y}_1) + \frac{s_0}{s_0}\left(\frac{A}{2}\right)(\bar{y}_2) = \frac{A}{2}(\bar{y}_1 + \bar{y}_2) \tag{11}$$

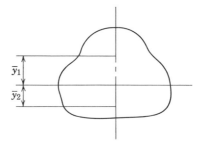

Figure 2.17

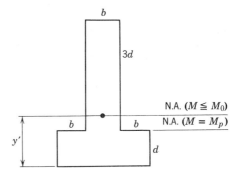

Figure 2.18

where A is the area of the total cross section. With two axes of symmetry we have $\bar{y}_1 = \bar{y}_2 = \bar{y}$ and

$$Z_p = A\bar{y} \qquad (12)$$

where $\bar{y}$ is now the distance from mid-depth to the centroid of the half-area. Again, this checks the rectangle for $A = bd$ and $\bar{y} = d/4$. Thus

$$M_p = s_0 Z_p = \frac{s_0 b d^2}{4} \qquad (13)$$

For the Tee-section shown in Figure 2.18 we find the centroidal axis to be a distance y' from the base and equal to

$$y' = \frac{(b)(4d)(2d) + (2)(b)(d)(d/2)}{(b)(4d) + (2)(b)(d)} = \frac{3d}{2} \qquad (14)$$

This represents the location of the neutral axis as long as all fibers are strained within the elastic range. The axis that divides the total area into halves is located a distance d from the base and represents the neutral axis at full plastification. We conclude, therefore, that unless the centroidal axis itself divides the total area in half, the neutral axis will shift* gradually from the centroid of the section (when all fibers are elastically deformed) to an axis that halves the area (when all fibers are plastically deformed).

Example 2.5.1 Find the location of the neutral axis for the elastic range, the location of the neutral axis for complete plastification, and the shape factor for the *I*-section of Figure 2.19. We begin by locating the centroid relative to the base, finding

$$y' = \frac{(3)(0.5) + (2)(2) + (5)(3.5)}{10} = 2.3 \text{ in.} \qquad (15)$$

This is the location of the neutral axis when all fibers are deformed elastically.

---

* This shifting was anticipated nearly two hundred years ago by the French engineer and physicist, Augustin Coulomb (1736–1806), in his early discussion of fiber stresses.

We note that the area of the top flange equals the sum of the areas of web and lower flange. Hence, the axis dividing the cross section in half lies at the base of the top flange—the position that the neutral axis approaches in the limit as the bending moment applied to the section approaches the fully plastic moment and the section undergoes complete plastification. The moment of inertia of this cross section about a horizontal principal axis is given by

$$I = \frac{(1)(2)^3}{12} + 2(0.3)^2 + \frac{(3)(1)^3}{12} + 3(1.8)^2 + \frac{(5)(1)^3}{12} + 5(1.2)^2 = 18.44 \text{ in.}^2 \quad (16)$$

The elastic section modulus, Z, is thus equal to

$$Z = \frac{I}{c} = \frac{18.44}{2.3} = 8.02 \text{ in.}^3 \quad (17)$$

where c is taken as the distance from the centroid to the lower edge since first yielding occurs at that edge. The distances from the centroids of the two halves of the area from the base of the upper flange are

$$\bar{y}_1 = 0.5 \text{ in.}, \qquad \bar{y}_2 = \frac{(2)(1) + (3)(2.5)}{5} = 1.9 \text{ in.} \quad (18)$$

The plastic section modulus is thus given by

$$Z_p = \tfrac{10}{2}(0.5 + 1.9) = 12 \text{ in.}^3 \quad (19)$$

Finally the shape factor for this section is

$$\alpha = \frac{Z_p}{Z} = \frac{12}{8.02} = 1.496 \quad (20)$$

This I-section has a reserve of strength of 49.6% beyond that necessary to resist first yielding.

Example 2.5.2 Determine the bending moment necessary to deform the rectangular section of Figure 2.20 to give a strain at the outer fiber of ϵ_c, and plot

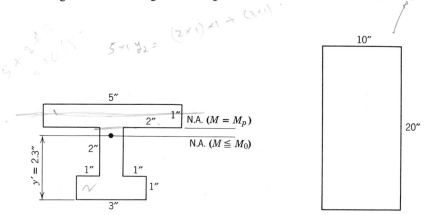

Figure 2.19   Figure 2.20

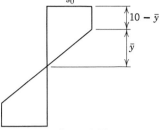

Figure 2.21

a curve of bending moment versus strain at outer fiber. Here, we note that the yield strain occurs at a distance $\bar{y}$ above the centroidal axis. We now note that

$$\frac{\bar{y}}{10} = \frac{\epsilon_0}{\epsilon_c} = \frac{1}{\gamma} \tag{21}$$

where γ, some constant, is given by

$$\gamma = \frac{\epsilon_c}{\epsilon_0} \tag{22}$$

The stress above this level is s_0 and the bending moment causing such a state of stress is given by (see Figure 2.21)

$$M = \frac{2(s_0)(10 - \bar{y})(10 + \bar{y})(10)}{2} + \frac{s_0(10)\bar{y}}{2}(2)\left(\frac{2\bar{y}}{3}\right) = 10s_0\left(100 - \frac{\bar{y}^2}{3}\right) \tag{23}$$

Using $s_0 = 33$ ksi and equation 2.5.21, we find

$$M = 11,000\left(3 - \frac{1}{\gamma^2}\right) \tag{24}$$

The curve of Figure 2.22 is plotted using the values in Table 2.1. We choose

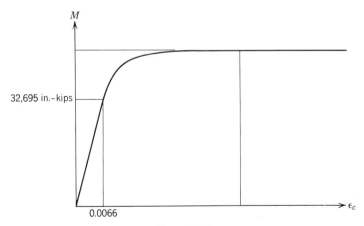

Figure 2.22

the values of γ shown and use 2.5.24 to calculate M and 2.5.22 to calculate ϵ_c.

TABLE 2.1

γ	M	ϵ_c
1.0	22,000 in.-kips	0.0011
1.5	28,116 in.-kips	0.0017
2.0	30,250 in.-kips	0.0022
3.0	31,777 in.-kips	0.0033
6.0	32,695 in.-kips	0.0066
∞	33,000 in.-kips	∞

2.6 Reversal of Normal Stresses

Thus far we have been concerned only with the stresses and strains produced by an axial force or bending moment being applied to the cross section of an elastic or an elastoplastic member. We now inquire into the normal stresses and strains associated with the total or partial removal of the stress resultants.

When an axial force is applied to a straight member it causes all fibers to be strained equally. When the material is elastic the stress-strain variation on loading is linear in accordance with Hooke's law. If the force is reduced, the stress level is reduced. Hooke's law indicates that the change in stress is always proportional to the change in strain. Hence, if the stress changes an amount Δs, we expect a change in strain $\Delta \epsilon$ of

$$\Delta \epsilon = \frac{\Delta s}{E} \tag{1}$$

This suggests that upon unloading the stress-strain curve will return along the loading curve as indicated in Figure 2.23. For the perfectly elastic material we have a linear stress-strain curve up to any stress or strain level. Hence, regardless of the previous loading history of the member we may always determine the stress in the member by dividing the axial force by the cross sectional area.

This will not be true for the elastoplastic material. Experiments indicate that when a member is strained beyond the yield strain and then subjected to a reversal of loading (which is equivalent to unloading), the stress-strain curve on unloading is a straight line parallel to the initial portion of the loading curve as shown by line AC in Figure 2.24. The stress may be reduced to such an extent that the curve crosses the ϵ axis and the straight line may continue until the yield stress level in compression is reached. At this point, *unconfined plastic flow* may occur in the negative

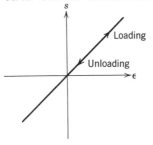

Figure 2.23

direction as shown by line *BD* in Figure 2.24. If, for example, an axial load of 33 kips were applied to a bar of one square inch area it would cause the stresses to reach the yield value and nothing would prevent the bar from undergoing an unconfined plastic flow resulting in a greater and greater elongation. If, say at point *A* in Figure 2.24, at a strain of 0.003 in./in. the force is removed, there will be an elastic recovery indicated by some portion of the line *AB* in Figure 2.24. The removal of a 33-kip tensile force is equivalent to the addition of a 33-kip compressive force to the existing 33-kip tensile force. Such an addition is associated with a change in stress of 33 ksi. Moving from *A* along *AB* until we have affected a change of 33 ksi, we find that we reach point *C*. This indicates that upon removal of the load there is no residual normal stress but there is a residual strain of $(0.003 - 33/E)$ or 0.0019 in./in. If to the 33-kip tensile force we add a 66-kip compressive force, we find that we move from point *A* to *B*, giving a final stress of 33 ksi compression which is equal to the yield stress in compression. At point *B* the strain is 0.0008 in./in. At this stress level we expect the strain to change indefinitely from the value 0.0008 in./in. showing an unconfined plastic flow in compression.

The behavior of the fibers of a member subject to bending is quite different from the behavior under the action of axial forces. In the latter, when first yielding of the cross section occurs, all fibers yield and unconfined plastic flow follows. First yielding for bending, on the other hand, occurs only in the outer fibers and the interior fibers, still behaving elastically, offer resistance to unconfined deformation of the outer fibers. This creates *confined plastic flow*. Only when all fibers have reached their yield strain can unconfined plastic flow occur.

Upon applying a bending moment that is greater than the yield moment, we find the various fibers to be at different levels of strain and stress. At the neutral axis the strain is zero (point 0 in Figure 2.25). At one location below and one location above the neutral axis the strain is equal to the yield strain (points *B* and *F* in Figure 2.25). Between these locations all fibers are elastic (i.e., points *A* and *E*). At the outer fibers the strains may be as given by D and H. Locations between the elastic core and the extreme fibers may be strained to, say, points C and G.

After each fiber is unloaded, a stress-strain curve such as given in Figure 2.24 will follow. Fibers within the elastic core will return along a straight line from A or E toward the origin. Fibers strained beyond the yield strain will return along lines (shown dotted) parallel to the initial portion of the curve.

Figure 2.26 shows the states of strain and stress for a member subjected to a bending moment greater than the yield moment, which is subsequently reduced. In the strain diagrams the distribution remains linear according to Navier's hypothesis, and it reaches a maximum value ϵ_c of three times the yield strain (shown by point D in Figure 2.25) and then is reduced to zero. When the strain $\epsilon_c = 3\epsilon_0$ fiber #3 separates the elastic from the plastic zone as shown in Figure 2.26b. When the strain ϵ_c is reduced to $2\epsilon_0$ as shown in Figure 2.26c, the stress on the extreme fiber becomes zero since point D follows the dotted line of Figure 2.25 for a reduction of strain equal to ϵ_0 reaching point D'. Fiber #2 which reached point C has a strain reduction of $2\epsilon_0 - \frac{4}{3}\epsilon_0 = \frac{2}{3}\epsilon_0$ and a stress reduction of $\frac{2}{3}s_0$, which brings it to the new position C' where $s = \frac{1}{3}s_0$. Fiber #3 stressed to a point B has a reduction in strain of $\epsilon_0 - \frac{1}{3}\epsilon_0 = \frac{2}{3}\epsilon_0$, which brings it to a new position B' where $\epsilon = \frac{2}{3}\epsilon_0$. The new stress distribution is given in Figure 2.26c. Figure 2.26d shows the strain and stress distributions as the moment is further reduced so that the outer fiber is strained to ϵ_0. Note that the outer fibers have now suffered a reversal of stress. Finally

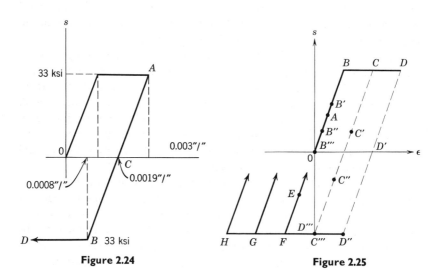

Figure 2.24   Figure 2.25

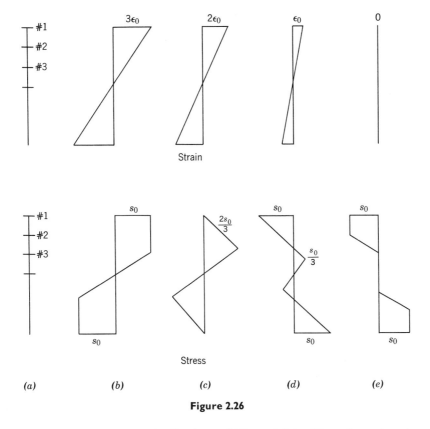

Figure 2.26

when $\epsilon_c = 0$ we get the distributions of Figure 2.26e. Note there that the outer fiber stresses cannot exceed s_0, and that the fibers that were always in the elastic core return to a condition of zero stress. As indicated by Figure 2.26e, a resulting bending moment is associated with the condition of zero strain everywhere. Thus, we do not remove all stresses merely by removing all strains. The moment causing the stress distribution of 2.26b is, for a rectangular beam of width b and depth d,

$$M = \left(\frac{s_0 bd}{3}\right)\left(\frac{2d}{3}\right) + 2\left(\frac{s_0 bd}{12}\right)\left(\frac{d}{9}\right) = \tfrac{13}{54}s_0 bd^2 = 0.241 s_0 bd^2 \qquad (2)$$

The residual moment associated with the removal of all strain is

$$M = -\left(\frac{s_0 bd}{6}\right)\left(\frac{5d}{6}\right) - \left(\frac{s_0 bd}{12}\right)\left(\frac{5d}{9}\right) = -\tfrac{5}{27}s_0 bd^2 = -0.185 s_0 bd^2 \qquad (3)$$

Thus in order to remove all strain caused by a moment of $0.241 s_0 bd^2$ it is necessary to apply an opposite moment of $(0.241 + 0.185)s_0bd^2 = 0.426s_0bd^2$.

In passing from the condition represented by Figure 2.26b to that represented by 2.26c, we note that the changes in strain are all less than $2\epsilon_0$. This means, from Figure 2.25, that changes in stress are linear. Since the outer fiber strain is changed by ϵ_0, the outer fiber stress changes by s_0. We may thus find the distribution of 2.26c very simply from 2.26b by adding to the distribution of 2.26b a distribution representing a purely elastic change having $s = -s_0$ at the top fiber as shown in Figure 2.27.

We now use this superposition technique to find the residual state of stress when a bending moment greater than the yield moment is totally removed. We have found that the moment causing the distribution of stress of Figure 2.26b was given by $M = 0.241s_0bd^2$. What will be the distribution of stress if we now add $M = -0.241bd^2$ to the section (which is equivalent to removing the applied moment)? If this moment causes only elastic changes in stress, we find that according to elastic theory the stresses at the outer fibers equal

$$s = \frac{M}{Z} = 0.241s_0bd^2 \left(\frac{6}{bd^2}\right) = 1.446s_0 \qquad (4)$$

All stresses inside the section are less than $1.446s_0$. We note from Figure 2.25 that a total change in stress of $2s_0$ is permissible for any fiber strained beyond the yield strain, but that changes greater than $2s_0$ are impossible since reverse plastic flow occurs exactly at a change of $2s_0$. It would follow, therefore, that since our partially plastified section undergoes only elastic deformations due to the removal of the moment that the distribution of normal stress can be found graphically as shown in Figure 2.28. A check of the resulting moment associated with 2.28c indicates that it is zero, meaning that the moment has been completely removed. The residual stresses are trapped in the member and must be taken into account if

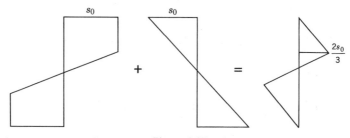

Figure 2.27

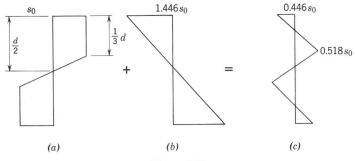

Figure 2.28

the member is reloaded. This is so, for example in the cold bending, welding, or cooling of a member. The apparent yield strain at any fiber is reduced as a consequence although there is no reduction in the value of M_p.

Finally, imagine that an applied moment has caused the stress distribution of Figure 2.29. This corresponds to an outer fiber strain of $4\epsilon_0$. The greatest negative moment that can be applied and give only elastic (or linear) changes in stress is the couple corresponding to an outer fiber stress of $2s_0$. The applied moment is given by

$$M = \left(\frac{3s_0bd}{8}\right)\left(\frac{5d}{8}\right) + \left(\frac{s_0bd}{16}\right)\left(\frac{d}{12}\right) = \tfrac{23}{96}s_0bd^2 \tag{5}$$

In order to remove the moment elastically we would have to add a linear stress distribution with an extreme fiber stress of

$$s = \frac{M}{Z} = \frac{23}{96}\left(\frac{s_0bd^2}{bd^2}\right)(6) = \tfrac{23}{16}s_0 \tag{6}$$

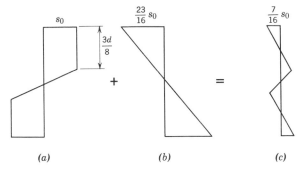

Figure 2.29

which is less than $s = 2s_0$. Thus superposition is permissible and the final stress distribution upon removal of the bending moment is as shown in Figure 2.29c.

2.7 Shear Stresses in Members Subject to Bending

In this section we shall investigate the shear stresses on the cross section of a beam in bending.* We begin by cutting an element of length from a beam and showing a free body diagram which indicates the stress resultants acting, Figure 2.30a, and the normal stresses present, Figure 2.30b. It is assumed that bending occurs about a principal axis so that we may write

$$s = \frac{My}{I} \tag{1}$$

We now cut a portion of the element and show it as a free body diagram in Figure 2.30c. Acting to the left are the normal stresses on the left. Acting to the right are the normal stresses on the right which on any elemental area are greater than the stresses on the left. Equilibrium can be maintained only if we have a horizontal force acting on the top surface and giving an average horizontal shear stress of s_{xy}, or more simply, in this instance, s_s. We have chosen b as the width of the member at the location of the cut and dx is the length of the elemental section. We sum forces on the free body of Figure 2.30c to write

$$s_s b\, dx = \int_y^c \frac{(M + dM)y}{I} b\, dy - \int_y^c \frac{Myb\, dy}{I} \tag{2}$$

or

$$s_s b\, dx = \int_y^c \frac{(dM)y\, dy}{I} \tag{3}$$

But since

$$V = \frac{dM}{dx} \tag{4}$$

we may write

$$s_s = \frac{V}{I} \int_y^c y\, dy \tag{5}$$

The integral

$$Q = \int_y^c yb\, dy \tag{6}$$

is the first moment of the area between elevation y and the outer fiber of

* The Russian engineer, D. J. Jourawski (1821–1891) developed this theory of shearing stresses in beams during the course of his prize-winning research on railway bridges.

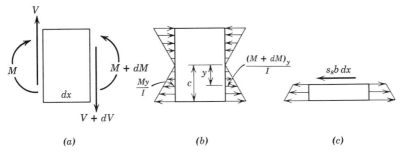

(a)   *(b)*   *(c)*

Figure 2.30

the cross section taken about the centroidal axis of the total cross section. We introduce this into 2.7.5 and write finally

$$s_s = \frac{VQ}{Ib} \tag{7}$$

Since the horizontal shear stress along the length of the member must equal the vertical shear stress on the cross section, we may interpret 2.7.7 as giving the vertical shear stress at any point on the cross section of a member.

Example 2.7.1 Find the shear stress just below the flange of the beam cross section shown in Figure 2.31*a*. We first locate the centroid to be in the position shown. The moment of inertia is

$$I = (\tfrac{1}{12})(6)(2)^3 + (12)(1.2)^2 + (\tfrac{1}{12})(2)(4)^3 + (8)(1.8)^2 = 57.87 \text{ in.}^4$$

Just below the flange we have $b = 2$ in. We find also

$$Q = (6)(2)(1.2) = 14.4 \text{ in.}^2$$

Thus we find

$$s_s = \frac{V(14.4)}{(2)(57.87)} = 0.124V \tag{8}$$

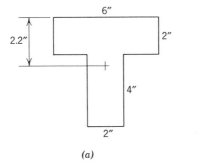

(a)   *(b)*

Figure 2.31

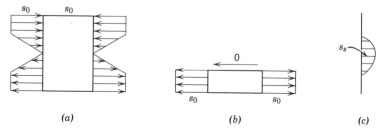

Figure 2.32

Just above the flange we have

$$s_s = \frac{V(14.4)}{(6)(57.87)} = 0.041V \tag{9}$$

The variation in shear stress over the cross section is shown in Figure 2.31b.

If the member is made from an elastoplastic material and is stressed so as to partially plastify the cross section, we have the free body of the elemental length shown in Figure 2.32a. A free-body diagram of a portion of this element taken near the base is shown in Figure 2.32b. Note that the total force acting on the right is now exactly equal to the total force acting on the left. Hence, there is no shear necessary to preserve the equilibrium, which indicates that the shear force gives rise to shear stresses only over the elastic core as indicated for a rectangular cross section in Figure 2.32c. Now since the stress resultant V is given by

$$V = \int_A s_s \, dA \tag{10}$$

it follows that as the area of the elastic core diminishes with increasing plastification, the maximum shearing stress increases. Full plastification is seen to be physically impossible again since it would mean infinite shearing stresses. In terms of Figure 2.13e this means that the stress diagram cannot become horizontal at the neutral axis but can only approach a horizontal line as a limit.

2.8 Shear Stresses in Members Subject to Twisting

When a bar is made from an elastic material, the shear stress at any point is directly proportional to shearing (or angular) strain. Hooke's law here becomes

$$s_s = G\epsilon_s \tag{1}$$

where G is the *modulus of elasticity in shear* and ϵ_s is the shearing strain. If an element of an elastic body is acted on by shearing stresses as shown

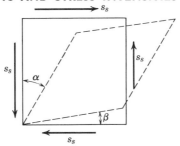

Figure 2.33

in Figure 2.33, the change $(\alpha + \beta)$ in angle, measured in radians, is defined as the *shearing strain*. A plot of shear stress versus shearing strain for the elastic material is shown by the solid line of Figure 2.34. For an elasto-plastic material we assume that the dotted line shown in this figure represents the shear stress-shear strain curve where ϵ_{s0} is the yield strain.

Because the presence of a torque suggests a rotation, it will be most convenient for us here to use cylindrical coordinates. An element of volume in these coordinates is shown in Figure 2.35. Due to twisting, the angle ABD becomes ABD' corresponding to a shear strain. If we assume that plane sections normal to the axis of the member before twisting remain plane and normal after twisting, in a manner analogous to Navier's hypothesis used in studying flexure, we are assuming that ODC remains in the same plane and that $O'BA$ remains in its same plane. The shear strain, measured by the change in angle ABD is due exclusively to the rotation of side BD since AB does not rotate. As the ends of this element are twisted, point D moves to a new position D' due to angle change at 0 of φ. If the radius at D is r, the distance DD' is $r\varphi$. The change in angle ABD is DD'/BD. Thus

$$\epsilon_s = \frac{r\varphi}{BD} = C'r \qquad (2)$$

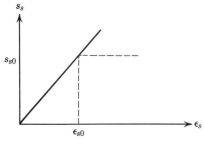

Figure 2.34

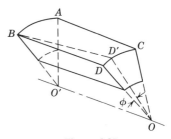

Figure 2.35

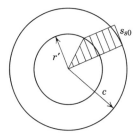

Figure 2.36

where C' is a constant representing φ divided by BD. The shearing strain is thus proportional to distance r from the origin of the coordinates. Navier's hypothesis leads to a linear variation of normal strain in bending; here an analogous assumption leads to a linear distribution of shear strain.

For the elastic material we have by Hooke's law

$$s_s = G\epsilon_s = GC'r = Cr \tag{3}$$

where C is a new constant. Equilibrium requires that the twisting moment (or torque) be given by

$$T = \int_A s_s r\, dA = C \int_A r^2\, dA \tag{4}$$

But

$$\int_A r^2\, dA = I_p \tag{5}$$

where I_p is a polar moment of inertia. Thus we have the constant given by

$$C = \frac{T}{I_p} \tag{6}$$

and from equation 2.8.3 we have

$$s_s = \frac{Tr}{I_p} \tag{7}$$

This simple expression, unfortunately, is of rather limited use since experiments indicate that plane sections do not remain plane, except for cross sections with circular symmetry, such as the solid or hollow circular section. Otherwise, the cross section is always warped. The warped section involves analytical methods beyond the scope of this work.* Several useful results are summarized in § 3.8.

For an elastoplastic member in torsion we have a distribution of shear stress such as that shown in Figure 2.36 when the torque applied is great

---

* The reader is referred to standard texts on the mathematical theory of elasticity and advanced mechanics of materials for formulas relating to other cross sections.

enough to cause the shear stresses s_{s0}. The elastic core here has a radius of r'. The resulting torque is given by

$$T = \int_A s_s r \, dA = \int_0^{r'} \frac{s_{s0}r}{r'} r \, dA + \int_{r'}^{c} s_{s0}r \, dA \qquad (8)$$

With $dA = 2\pi r \, dr$

$$T = \frac{2\pi s_{s0}}{r'} \frac{r'^4}{4} + 2\pi s_{s0} \left(\frac{c^2}{3} - \frac{r'^3}{3}\right) \qquad (9)$$

or

$$T = 2\pi s_{s0} \left(\frac{c^3}{3} - \frac{r'^3}{12}\right) \qquad (9)$$

When $r' = 0$, we find the limiting case of complete plastification with

$$T_p = \tfrac{2}{3}\pi s_{s0}c^3 \qquad (10)$$

The torque that causes first yielding is found from 2.8.7 to be

$$T_0 = \frac{s_{s0}}{c} \frac{\pi c^4}{2} = \tfrac{1}{2}\pi s_{s0}c^3 \qquad (11)$$

which is three-fourths of the fully plastic torque.

2.9 Shear Flow and the Shear Center

The shear stress associated with the shear force V in the beam is given by equation 2.7.7. For the beam in Figure 2.37, the vertical shear stress at section a–a is given by

$$s_s = \frac{VQ}{It_2} \qquad (1)$$

where Q is the first moment of the shaded area about the centroidal axis of the total area. Both sides are multiplied through by t_2 to obtain the shear force per unit of length along the web. This is called the *shear flow* and is given the symbol q.

$$q_2 = \frac{VQ}{I} \qquad (2)$$

Now if we wish to find the horizontal shear stress on the plane b–b in Figure 2.38, we may equally well make use of 2.9.1 where Q is the first moment of the shaded area about the horizontal centroidal axis of the total area. This is easily shown by using the same development as given in § 2.7. There will be an equal and opposite shear stress acting on the front face in the horizontal direction. The shear flow on that portion of the section is $q_1 = s_s t_1$ (see Figure 2.39). The variation in shear flow is also

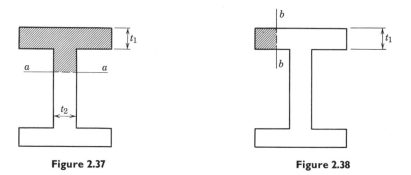

Figure 2.37   **Figure 2.38**

shown in Figure 2.39. From the symmetry of the distribution we recognize that the resultant shear force V passes through the centroid of the total area.

Consider now the channel section of Figure 2.40. Let the cross section shown be at the end of an element of length that resists the greatest positive bending moment (see Figure 2.30a). The area to the right of a–a in Figure 2.40 must have a shear flow direction as shown. Similarly at b–b and at c–c we find the direction indicated. The resultant of these shear flows is the vertical shear force V but it is evident that it must act some distance x_0 to the left of the cross section as shown. If it acts elsewhere there will be an accompanying torque.

We saw earlier that a normal force must act at the centroid of a cross section in order not to give rise to bending moments. We see now that a

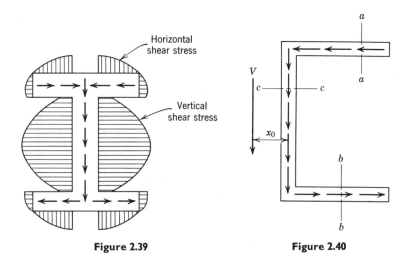

Figure 2.39   **Figure 2.40**

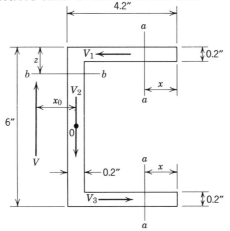

Figure 2.41

shear force must act a distance x_0 to the left of the channel section in order not to give rise to twisting moments. This point of application is called the *shear center** of the cross section. For structures with two axes of symmetry the centroid and the shear center coincide.

Example 2.9.1 Find the shear center for the channel of Figure 2.41. At any location a–a we find $Q = (0.2)(x)(2.9)$. The total horizontal shear force on each flange is taken as

$$V_1 = \int_0^4 q\, dx = \int_0^4 \frac{VQ\, dx}{I} = \frac{V}{I}\int_0^4 (0.58x)\, dx = \frac{4.64V}{I} \tag{3}$$

Considering only the web area we now find for any location b–b, $Q = (0.2)(z)(3 - 0.5z)$. The total shear flow in the web is thus V since the web takes all the vertical shear, the flanges being so thin. Summing moments about 0 we find distance x_0 to be

$$V x_0 = (V_1)(2.9) + (V_3)(2.9) = 5.8 V_1 = \frac{(5.8)(4.64)V}{I}$$

or

$$x_0 = \frac{26.9}{I}$$

2.10 Twisting of Cellular Cross Sections

For cellular cross sections, the method of computation is somewhat different from that described in earlier sections. In particular, we consider a straight member having a constant hollow section and subjected to equal

---

* The great Swiss structural engineer, Robert Maillart, introduced the notion of the shear center and showed how it could be calculated.

and opposite twisting moments at its ends. The stress distribution is exactly the same on all cross sections and the product of shear stress and wall thickness, called the shear flow, q, in § 2.9 remains constant. The shear flow, q, is assumed to act along the centerline of the wall thickness.

The shear force in pounds acting on a length ds of cross section is $q\,ds$. The moment of this force about any center O is given by $qr\,ds$ where r is the perpendicular distance from O to the force as shown in Figure 2.42. This value of the moment corresponds to the product of q and twice the shaded area AOB described by the arc length ds and the radial rays from O. The sum of moments of all such forces will be equal to the shear flow q times twice the enclosed area of the centerline, and equal to the torque. Thus

$$T = 2qA \tag{1}$$

or

$$q = \frac{T}{2A} \tag{2}$$

If a vector diagram of forces is prepared of the shear flow forces around the cell, it will close, indicating that there is no resultant shear force on the cross section. If a vector diagram of forces is drawn for only a portion MN of the contour of the cell, it will be observed that the resultant shear force acts along the line parallel to the chord connecting the end points of that portion as shown in Figure 2.43. The magnitude of the moment of that resultant is given by the shear flow q times twice the area A_0 enclosed by the centerline of the portion of the cell and rays connecting the ends of the portion to the moment center O as previously discussed. The resultant shear force is equal to q times the length of chord, L, associated with the portion of the cell. The distance, e, from the resulting shear force to the moment center is then given by

$$e = \frac{2A_0}{L} \tag{3}$$

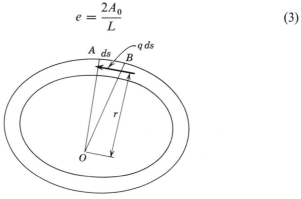

Figure 2.42

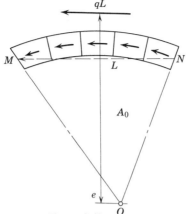

Figure 2.43

For a thin circular section of thickness t and centerline radius r we find $A = \pi r^2$ and obtain from 2.10.2

$$q = \frac{T}{2\pi r^2} \tag{4}$$

Using the result found for solid members in § 2.8, we have

$$I_p = \frac{\pi}{2}\left[\left(r + \frac{t}{2}\right)^4 - \left(r - \frac{t}{2}\right)^4\right] = 2\pi rt(r^2 + t^2) \tag{5}$$

where r is the mean radius and

$$q = s_s t = \frac{T}{2\pi(r^2 + t^2)} \tag{6}$$

Formula 2.10.4 was found by assuming the wall thickness to be very small. Here r is much greater than t and $(r^2 + t^2) = r^2$, which agrees with 2.10.6.

For a thin-walled square section of side length b along the centerline and thickness t we have $A = b^2$ and find

$$q = \frac{T}{b^2} \tag{7}$$

Problems

2.2.1 A plane area is acted on by a force of -30 kips at its centroid and moments of $+60$ in.-kips and -90 in.-kips about its y and z axes, respectively. Where would a single force have to be placed in order to be equivalent to these and what must its magnitude be?

2.2.2 Two columns of a given building are to be located 30 ft. apart along a line that is perpendicular to the property line. The two columns are to be supported by a single trapezoidal footing (a footing supporting two columns is called a combined footing). One of the conditions of design is that the pressure brought to the subgrade by the footing must be uniformly distributed and must not exceed 3 tons per sq. ft. The column nearest the property line carries an axial load of 600,000 lb. and the other (interior) column carries an axial load of 1,120,000 lb. The footing may not extend beyond the property line (which is 3 ft. from the center of the exterior column) nor more than 6 ft. beyond the interior column. Assume that the total weight of the footing will be 200,000 lb. Determine a satisfactory shape and size for the footing.

2.2.3 A plane area having the shape of an angle shown below is acted on by a single compressive force of 140,000 lb. as shown. Use centroidal axes

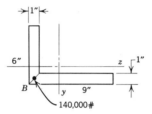

Problem 2.2.3

that are parallel to the sides of the angle, plot the neutral axis for this loading, and find the maximum compressive and tensile stresses on the section.

2.2.4 Given the figure in Problem 2.2.3, sketch the line along which a force must be placed in order to give a stress equal to zero at B.

2.2.5 Using equations 2.2.8 and the assumption that the y and z axes are principal axes, prepare a direct derivation of equation 2.2.15.

2.2.6 Given a rectangle of dimensions b and d, locate the point at which a single compressive force must be placed in order to place the neutral axis along the (a) upper edge, (b) lower edge, (c) right edge, and (d) left edge. Describe the area in which a single compressive force must be applied in order to give no tensile stresses on the section. This area is called the *kern*, *kernal*, or *core*.

2.2.7 Given a moment of $M_z = 1$ in.-kip. Find maximum tensile and compressive stresses on the cross section shown.

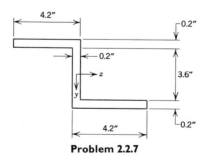

Problem 2.2.7

2.2.8 Draw the neutral axis and find the stress at point A.

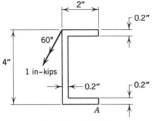

Problem 2.2.8

2.3.1 Prove that for a rectangle of width b and height h and radius of curvature r, that the value of J_v is given by $J_v = -r^2bh - r^3b \ln (2r - h/2r + h)$.

2.3.2 A bar 1 in. wide and $\frac{1}{2}$ in. thick is bent into a U shape with an inside radius of 1 in. as shown in the figure below. Assuming that $P = 100$ lbs.,

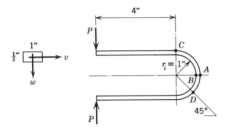

Problem 2.3.2

calculate the stresses at points A, B, C, and D and compare your results with those found using the assumption of linear distribution of stress.

2.3.3 The cross section of a curved member is symmetrical about the v-axis. Explain why the value of J_{vw} will (or will not) necessarily be zero.

2.3.4 Using equations 2.3.4 and 2.3.12 verify equation 2.3.13.

2.3.5 Using the figure of Problem 2.3.2, determine the normal stress at point A for the following values of r_i: 2 in., 5 in., 10 in., ∞ in. when the only loads are couples of 100 in. lbs. at the free ends.

2.4.1 For the truss shown, the area of each member in square inches is equal to the length of that member in feet. The material is mild steel. Determine the load necessary to cause first yielding to occur. (We assume for the present that

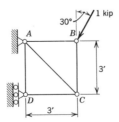

Problem 2.4.1

buckling will not occur in any of the compressed members.) Modify the area of AC such that it and one other member will yield simultaneously.

2.4.2 The load necessary to cause yielding on the structure shown is 60 kips. What is the necessary load to cause collapse?

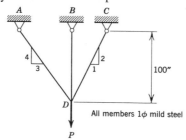

All members 1ϕ mild steel

Problem 2.4.2

2.5.1 Determine the shape factor for a 36W⁻ 150 section shown approximately in the figure below and compare it with the shape factor for a rectangle having the same overall dimensions.

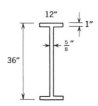

Problem 2.5.1

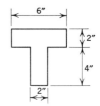

Problem 2.5.2

2.5.2 For the T-section shown, prepare a plot of e versus M where e is the distance of the neutral axis from the centroid and M is the applied bending moment. Plot at least three points. Plot e as ordinate.

2.5.3 Find the location of the neutral axis for full plastification for a rectangular section made from a material having a yield point in compression equal to one-half the yield point in tension.

2.5.4 Find the bending moment necessary to make $\epsilon = 3_{\epsilon 0}$ at the outer fiber of the figure shown.

Problem 2.5.4

2.5.5 For the T-section of Figure 2.5.2, determine the positive moment necessary to first produce yield at the base of the flange. Yield stress in tension is equal to yield stress in compression.

2.6.1 An elastoplastic beam of rectangular cross section has a width of 1 in. and depth of 2 in. It is subjected to bending moment equal to 120% of the yield moment. Determine the depth of the elastic core. Sketch the distribution of stress when the bending moment is reduced to zero.

2.6.2 For the section shown, a bending moment is applied about the z-axis of magnitude $2M_0$ and is then reduced to a value of $0.5M_0$. Plot on a single set of axes, the complete stress-strain history of fibers at A, B, and C.

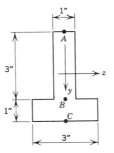

Problem 2.6.2

2.7.1 What percentage error in the maximum shear stress is introduced if we assume that the web of a 36W 150 section (see figure in Problem 2.5.1) carries all the shear stress, uniformly distributed, due to a shear force $V = 10,000$ lb?

2.7.2 Plot the distribution of vertical shear stress in terms of V for the figure shown.

Problem 2.7.2

2.7.3 Plot the distribution of shear stress of the figure shown in Problem 2,7.2 when the bending moment present is such as to cause an outer fiber strain of $3\epsilon_0$. Compare maximum stress with that found in Problem 2.7.2 if $V = 10,000$ lb.

2.8.1 What is the shear stress at the inner edge of a tubular cross section $(d_0 = 8$ in, $d_i = 6$ in.) due to a torque of 100 ft-kips?

2.8.2 Determine the torque necessary to cause yielding at the inner edge of the figure of Problem 2.8.1. Assume yielding in shear occurs at a stress of 18 ksi. Compare the shear stress distribution with that in Problem 2.8.1.

2.8.3 If moment is applied to a solid cross section of radius 2 in. having a magnitude $1.2T_0$ and is subsequently removed, plot the distribution of residual shear stress across the section.

2.9.1 Find the shear center and orientation of an angle $8 \times 8 \times \frac{1}{2}$ subject to a vertical load.

2.9.2 Plot the distribution of the horizontal shear stress in terms of V for each portion of the Z bar shown below.

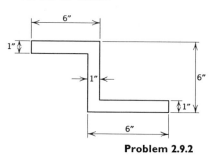

Problem 2.9.2

2.9.3 The section shown has a uniform wall thickness of 0.2 in. Locate the shear center.

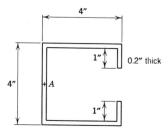

Problem 2.9.3

2.10.1 A hollow equilateral triangle has a 4-in. leg dimension and wall thickness of 0.2 in. What will be the shear stress at any point on the cross section due to a torque of a 100 in.-lbs?

2.10.2 A hollow concrete girder has the inside dimensions 36 in. × 18 in. and a uniform wall thickness of 4 in. Find the distribution of shear flow due to a vertical shear force of 100 kips and the distribution of shear flow due to a torque of 100 ft-kips.

3 ELASTIC DEFORMATION

3.1 Displacements Due to Axial Force

Consider an element of length dx cut from a straight elastic member that is subjected only to the action of axial forces N and $N + dN$ as shown in Figure 3.1. Let the displacement of any point on the left of this element be denoted by u and the displacement of any point on the right be denoted by $u + du$. The total elongation of any fiber of the element is $(u + du) - u = du$. We now define the *normal strain* ϵ_n as the change in length of a fiber divided by the original length in the undeformed state. In the present case we have dx as the original length and write

$$\epsilon_n = \frac{du}{dx} \tag{1}$$

Now if the member is elastic, we have Hooke's law

$$s_n = E\epsilon_n \tag{2}$$

which relates intensity of normal stress to normal strain through E, *Young's modulus of elasticity*. We combine 3.1.1 and 3.1.2 to obtain

$$s_n = E\frac{du}{dx} \tag{3}$$

For an axial force N, we find the intensity of normal stress to be uniform over the cross section with the magnitude

$$s_n = \frac{N}{A} \tag{4}$$

where A is the area of the cross section. We now combine 3.1.3 and 3.1.4 to find

$$du = \frac{N\,dx}{AE} = \epsilon_n\,dx \tag{5}$$

III

N $N + dN$

dx **Figure 3.1**

The change in displacement between any two locations $x = a$ and $x = b$ is now given by

$$\int_a^b du = u_b - u_a = \int_a^b \frac{N\,dx}{AE} = \int_a^b \epsilon_n\,dx \tag{6}$$

If N, A, or E happens to be constant over the distance from a to b, that term may be brought out of the integral sign. Both the differential form 3.1.5 and the integral form 3.1.6 find wide application in practical problems.

Example 3.1.1 The bar of Figure 3.2a has a variable area, is acted on by a concentrated tensile force of P at the right end, a uniformly distributed skin frictional force of p (units of force per unit of surface area) over the right third of the bar, and is fixed against any displacement at the left end. Draw the displacement diagram. Figure 3.2b shows the axial force diagram. The stress diagram is shown in Figure 3.2c and the strain diagram in Figure 3.2d. Since we know that the displacement at the left end is zero, we choose our x axis as shown in Figure 3.2a and write for the left third of the bar

$$u = \int_0^x \epsilon_n\,dx = \frac{P - 8bpL}{4b^2E} \int_0^x dx = \frac{P - 8bpL}{4b^2E}(x) \tag{7}$$

An alternate approach would be to interpret equation 3.1.6 as stating that the change in displacement between two sections a and b is equal to the area under the strain diagram between a and b. Here we have for $x = L$

$$u_L - u_0 = u_L = \left(\frac{P - 8bpL}{4b^2E}\right)(L) \tag{8}$$

which agrees with 3.1.7 when x is set equal to L. The ordinate of the strain diagram is thus the slope of the displacement diagram. The middle third of the bar has a constant strain that is larger than the strain over the left third of the bar. The slope of the displacement diagram over the middle third is thus still positive and of larger magnitude than over the left third. Over the right third the slope increases uniformly, and is always positive. The value of u at the right end of the bar is given by

$$u = \frac{L}{2b^2E}(3P - 22bpL) \tag{9}$$

This displacement diagram is given in Figure 3.2e. Note that if the load at the free end were zero, the normal stress and normal strain would also be zero at the right end, and by 3.1.1 the slope of the displacement diagram would be zero.

Example 3.1.2 Derive an expression for the axial forces in the vertical bars of Figure 3.3. The condition to be imposed is that the horizontal bar is absolutely rigid and suffers only a translation without rotation. We require the forces

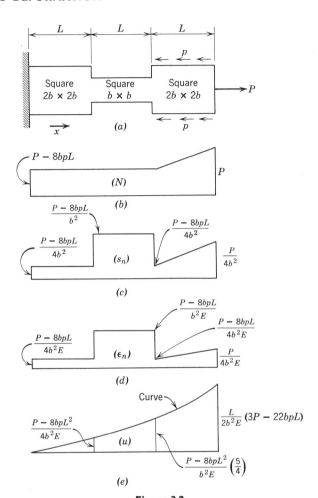

Figure 3.2

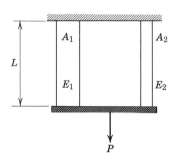

Figure 3.3

carried by each of the two vertical bars. To begin with, the total elongation of the two bars is equal. We use 3.1.6 to find the total elongation to be

$$\int_0^L \frac{N_1}{A_1 E_1}\, dx = \int_0^L \frac{N_2}{A_2 E_2}\, dx \tag{10}$$

or

$$\frac{N_1 L}{A_1 E_1} = \frac{N_2 L}{A_2 E_2} \tag{11}$$

and since

$$N_1 + N_2 = P \tag{12}$$

we may solve these two equations to obtain

$$N_1 = \frac{P}{\dfrac{A_2 E_2}{A_1 E_1} + 1}$$

$$N_2 = \frac{P}{\dfrac{A_1 E_1}{A_2 E_2} + 1} \tag{13}$$

We note for the bar of constant area and constant elastic modulus that the total elongation is directly proportional to the force N. We may also write

$$N = \frac{AE}{L}\Delta = k\Delta \tag{14}$$

where k is the constant of proportionality and is called the *spring constant* for the bar. It is measured in dimensions of force per unit length. We rewrite equations 3.1.13 using k as follows:

$$N_1 = P\left(\frac{k_1}{k_1 + k_2}\right)$$

$$N_2 = P\left(\frac{k_2}{k_1 + k_2}\right) \tag{15}$$

3.2 Displacements in Plane Trusses

In a truss, the bars are subjected to axial forces only, and hence their elongations or contractions may be calculated from the results of the previous section. For a bar of uniform area A, length L, modulus of elasticity E, and axial load N, the elongation Δ is given by

$$\Delta = \frac{NL}{AE} \tag{1}$$

The displacements of the joints of a truss depend on the bar elongations and may be determined as soon as the Δ values have been found. A

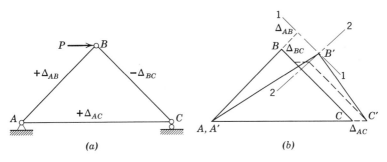

Figure 3.4

particularly simple method of finding these displacements is the graphical construction first proposed by Williot and subsequently improved by Mohr.*

To illustrate Williot's contribution, we consider the simple truss of Figure 3.4a. The applied load P creates axial forces in the various members, giving rise to the elongations Δ_{AB}, Δ_{BC}, and Δ_{AC}. Joint A, supported by a fixed hinge, suffers no translation. Joint C, supported by a roller, may suffer a translation in the horizontal direction. The absolute displacement of C is an amount Δ_{AC} to the right.

To find the final position of joint B, we first note that in the deformed state the bars of the truss must be longer (or shorter) than in the undeformed state by amounts Δ, that bars meeting at a joint before deformation must meet at a joint after deformation, and that the bars remain straight. The angles at the joints are *not* the same before and after deformation. Bar AB thus takes on the new length $AB + \Delta_{AB} = AB'$ and B' must lie on a line perpendicular to the end of $AB + \Delta_{AB}$ shown as line 1–1 in Figure 3.4b. Bar BC rotates about the new position of C; namely, C', and B' must lie on a line perpendicular to the end of $BC + \Delta_{BC}$ shown as line 2–2 in the figure. In order for B' to lie on lines 1–1 and 2–2, it must lie at the point of intersection of these lines. B' is thus located and the deformed truss is as drawn in the figure having joints A, B', and C'.

From this qualitative discussion we may be inclined to overlook the one important factor that makes the method as described of little practical use. That is, the deformations Δ are so small in comparison with the member lengths that we can hope for an accurate construction only if we use an

---

* M. Williot and Otto Mohr were but two of the European engineers who helped popularize graphical methods of structural analysis. The Williot-Mohr method of finding truss deflections and the Maxwell diagram for finding bar forces in trusses are the only two graphical methods discussed in this book, and are by far the most popular of the graphical methods still in general use.

inconveniently large scale. To remedy this, we consider a means of working only with the *relative displacements* of the joints rather than their absolute displacements.

If we look carefully at Figure 3.4b, we find that the displacement of one end of a member relative to the other end of the member can be considered in three parts. Consider a typical member EF such as may be present in any truss. The end E is displaced to the new position E' as shown in Figure 3.5. First the bar may move as a rigid body going from EF to position $E'F_1$. Secondly, the bar may deform and end F will move toward E (e.g., a contraction) or away from E (e.g., an elongation) in the direction of EF. Considering for the present that EF elongates an amount Δ_{EF}, we see that F reaches the new position F_2. Thirdly, the bar may rotate as a rigid body about the new position E'. Since the elongation is small in comparison with the length of the member, we can assume that F moves along a circular arc of radius $(E'F_1 + \Delta_{EF})$, which can be represented by a straight line perpendicular to EF and labeled line 1–1 in Figure 3.5. In summary, the displacement of F relative to E consists of the rigid body translation to F_1, the deformation to F_2, and the rigid body rotation to a new position F' on line 1–1.

Returning to the truss in Figure 3.4b, we now show the displacements of joints A, B, and C separately in 3.6a, 3.6b, and 3.6c. In Figure 3.6a the movement of joint A is represented by a single dot and labeled A and A'. This means that the initial position A and the final position A' are the same. In Figure 3.6b the movement of joint C is indicated by a single horizontal line labeled CC'. Considering the displacement of C relative to A in accordance with our previous discussion, we have no rigid body translation of bar AC. We have the deformation Δ_{AC} and no rigid body rotation of member AC. The total displacement of C then consists of the deformation Δ_{AC} as shown. Figure 3.6c shows the displacement of joint B to its new position at B'. Relative to joint A, B' suffers no rigid body translation. It suffers an elongation of amount Δ_{AB} and moves along the line labeled 1–1 that represents the arc of a circle having A as a center. We do not yet know

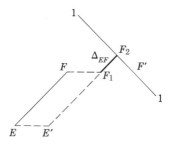

Figure 3.5

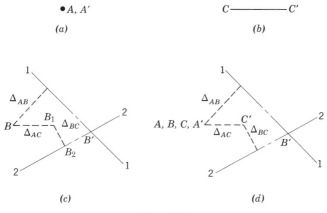

Figure 3.6

its final position on 1–1. Relative to C, B suffers a rigid body translation equal to the absolute displacement of joint C shown in Figure 3.6b. That rigid body translation moves the joint to the new position B_1 in Figure 3.6c. The shortening Δ_{BC} causes joint B to move toward C an amount Δ_{BC} to position B_2. The possible rigid body rotation of member BC causes joint B to move along a line 2–2 corresponding to the arc of a circle having its center at C'. The final position B' is at the point of intersection of lines 1–1 and 2–2.

Figure 3.6d shows all of the information in Figures 3.6a, 3.6b, and 3.6c. A single point represents the initial position of joints A, B, and C. That same point also represents A', the final position of joint A. The final positions of B and C are given by points B' and C'. A vector drawn from the point representing the initial position of any joint to the point that represents the final position of any joint represents the absolute displacement of that joint. The vector drawn from the final position of any joint to the final position of any other joint represents the relative displacement of the second joint to the first. We now have a systematic method of studying displacements. This figure is the *Williot diagram* and gives the relative and absolute displacements of all joints. Since only displacements are to be used, we may employ a scale that is large enough to give whatever accuracy we require.

In general, the Williot diagram gives the full story of joint displacements as long as we can begin by knowing the relative displacement (magnitude and direction) of any two adjacent joints in a truss and the absolute displacement of one joint of the truss. In Figure 3.4a we knew that the displacement of C relative to A was Δ_{AC} horizontal to the right of C and that joint A suffered no displacement.

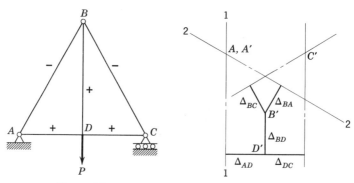

Figure 3.7   **Figure 3.8**

Example 3.2.1   Find the displacements of the truss in Figure 3.7. We know by symmetry that joints B and D both move in the vertical direction and since bar BD is in tension, joint B must move upward relative to joint D by an amount Δ_{BD} (or joint D moves downward relative to B by an amount Δ_{BD}). We also know that joint A does not move. The Williot diagram shown in Figure 3.8 gives us all the information we need. Positions B' and D' are laid off first. These are primed because they represent final positions. Joint A relative to D moves horizontally to the left an amount Δ_{AD} and on a line perpendicular thereto as given by 1–1. Joint A also moves relative to joint B up and to the right along a line parallel to AB an amount Δ_{AB} and then on a line perpendicular to it as shown by 2–2. We locate position A' at the intersection of 1–1 and 2–2. In a symmetrical fashion we locate position C'. Now since A does not move we denote point A' by A and read off absolute displacements of all joints by referring them to position A. For example, a vector Δ_{CA} drawn from A to C' gives the displacement of C relative to A which is the absolute displacement of C. A vector Δ_{CB} drawn from B' to C' gives the displacement of joint C relative to joint B. The absolute displacement of joint B, Δ_{BA}, is given by a vector from A to B'. Vectorially this gives

$$\Delta_C = \Delta_B \mathrel{+\!\!\!\rightarrow} \Delta_{CB}$$

which states that the absolute displacement of C is equal to the vector sum of the absolute displacement of B and the displacement of C relative to B. We get the vector diagram of Figure 3.9, which agrees with the value read directly from Figure 3.8.

Example 3.2.2   Find the displacements of the joints of the truss in Figure 3.10a due to an impressed shortening of bar BD. This may be considered the

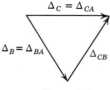

Figure 3.9

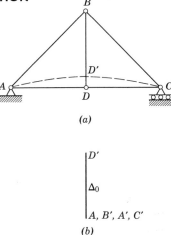

(a)

(b)

Figure 3.10

problem of a bar being cut shorter than required for a truss. Since the truss is statically determinate and stable, such a shortening causes no stress to be induced in any member. The bars move, as rigid bodies, suffering no deformation. The displacements will again be symmetrical relative to the bar BD with Δ_{BD} given as Δ_0 where Δ_0 is negative since the bar is shortening. The Williot diagram is shown in Figure 3.10b. We set all values of Δ_{AC}, etc., equal to zero except Δ_{BD} since there are no deformations. For example, A would normally move horizon- tally an amount Δ_{AD} relative to D and then along a line perpendicular thereto. Because Δ_{AD} equals zero, A must move along a vertical line through point D'. A', B', and C' all cluster at a given point. We conclude that B and C have no movement relative to A (no absolute displacement). The truss thus deforms as shown by the dotted line of Figure 3.10a.

In the more general structures we do not have the relative displacement of two adjacent joints known and the Williot diagram does not give us the absolute displacements of the joints. This is illustrated for the truss of Figure 3.11. There is no definite information here about the relative displacement of any two adjacent joints. We only know the bar elonga- tions and that joint A does not move and that joint C moves only horizon- tally. We draw the Williot diagram of Figure 3.12 by *assuming* a relative

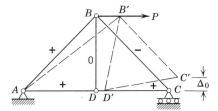

Figure 3.11

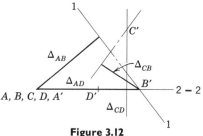

Figure 3.12

displacement of two adjacent joints; in this case, that joint D moves horizontally an amount Δ_{AD} relative to A. On this basis we can construct the diagram. To locate B' we make use of the existing positions of A' and D'. B relative to A moves up and to the right an amount Δ_{AB} and then along a line perpendicular thereto labeled 1–1. B relative to D moves vertically an amount Δ_{BD} and then along a line perpendicular thereto. Since Δ_{BD} equals zero, B is located on a horizontal line through D labeled 2–2. The intersection of lines 1–1 and 2–2 gives the position of B'. With B' and D' now known, C' is located as shown. The displacements found are shown by the dotted outline in Figure 3.11. It is obviously not the correct displacement diagram since C is shown with a vertical component of displacement of amount Δ_0.

In Figure 3.13*b* we are given the diagram corresponding to the rigid-body rotation of our truss due only to an upward displacement of joint C. We call this the *Mohr diagram*. If we take the vector corresponding to the displacement of any joint in Figure 3.12 and subtract from it the vector corresponding to the displacement of the same joint in 3.13*a* we will get the vector corresponding to the absolute displacement of that joint for the original problem. To illustrate, consider joint B. From Figure 3.12

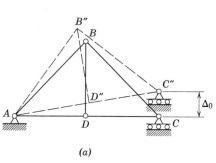

(a)   (b)

Figure 3.13

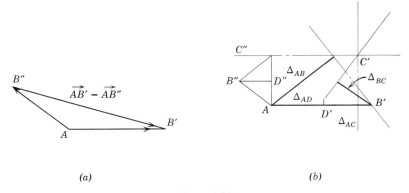

(a)   *(b)*

Figure 3.14

the displacement is given by the vector **AB'**. This displacement incorporates the effect of bar deformations. In Figure 3.13*b* the displacement of *B* is given by the vector **AB''**. The vector difference (**AB'** − **AB''**) is given by the diagonal of the vector diagram from *B''* to *B'*. Thus

$$\mathbf{AB'} - \mathbf{AB''} = \mathbf{B''B'} \tag{2}$$

as shown in Figure 3.14*a*. In a similar manner we find the absolute displacements of joints *C* and *D* to be

$$\begin{aligned} \mathbf{AD'} - \mathbf{AD''} &= \mathbf{D''D'} \\ \mathbf{AC'} - \mathbf{AC''} &= \mathbf{C''C'} \end{aligned} \tag{3}$$

The information from the two diagrams is conveniently presented in one diagram in Figure 3.14*b*. The rotation diagram is drawn with point *A*

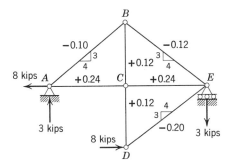

Mem.	N	$\dfrac{L}{AE}$	$\Delta = \dfrac{NL}{AE}$
AB	−5 kips	0.02	−0.10 in.
AC	+12 kips		+0.24 in.
BC	+6 kips		+0.12 in.
BE	−5 kips		−0.10 in.
CE	+12 kips		+0.24 in.
CD	+6 kips		+0.12 in.
DE	−10 kips		−0.20 in.

Figure 3.15

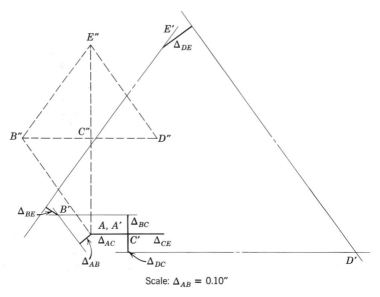

Scale: $\Delta_{AB} = 0.10''$

Figure 3.16

common to both diagrams and with a scale such that AC'' equals the vertical component of the vector $\mathbf{AC'}$. The absolute displacement of any joint is given by the vector originating at the joint in the Mohr diagram and terminating at the joint in the Williot diagram.

Example 3.2.3 Draw the Williot-Mohr diagram representing the displacements of the joints in Figure 3.15. Let the value of L/AE for each bar be 0.02 in-kips. Equilibrium requires the bar forces to be as follows: $N_{AB} = N_{BE} = -5$ kips, $N_{AC} = N_{CE} = +12$ kips, $N_{BC} = N_{CD} = +6$ kips, $N_{DE} = -10$ kips. The elongations are as shown on the figure. The final diagram is shown in Figure 3.16.

3.3 Displacements Due to Bending Moment

In this section we consider the deformations of a straight beam in bending about a principal axis of inertia. We let the axis of the undeformed beam coincide with the x-axis and let the deflection of any point on the beam axis due to bending be denoted* by y. The positive direction of y is taken downward and x is taken positive to the right. The equation of the

---

* The symbol y has been previously used to indicate one coordinate of a point on a cross section of a beam relative to the centroidal axes of the section. The use of the same symbol here will not lead to any confusion.

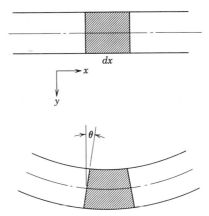

Figure 3.17

deflected beam axis, called the *elastic curve*, is some function of x.

$$y = f(x) \tag{1}$$

The slope θ of the elastic curve is given by the first derivative of y with respect to x. Thus

$$\theta = \frac{dy}{dx} = f'(x) \tag{2}$$

For the axis chosen we see that the slope will be positive when a tangent to the curve slopes down and to the right.

An element cut from the undeformed beam would be shaped as shown in Figure 3.17. In the deformed beam (due to the action of positive bending moments) we find that fibers at the top of the element have shortened and those at the bottom have lengthened. By *Navier's hypothesis*, the angle of rotation of a plane section normal to the axis of the beam must be equal to the slope of the elastic curve as shown. Referring to Figure 3.18, we note that a fiber located a distance* ζ from the centroid of the cross section suffers a displacement of u at the left end of the element and $u + du$ at the right end. These correspond to slopes of u/ζ and

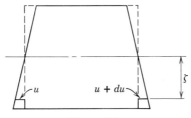

Figure 3.18

---

* Use is made of ζ here instead of y, as would be consistent with Chapter 2, so as to prevent any confusion.

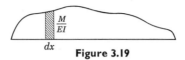

dx

Figure 3.19

$(u + du)/\zeta$ for the elastic axis at the two ends. The change in slope is negative from left end to right end and is thus given by

$$-d\theta = \frac{u + du}{\zeta} - \frac{u}{\zeta} = \frac{du}{\zeta} \tag{3}$$

The strain at the fiber located the distance ζ away from the centroid is given by

$$\epsilon_n = \frac{s_n}{E} = \frac{M\zeta}{EI} = \frac{du}{dx} \tag{4}$$

Substituting du from 3.3.4 into 3.3.3 and clearing, we find

$$\frac{d\theta}{dx} = -\frac{M}{EI} \tag{5}$$

We rewrite 3.3.5 as

$$d\theta = -\frac{M\,dx}{EI} \tag{6}$$

and integrate over a length of beam from $x = a$ to $x = b$ to find

$$\theta_b - \theta_a = -\int_a^b \frac{M\,dx}{EI} \tag{7}$$

If the value of M/EI is plotted for all points along the length of a beam as shown in Figure 3.19, we note that the quantity $M\,dx/EI$ is an element of area under the curve. We may state equation 3.3.7 in the following way:

The difference in slope between any two sections of a straight elastic beam is equal to minus the area under the M/EI diagram between these sections.

This is known as the *moment-area theorem.**

By substituting θ from 3.3.2 into 3.3.5 we get the equation

$$\frac{d^2y}{dx^2} = -\frac{M}{EI} \tag{8}$$

When the equation for the bending moment is known, we may integrate equation 3.3.8 once to get the equation for slope and integrate the second time to get the equation for the deflection at any point.

$$y = -\int\int \frac{M}{EI}\,dx\,dx + C_1x + C_2 \tag{9}$$

These equations contain constants of integration that can be evaluated by

---

* A second moment-area theorem is presented in Chapter 6.

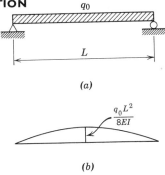

(a)

(b)

Figure 3.20

using known values for slope and deflection at prescribed points on the beam. The following two examples illustrate the method.

Example 3.3.1 Find the slope at the left support of the beam in Figure 3.20. We first make use of 3.3.5 and write the bending moment equation for the beam

$$M = \frac{q_0 L x}{2} - \frac{q_0 x^2}{2} \qquad (10)$$

If EI is constant throughout we may write 3.3.5 as

$$d\theta = -\frac{q_0}{2EI}\left(Lx - x^2\right)dx \qquad (11)$$

Integrating we find

$$\theta = -\frac{q_0}{2EI}\left[\frac{Lx^2}{2} - \frac{x^3}{3}\right] + C \qquad (12)$$

From symmetry, we note that $\theta = 0$ at midspan. Applying this to 3.3.12, we obtain

$$[\theta]_{x=L/2} = 0 = -\frac{q_0}{2EI}\left(\frac{L^3}{8} - \frac{L^3}{24}\right) + C$$

or

$$C = \frac{q_0 L^3}{24EI} \qquad (13)$$

giving the slope equation as

$$\theta = -\frac{q_0}{EI}\left(\frac{Lx^2}{4} - \frac{x^3}{6} - \frac{L^3}{24}\right) \qquad (14)$$

At the left support the slope is given by

$$[\theta]_{x=0} = +\frac{q_0 L^3}{24EI} \qquad (15)$$

Now using 3.3.7 we draw the M/EI diagram as shown in Figure 3.20*b* and note that from symmetry the slope at midspan is zero. The change in slope between the left support and midspan is thus equal to half the total area under the M/EI diagram and leads to

$$[\theta]_{x=L/2} - [\theta]_{x=0} = -\left(\frac{1}{2}\right)\left(\frac{q_0 L^2}{8EI}\right)\left(\frac{2}{3}L\right) = -\frac{q_0 L^2}{24EI} \tag{15}$$

or

$$[\theta]_{x=0} = +\frac{q_0 L^3}{24EI}$$

as before.

Example 3.3.2   Find the deflection at midspan for the beam in Figure 3.20. Using 3.3.10 and 3.3.8 we write

$$\frac{d^2 y}{dx^2} = -\frac{q_0}{2EI}(Lx - x^2) \tag{16}$$

Integrating twice, we find

$$y = -\frac{q_0 x^3 L}{12EI} + \frac{q_0 x^4}{24EI} + C_1 x + C_2 \tag{17}$$

We note that the deflection is zero when $x = 0$ and when $x = L$. Thus

$$[y]_{x=0} = 0 = C_2$$

or

$$C_2 = 0$$

and

$$[y]_{x=L} = -\frac{q_0 L^4}{12EI} + \frac{q_0 L^4}{24EI} + C_1 L = 0$$

or

$$C_1 = \frac{q_0 L^3}{24EI}$$

and 3.3.17 becomes

$$y = \frac{q_0 L^4}{24EI}\left[-2\left(\frac{x}{L}\right)^3 + \left(\frac{x}{L}\right)^4 + \left(\frac{x}{L}\right)\right] \tag{18}$$

At midspan this gives

$$[y]_{x=L/2} = \frac{5q_0 L^4}{384\,EI} \tag{19}$$

We may now check 3.3.14 by taking the derivative of y in 3.3.18 with respect to x. In finding the deflection equation we may equally well have used the conditions $y = 0$ at $x = 0$ and $\theta = 0$ at $x = L/2$.

Now by combining equation 3.3.8 and 1.6.5, we obtain the relation between shear force V and deflection to be

$$\frac{d^3 y}{dx^3} = -\frac{V}{EI} \tag{20}$$

Furthermore, by combining 3.3.8 with 1.7.6 or 3.3.20 with 1.7.1, we obtain

$$\frac{d^4 y}{dx^4} = \frac{q(x)}{EI} \tag{21}$$

where $q(x)$ is the intensity of load per unit of length. We speak of 3.3.21 as the *basic equation of elasticity* for the beam. It includes all requirements on the beam to satisfy the equilibrium equations, Navier's hypothesis, and Hooke's law.

By successive integrations, we find from 3.3.20 and 3.3.21 that

$$y = -\int\int\int \frac{V}{EI}\,dx\,dx\,dx + C_1 x^2 + C_2 x + C_3 \tag{22}$$

or

$$y = +\int\int\int\int \frac{q(x)}{EI}\,dx\,dx\,dx\,dx + C_1 x^3 + C_2 x^2 + C_3 x + C_4 \tag{23}$$

Example 3.3.3 Use the basic equation of elasticity to find the deflection equation for the beam in Figure 3.20. The prescribed end conditions for simply supported beams are that deflections and bending moments be zero at the end supports. This gives

$$[y]_{x=0} = [y]_{x=L} = 0 \tag{24}$$

$$[M]_{x=0} = [M]_{x=L} = 0 \tag{25}$$

Using 3.3.8 we interpret 3.3.4 to give

$$\left[\frac{d^2y}{dx^2}\right]_{x=0} = \left[\frac{d^2y}{dx^2}\right]_{x=L} = 0$$

Since $q(x) = q_0$, a constant, for the present problem, we evaluate 3.3.23 to get

$$y = \frac{q_0 x^4}{24EI} + C_1 x^3 + C_2 x^2 + C_3 x + C_4 \tag{26}$$

Applying the first of conditions 3.3.24, we find $C_4 = 0$. Applying the first condition of 3.3.25, we find $C_2 = 0$. Applying the second of conditions 3.3.24 and the second condition of 3.3.25, we find

$$[y]_{x=L} = 0 = \frac{q_0 L^4}{24EI} + C_1 L^3 + C_3 L \tag{27}$$

$$[y'']_{x=L} = 0 = \frac{q_0 L^2}{2EI} + 6C_1 L \tag{28}$$

The last of these yields

$$C_1 = -\frac{q_0 L}{12EI} \tag{29}$$

Substituting this value of C_1 into 3.2.27, we get

$$C_3 = -\frac{q_0 L^3}{24EI} + \frac{q_0 L^3}{12EI} = \frac{q_0 L^3}{24EI} \tag{30}$$

Finally, we substitute the newly found values of the constants into 3.3.26 to get the equation for the deflection at any point. Thus

$$y = \frac{q_0 L^4}{24EI}\left[-2\left(\frac{x}{L}\right)^3 + \left(\frac{x}{L}\right)^4 + \frac{x}{L}\right] \tag{31}$$

which is identical to 3.3.18.

Whenever the load $q(x)$ can be represented by a single expression, the deflection, y, may be easily found using equation 3.3.21 and its solution 3.3.23.

A much better method for finding slopes and deflections for loadings which are uniformly distributed and/or concentrated is given in the next section.

3.4 Conjugate Beam

A very useful method of finding deflections and slopes which reduces considerably the tedium of the direct approach given in § 3.3 makes use of the mathematical analogy existing between equations 1.7.6 and 3.9.8. Writing these side by side, we have

$$\frac{d^2y}{dx^2} = -\frac{M}{EI}, \qquad \frac{d^2M}{dx^2} = -q(x) \tag{1}$$

Each of these has the same structure, being a second-order, linear, non-homogeneous, ordinary, differential equation with constant coefficients. The solutions are also of the same structure as seen in equations 1.6.7 and 3.3.9. If the variation with x of M/EI in the first is considered analogous to the variation with x of the load q, the variation with x of the deflection in the first corresponds to the variation with x of the bending moment of the second. These suggest the following:

(1) Let the M/EI diagram of a given beam be considered to be the q diagram in a new, analogous beam.

(2) The deflection diagram of the given beam will then correspond to the bending moment diagram of the analogous beam.

(3) The slope diagram of the given beam (being the derivative of the deflection) will correspond to the shear force diagram (being the derivative of the bending moment) in the analogous beam.

We call the analogous beam the *conjugate beam* and summarize the foregoing statements in the following manner.

Given Beam	Conjugate Beam
M/EI	$q(x)$
y	M
θ	V

The conjugate beam has the same length as the given beam and must have its supports chosen so that these tabulated conditions apply. For example, a *simple support* in a given beam has associated with it the conditions of zero deflection but nonzero slope. Therefore, in the conjugate beam we must insist on zero bending moment and nonzero shear force. These latter conditions are also characteristic of a simple support. Hence, a simple support in a given beam corresponds to a simple support in the conjugate beam.

At the *fixed end* of a given beam is zero deflection and zero slope. In the conjugate beam there must be zero bending moment and zero shear force. Hence, the fixed end of a given beam becomes a free end in the conjugate.

At an *interior support* in a given beam there is zero deflection and no sudden change in slope (a slope at an infinitesimally small distance to the right is the same as the slope at an infinitesimally small distance to the left). In the conjugate we must have zero bending moment and no sudden change in shear force. Thus an interior support in the given beam corresponds to an interior hinge in the conjugate beam.

At an *interior hinge* in a given beam, there is nonzero deflection and the possibility of a sudden change in slope. In the conjugate there is a nonzero bending moment and the possibility of a sudden change in shear force. An interior hinge in the given beam must therefore correspond to an interior support in the conjugate.

At an *interior shear connector* in a given beam, we find a sudden change in deflection but no sudden change in slope. In the conjugate this requires a sudden change in bending moment but no sudden change in shear force. The interior shear connector must then be represented by an applied couple.

These are summarized in Figure 3.21. In Figure 3.22 a number of beams and their conjugates are shown.

Example 3.4.1 Use the conjugate beam method to find the slopes at the ends and the deflection at midspan of the elastic curve of the uniformly loaded, simply supported beam of Figure 3.20. Since a simple support in the given beam remains a simple support in the conjugate beam, our simply supported beam does not change. The load on the conjugate beam is the M/EI diagram for the loaded given beam which is shown in Figure 3.20b. Figure 3.23 shows the conjugate beam with the correct analogous loading. The moment ordinates are

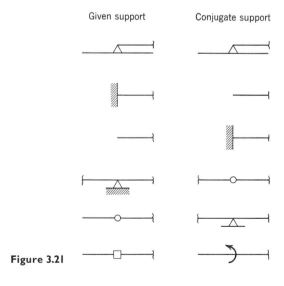

Given support   Conjugate support

Figure 3.21

Given beam⁻   Conjugate beam

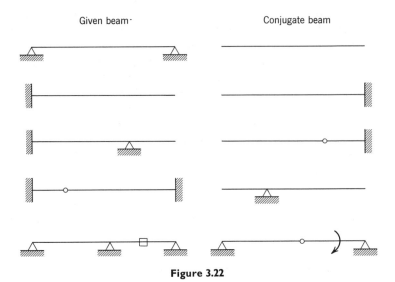

Figure 3.22

positive; thus, the loading on the conjugate beam is positive and is directed downward as shown. The total area of the parabolic diagram is

$$(\tfrac{2}{3})(L)\left(\frac{q_0 L^2}{8EI}\right) = \frac{q_0 L^3}{12EI}$$

This represents the total load acting on the beam. Half of this goes to each support. The reactions of the conjugate are then given by

$$R_L = R_R = \frac{q_0 L^3}{24EI} \tag{2}$$

These act upward. An upwardly directed left reaction corresponds to a positive shear force at the end. A positive shear force in the conjugate beam corresponds to a positive slope in the given beam. Thus, the slope at $x = 0$ is

$$[\theta]_{x=0} = +\frac{q_0 L^3}{24EI} \tag{3}$$

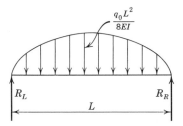

Figure 3.23

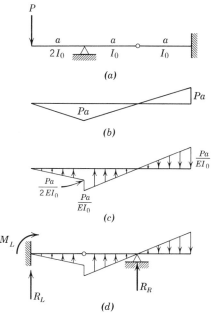

Figure 3.24

Furthermore, the right reaction acting upward corresponds to a negative shear force in the conjugate. Thus, in the given beam we have

$$[\theta]_{x=L} = -\frac{q_0 L^3}{24EI} \tag{4}$$

These agree with values found in § 3.3. The signs are correct since we take deflection, y, as positive downward. Now with the reactions known we can find the bending moment at midspan in the conjugate beam and thereby have the deflection at midspan in the given beam. This gives

$$[y]_{x=L/2} = \frac{q_0 L^3}{24EI}\left(\frac{L}{2}\right) - \left(\frac{1}{2}\right)\left(\frac{q_0 L^3}{12EI}\right)\left(\frac{3}{8}\right)\left(\frac{L}{2}\right) = +\frac{5q_0 L^4}{384} \tag{5}$$

This is the same positive value found in 3.3.19.

Example 3.4.2 Find the deflection at the left end of the beam loaded as shown in Figure 3.24a. The beam is statically determinate and has the bending moment diagram shown in Figure 3.24b. The moment of inertia for the overhang is twice that for the remainder of the beam. This causes the M/EI diagram to have a different shape from the M diagram as seen in Figure 3.24c. The loaded conjugate beam is shown in Figure 3.24d. Now the equation for the deflection of the given beam corresponds to the equation of the bending moment in the conjugate beam. The equation for the slope in the real beam corresponds to the equation for the shear force of the conjugate beam. The right reaction of the conjugate beam is quickly found by setting the sum of moments equal to zero to the right of the hinge.

$$\left(\frac{Pa}{EI_0}\right)\left(\frac{a}{2}\right)\left(a + \frac{2a}{3}\right) - \left(\frac{Pa}{EI_0}\right)\left(\frac{a}{2}\right)\left(\frac{a}{3}\right) - R_R a = 0$$

or

$$R_R = \frac{2}{3}\frac{Pa^2}{EI_0} \tag{6}$$

The left reaction, R_L, is now found by setting the sum of vertical forces on the entire beam equal to zero. Thus

$$\left(\frac{Pa}{EI_0}\right)\left(\frac{a}{2}\right) - R_R - \left(\frac{Pa}{2EI_0}\right)\left(\frac{a}{2}\right) - \left(\frac{Pa}{EI_0}\right)\left(\frac{a}{2}\right) - R_L = 0$$

or

$$R_L = -\frac{11}{12}\frac{Pa^2}{EI_0} \tag{7}$$

The minus sign indicates that we assumed the wrong direction on R_L. It must act vertically downward. The end moment M_L is now found by setting the sum of moments to the left of the hinge equal to zero to obtain

$$\frac{11}{12}\frac{Pa^2}{EI_0}(a) - \left(\frac{Pa}{2EI_0}\right)\left(\frac{a}{2}\right)\left(\frac{a}{3}\right) - M_L = 0$$

or

$$M_L = \frac{5Pa^3}{8EI_0} \tag{8}$$

This positive bending moment in the conjugate beam corresponds to a positive (downward) deflection in the given beam. Thus, y at the free end is given by

$$y = \frac{5}{8}\frac{Pa^3}{EI_0} \tag{9}$$

3.5 Conjugate Beam Method Applied to Plane Bents

The conjugate beam developed for straight beams in § 3.4 is equally applicable to statically determinate plane bents. When the joints are hinged, the angles formed by members framing into a joint do not necessarily remain constant when the frame is loaded. For rigid joints, these angles will be assumed to remain constant under load although they are free to rotate. The application of the conjugate beam method to structures having hinged or rigid joints is illustrated in the following two examples.

Example 3.5.1 Determine the slopes and deflections at the ends of all members of the rigid frame shown in Figure 3.25a. We begin by making the following observations:

(1) The horizontal displacements of joints C and D will be equal if we neglect the effect of axial forces on deformations.

(2) The joint at A is rigid and the column framing into A will retain its original slope at A.

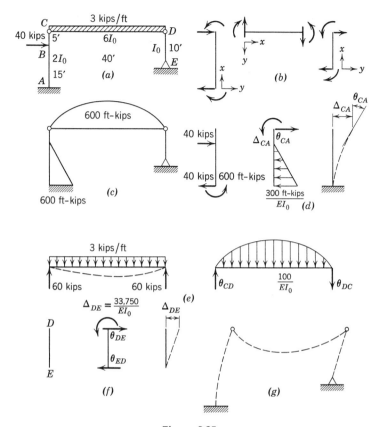

Figure 3.25

(3) Joints C, D, and E are hinged and the angles formed at the joints will change under load.

(4) For rectangular frames such as this, we will choose the origin of coordinates for any horizontal member with x measured positive to the right and y measured positive downward. We will view any vertical member from its right side, choosing the origin of coordinates at the base of the member with axes positive as shown in Figure 3.25b.

(5) Unknown bending moments and shear forces will be assumed positive as shown in Figure 3.25b in accordance with the convention established in Chapter 1.

(6) Bending moment diagrams will always be drawn on the compression side of any member.

We begin our analysis by drawing the bending moment diagram shown in Figure 3.25c for the given structure. Next we isolate member AC as a free body and show its associated conjugate in Figure 3.25d. The load on the conjugate is the M/EI diagram of the given member. The deflection Δ and the slope θ at end A are zero; hence, the bending moment and shear force at end A of the conjugate are zero (giving a free end). The deflection Δ and slope θ at end C of the given member are nonzero; hence, the bending moment and shear force at point C of the conjugate are nonzero. These are assumed positive and shown in the figure. Equilibrium requires that

$$\left(\frac{300}{EI_0}\right)\left(\frac{15}{2}\right) - \theta_{CA} = 0 \tag{1}$$

$$\left(\frac{300}{EI_0}\right)\left(\frac{15}{2}\right)(15) - \Delta_{CA} = 0 \tag{2}$$

Thus

$$\theta_{CA} = \frac{2250}{EI_0} \quad \text{and} \quad \Delta_{CA} = \frac{33,750}{EI_0} \tag{3}$$

The positive values indicate that the unknowns were chosen in the correct directions. Thus the member deflects as shown in the figure.

We now isolate member CD and show its free body diagram as well as its associated conjugate in Figure 3.25e. The load on the conjugate is again the M/EI diagram for the given member. The deflections Δ at ends C and D are each zero; hence, bending moments in the conjugate, at C and D are zero. The slopes at ends C and D in the given member as well as the shear forces at ends C and D of the conjugate are nonzero. They are assumed positive as shown in the figure. Equilibrium requires

$$\theta_{CD} = -\theta_{DC} = \left(\frac{1}{2}\right)\left(\frac{2}{3}\right)\left(\frac{100}{EI_0}\right)(40) \tag{4}$$

$$\theta_{CD} = \frac{1333}{EI_0} \quad \text{and} \quad \theta_{DC} = -\frac{1333}{EI_0} \tag{5}$$

The deflected member is also shown in the figure.

We complete the problem by isolating member DE and showing its free body diagram and associated conjugate in Figure 3.25f. Since there is no bending moment in the given member, there is no load on the conjugate. The horizontal displacement of joint D, being equal to the horizontal displacement of C, is given by equation 3.5.3.

$$\Delta_{DE} = \Delta_{CA} = \frac{33,750}{EI_0} \tag{6}$$

This positive deflection corresponds to a positive bending moment as shown in the conjugate. The slope at end D and the slope at end E are seen to be nonzero in the given member. They are assumed positive and shown for the conjugate member. The deflection at end E of the given member is zero; hence, the bending moment at end E of the conjugate is zero. Equilibrium for the conjugate requires

$$10\,\theta_{ED} - \frac{33,750}{EI_0} = 0 \tag{7}$$

$$\theta_{ED} - \theta_{DE} = 0 \tag{8}$$

or

$$\theta_{ED} = \theta_{DE} = \frac{3375}{EI_0} \tag{9}$$

The bending moment varies linearly along the conjugate member; hence, the

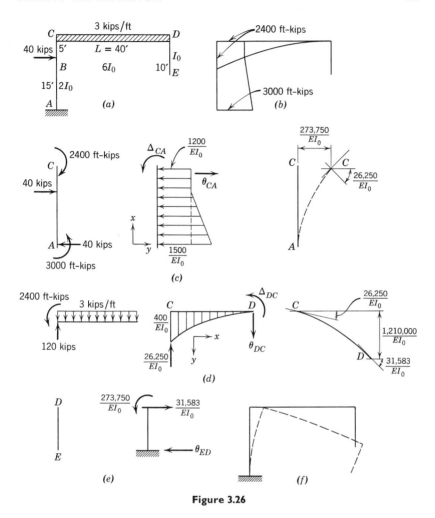

Figure 3.26

deflection diagram is linear as shown for the given member. The final deflected structure is shown in Figure 3.25g.

Example 3.5.2 Find the slopes and deflections at the ends of each member of the structure shown in Figure 3.26a. We begin by making the following observations:

(1) Joint E is free.

(2) Joints C, D, and A are rigid. For joints C and D, this means that the members framing into a joint suffer no rotation relative to one another although they may rotate and translate as a unit.

(3) The horizontal displacements at joints C and D are equal. The M/EI diagram for the structure is shown in Figure 3.26b.

(4) The vertical displacement of joint C is zero.

We know the deflection at end A of member AC and begin our analysis with that member. The free body diagram for member AC and its conjugate are shown in Figure 3.26c. Equilibrium of the conjugate requires

$$\left(\frac{300}{EI_0}\right)\left(\frac{1}{2}\right)(15) + \left(\frac{1200}{EI_0}\right)(20) - \theta_{CA} = 0 \tag{10}$$

$$\left(\frac{300}{EI_0}\right)\left(\frac{1}{2}\right)(15)(15) + \left(\frac{1200}{EI_0}\right)(20)(10) - \Delta_{CA} = 0 \tag{11}$$

or

$$\theta_{CA} = \frac{26,250}{EI_0} \quad \text{and} \quad \Delta_{CA} = \frac{273,750}{EI_0} \tag{12}$$

The deflection of member AC is also shown in the figure.

Figure 3.26d shows the free body diagram of the member CD and its conjugate. Joint C, being a rigid joint, requires that the members at that joint rotate the same amount. From 3.5.12 we find that member CA translates an amount Δ_{CA}, and that the joint rotates clockwise an amount equal to $26,250/EI_0$. The rotation of end C of the member CD must also rotate clockwise an amount equal to $26,250/EI_0$. This clockwise rotation corresponds to a positive slope θ_{CD}. At end D, the slope and deflection are nonzero and assumed positive. Equilibrium of the conjugate member requires

$$\frac{26,250}{EI_0} + \left(\frac{1}{3}\right)\left(\frac{400}{EI_0}\right)(40) - \theta_{DC} = 0 \tag{13}$$

$$\frac{26,250}{EI_0}(40) + \left(\frac{1}{3}\right)\left(\frac{400}{EI_0}\right)(40)(\tfrac{3}{4})(40) - \Delta_{DC} = 0 \tag{14}$$

or

$$\theta_{DC} = \frac{31,583}{EI_0} \quad \text{and} \quad \Delta_{DC} = \frac{1,210,000}{EI_0} \tag{15}$$

The deflected shape of member CD is shown in the figure.

The free-body diagram of member DE and its conjugate are shown in Figure 3.26e. The deflection of end D is positive and equal to Δ_{CA} found in equation 3.5.12. The rotation of end D equals the rotation of end D of member CD, which was found to be clockwise an amount equal to $31,583/EI_0$. A clockwise rotation gives rise to a positive value of θ_{DE}. The deflection Δ_{DE} is positive an amount $273,750/EI_0$. Equilibrium of the conjugate requires

$$\theta_{ED} = \frac{31,583}{EI_0} \quad \text{and} \quad \Delta_{ED} = -\frac{42,080}{EI_0} \tag{16}$$

The deflected structure is shown in the figure.

3.6 Displacements Due to Shear Force

In the previous section it has been assumed that the deflection of a bar is due exclusively to the presence of bending moments distributed along the length of the bar. This is not totally true, however, since shear forces contribute to an increase in the slope of a bar which in turn contributes to an increase in deflection. The shear strain is denoted by the symbol ϵ_s and is related to the shear stress, s_s, through Hooke's law.

$$s_s = G\epsilon_s \tag{1}$$

where G is the *modulus of elasticity in shear* of the material. Since the shear stress is distributed over the cross section of the beam we can relate average stress to shear force through the relation

$$V = s_{s_{avg}} A \tag{2}$$

where A is the area of the cross section. In terms of the shear stress, $\bar{s}_s$, at the centroid of the cross section, we write

$$s_{s_{avg}} = \mu \bar{s}_s \tag{3}$$

where μ is a dimensionless coefficient that varies with the shape of the cross section and is defined as the *shape factor in shear*. Combining 3.6.1 and 3.6.3 we obtain

$$V = \mu A G \epsilon_s \tag{4}$$

We now set the total deflection, y, of the bar equal to the sum of the deflection due to bending and the deflection due to shear.

$$y = y_b + y_s \tag{5}$$

and the slope becomes

$$\frac{dy}{dx} = \frac{dy_b}{dx} + \frac{dy_s}{dx} \tag{6}$$

The slope due to shear is equal to the shearing strain (see Figure 2.33) and we write

$$\epsilon_s = \frac{dy_s}{dx} \tag{7}$$

The stress resultants M and V can now be expressed in terms of deflection components as follows:

$$M = -EI \frac{d^2 y_b}{dx^2} \tag{8}$$

$$V = \mu A G \frac{dy_s}{dx} \tag{9}$$

When shear effects are neglected we have $y = y_b$ and 3.6.8 reverts to 3.3.8. From purely equilibrium considerations we found

$$\frac{dM}{dx} = V \tag{10}$$

and

$$\frac{dV}{dx} = -q(x) \tag{11}$$

Combining 3.6.9 and 3.6.11 we obtain

$$\frac{d^2y_s}{dx^2} = -\frac{q(x)}{\mu AG} \tag{12}$$

Combining 3.6.8, 3.6.10, and 3.6.11 we obtain

$$\frac{d^4y_b}{dx^4} = +\frac{q(x)}{EI} \tag{13}$$

For a given distribution of load, we find y_s from 3.6.12 and y_b from 3.6.13. The total deflection, y, is given by the sum as stated in 3.6.5.

The problem of end conditions is of particular concern. At a *simple support*, the total deflection and the bending moment are zero and we write

$$y = y_s + y_b = 0$$
$$-\frac{M}{EI} = \frac{d^2y_b}{dx^2} = 0 \tag{14}$$

At a *free end*, the shear force and bending moment are zero and we write

$$\frac{V}{\mu AG} = \frac{dy_s}{dx} = 0$$
$$-\frac{M}{EI} = \frac{d^2y_b}{dx^2} = 0 \tag{15}$$

At a *fixed end* we require the total deflection and the slope due to bending to be equal to zero. We thus have

$$y = y_b + y_s = 0$$
$$\frac{dy_b}{dx} = 0 \tag{16}$$

The slope due to shear cannot be zero since from 3.6.9 the shear force is not necessarily zero there.

Example 3.6.1 Find the deflection equation for the cantilever beam of Figure 3.27 with a single concentrated load at its free end $x = L$. Along the length of the beam, we have

$$q(x) = 0 \tag{17}$$

From 3.6.12 and 3.6.13 we have

$$y_s = A + Bx \tag{18}$$
$$y_b = C + Dx + Ex^2 + Fx^3 \tag{19}$$

where A, B, C, D, E, and F are constants to be determined from six prescribed

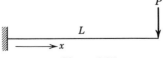

Figure 3.27

end conditions. At the fixed end, we have the total deflection equal to zero and the slope due to bending equal to zero. Thus we have

$$A + C = 0 \tag{20}$$
$$D = 0 \tag{21}$$

At the free end, $x = L$, the shear force is given by

$$V = P \tag{22}$$

and the bending moment is zero. From 3.6.9 we obtain

$$B = \frac{P}{\mu AG} \tag{23}$$

From 3.6.10 and 3.6.8 we obtain

$$V = -EI \frac{d^3 y_b}{dx^3} \tag{24}$$

and using 3.6.19, we get

$$F = -\frac{P}{6EI} \tag{25}$$

From 3.6.8 and 3.6.19 we get

$$2E + 6PL = 0 \tag{26}$$

and using 3.6.25 we obtain

$$E = \frac{PL}{2EI} \tag{27}$$

The total deflection is thus

$$y = \frac{Px}{\mu AG} + \frac{PLx^2}{2EI} - \frac{Px^3}{6EI} \tag{28}$$

This compares with

$$y = \frac{PLx^2}{2EI} - \frac{Px^3}{6EI} \tag{29}$$

when bending effects only are considered. The additional deflection at the free end, for example, is given by

$$\Delta = \frac{PL}{\mu AG} \tag{30}$$

Example 3.6.2 Find the value of the shear shape factor μ for a rectangular cross section of width b and depth d. Here the shear stress at the centroid is $\bar{s}_s = \frac{3}{2}(V/A)$. The average shear stress is $s_{s_{avg}} = (V/A)$. Thus, using 3.6.3 we find $\mu = s_{s_{avg}}/\bar{s}_s = \frac{2}{3}$. A more exact means of computing μ is given in §4.3.

3.7 Displacements Due to Twisting Moment

In §2.8 it was shown that the twisting moment, T, applied to the end of a straight bar of circular cross section is related to the shear stress, s_s, at any radial distance r, by the formula

$$s_s = \frac{Tr}{I_p} \tag{1}$$

where I_p is the polar moment of inertia of the cross sectional area. Due to the twisting a line etched on the mantle of the rod parallel to the axis of the rod will rotate through an angle ϵ_s, representing the shearing strain. Over a length of rod dx this angle is given by

$$\tan \epsilon_s = \frac{r\,d\varphi}{dx} \approx \epsilon_s \tag{2}$$

where $r\,d\varphi$ is the arc dimension shown in Figure 2.33. Tan ϵ_s is assumed to be equal to ϵ_s since ϵ_s is very small. Incorporating 3.7.2 with Hooke's law we obtain

$$s_s = G\epsilon_s = \frac{Gr\,d\varphi}{dx} \tag{3}$$

Combining this with 3.7.1 we find

$$T = GI_p \frac{d\varphi}{dx} \tag{4}$$

Over the length L of the rod, the twisting moment T is constant and we write

$$\int_0^L T\,dx = GI_p \int_0^\varphi d\varphi \tag{5}$$

or

$$T = \frac{GI_p \varphi}{L} \tag{6}$$

where φ is the total angle of twist. Rearranging, we also write

$$\varphi = \frac{TL}{GI_p} \tag{7}$$

When the twisting moment varies over the length of the rod, we write

$$\varphi = \frac{1}{GI_p} \int_0^L T\,dx \tag{8}$$

It is interesting to note the similarity between 3.7.4 and the expression

$$M = -EI \frac{d^2y}{dx^2} = -EI \frac{d\theta}{dx} \tag{9}$$

relating bending moment to change in slope. In 3.7.9 we have the constant EI called the *flexural rigidity*. In 3.7.4 we have the constant GI_p called the *torsional rigidity*.

When a general cross section is employed, we must modify formula 3.7.8 by introducing a shape factor C which is equal to the polar moment of inertia only when the shape is that of a circle. Thus

$$T = \frac{GC\varphi}{L} \tag{10}$$

For a rectangular section of dimensions a and b we have

$$C = k_1 a^3 b \tag{11}$$

where k_1 varies with the ratio b/a. The following table given by Timo-shenko* indicates approximate values of k_1 based on a more exact method of analysis.

TABLE 3.1

b/a	k_1	k_2	b/a	k_1	k_2
1.0	0.1406	0.208	3.0	0.263	0.267
1.2	0.166	0.219	4.0	0.281	0.282
1.5	0.196	0.231	5.0	0.291	0.291
2.0	0.229	0.246	10.0	0.312	0.312
2.5	0.249	0.258	∞	0.333	0.333

Corresponding to formula 3.7.1 for the circular cross section is the maximum shear stress for a rectangular section given by

$$s_{s_{max}} = \frac{T}{k_2 a^2 b} \tag{12}$$

where values of k_2 are also given on Table 3.1. This maximum shear stress occurs at the midpoint of the long sides of the rectangle.

3.8 Twisting of Thin-Walled Members

In the previous section the relation between twisting moment and angle of twist per unit of length (φ/L) was given for rectangular sections. When the cross section is a narrow rectangle we have a good approximation by using the values of k tabulated for the ratio $b/a = \infty$. In particular, $k_1 = k_2 = \frac{1}{3}$. We have

$$\varphi = 3\frac{T}{Ga^3b} \tag{1}$$

$$s_{s_{max}} = 3\frac{T}{a^2b} \tag{2}$$

When rolled sections such as channels, I-beams, and angles are twisted, convenient and reasonable values are found by using instead of a^3b and a^2b, values corresponding to $\Sigma\, a^3b$ and $\Sigma\, a^2b$ where all elements of the rolled shape are included. In Figure 3.28, for example, a^3b in 3.8.1 is replaced by $a^3(c - a/2) + d^3(c - a/2)$ and a^2b in 3.8.2 is replaced by $a^2(c - d/2) + d^2(c - a/2)$.

* Timoshenko, S. P., and Goodier, J. N. *Theory of Elasticity*, McGraw-Hill Book Company, New York, Second Edition, 1951.

MECHANICS OF ENGINEERING STRUCTURES

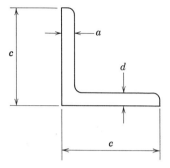

Figure 3.28

Problems

3.1.1 Support F settles vertically an amount Δ. Find the axial forces induced in the bars and express in terms of their spring constants.

Problem 3.1.1

3.1.2 A pile is subjected to a static load *in situ*. The applied force is 200 kips. The pile is made of concrete and is circular with a diameter of 1 ft. The skin friction is uniformly distributed of magnitude 100 psf. If the pile is 50 ft. long, what force will be transmitted at the base of the pile? What will be the total amount of shortening? Plot a strain diagram for the pile and relate the area below it to the shortening.

3.2.1 Find the displacements for joints C, E, and H in the figure below. $AE = 20 \times 10^3$ kips for each member.

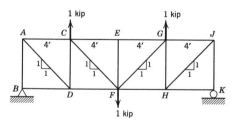

Problem 3.2.1

3.2.2 Find the vertical and horizontal components of the deflection of each joint in the figure shown. Find the magnitude and direction of the displacement of C relative to E. $L/AE = 0.00001$ for each member.

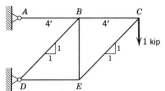

Problem 3.2.2

3.2.3 Find the displacements of all joints due to a shortening of 1 in. of member *CF*.

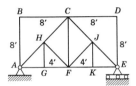

Problem 3.2.3

3.2.4 Find the displacement components at the loaded joint. $AE = 20,000$ kips for each member.

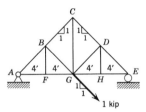

Problem 3.2.4

3.2.5 Find the displacement of joint *E*. $AE = 20,000$ kips.

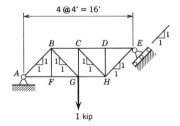

Problem 3.2.5

3.2.6 Draw the Williot-Mohr diagram for the figure shown on page 144. $E = 10 \times 10^3$ ksi, $A = 2$ in.^{2} for each bar.

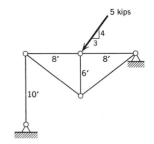

Problem 3.2.6

3.3.1 Find the slopes at sections A and B of the following beams using the differential equation.

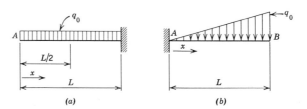

Problem 3.3.1

3.3.2 (a) Find the slopes at sections A and B using the moment-area theorem.
(b) Find the slopes at sections A and B using the moment-area theorem.
(c) Find the slopes at sections A and B using the moment-area theorem.

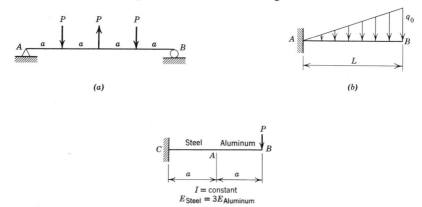

Problem 3.3.2

3.3.3 Use the differential equation to find the deflection equations for the beams of Problem 3.3.1.

3.4.1 Draw the conjugate beam for each of the following structures.

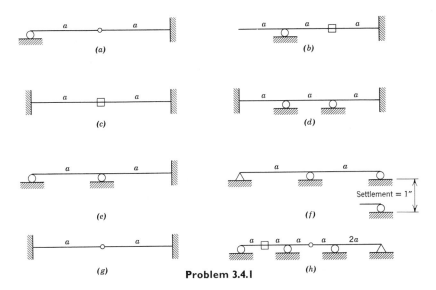

(a)

(b)

(c)

(d)

(e)

(f)

Settlement = 1″

(g)

Problem 3.4.1

(h)

3.4.2 Show the conjugate beam and its loading for each of the following structures. $EI = $ constant.

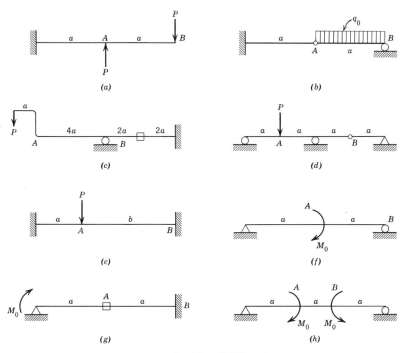

(a)

(b)

(c)

(d)

(e)

(f)

(g)

(h)

Problem 3.4.2

3.4.3 Find the slope and deflection at points A and B for each of the beams of Problem 3.4.2.

3.4.4 Use the conjugate beam method to write the deflection equations for the beams of Problems 3.4.2a and 3.4.2b.

3.5.1 Find the slopes and deflections at the ends of all members of the figure shown. Sketch the deflected structure.

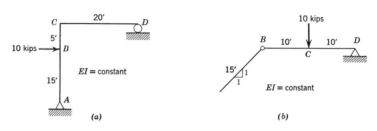

(a)

Problem 3.5.1a

(b)

Problem 3.5.1b

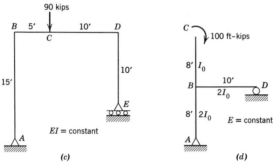

(c)

Problem 3.5.1c

(d)

Problem 3.5.1d

3.6.1 Find the effects of shear on the midspan deflection of a simply supported rectangular beam subjected to a uniformly distributed load.

3.6.2 Study the influence of shear forces on the beam of Problem 3.6.1 as the ratio of d/L varies. L is span length and d is depth of beam. Plot your results as Δ/Δ_b versus d/L where Δ is midspan deflection due to shear and bending and Δ_b is deflection due to bending alone.

3.7.1 Develop a theorem for twisting comparable to the moment-area method in § 3.3.

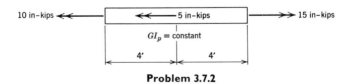

Problem 3.7.2

3.7.2   What will be the total change in angle of twist between the end sections of the bar shown?

3.7.3   A circular bar 1 ft. diameter is vertically placed in a medium capable of supplying resistance to twist along the mantle of the bar. A torque of 10 ft-kips is externally applied to the bar at its top section. $G = 500$ ksi. Find the change in angle of twist over the 10-ft. length of the bar. Assume resistance to twist is uniformly distributed along the mantle and that no resistance to twist is present along the base.

3.7.4   Prepare a plot for the maximum shear stress present in a solid rectangular bar subjected to twisting for values of b/A between 1 and infinity.

3.8.1   Which one of the sections in the figure provides the greatest resistance to twisting per unit of length? All thickness equal a.

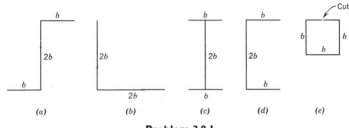

Problem 3.8.1

4 ENERGY PRINCIPLES

4.1 External Work and Internal Strain Energy in Axially Loaded Bars

When a straight bar is acted on by equal and opposite axial forces as shown in Figure 4.1, it elongates or contracts. If the forces are gradually applied tensile forces of magnitude P_1 and if the elongation is Δ, then the forces, in undergoing the displacement associated with this elongation, do external work. For an elastic bar the external work, W, done is given by

$$W_1 = \tfrac{1}{2}P_1\Delta_1 \tag{1}$$

since the force and elongation increase linearly from zero to their values of P_1 and Δ_1. If now for this elastic bar a second gradually applied force P_2

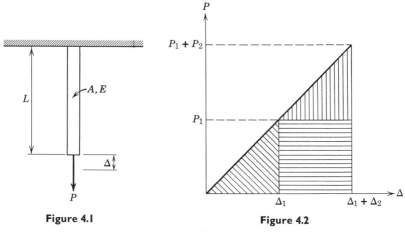

Figure 4.1   Figure 4.2

is added, causing an additional elongation Δ_2, additional external work will be performed. The force P_1 will be present throughout the additional displacement and will do an additional amount of work $P_1\Delta_2$. The force P_2, being gradually applied during the additional elongation, will do an amount of work $\frac{1}{2}P_2\Delta_2$. The total work done will then be

$$W_1 + W_2 = \tfrac{1}{2}P_1\Delta_1 + P_1\Delta_2 + \tfrac{1}{2}P_2\Delta_2 \tag{2}$$

Figure 4.2 shows a plot of load versus elongation. The work done initially by P_1 is the triangular area under the curve to the left of an ordinate through Δ_1. The work $P_1\Delta_2$ corresponds to the rectangular area. The work $\frac{1}{2}P_2\Delta_2$ corresponds to the upper triangular area. Within the elastic range it is evident, therefore, that the total work could equally well be represented by

$$W_1 + W_2 = \tfrac{1}{2}(P_1 + P_2)(\Delta_1 + \Delta_2) \tag{3}$$

Equating the right hand sides of 4.1.2 and 4.1.3, we find

$$P_1\Delta_2 = \tfrac{1}{2}(P_1\Delta_2 + P_2\Delta_1) \tag{4}$$

or

$$\frac{P_1\Delta_2}{2} = \frac{P_2\Delta_1}{2} \tag{5}$$

This is a specialized form of a general principle to be discussed later. For the present we interpret it to mean that the work done by the force P_1 acting through the displacement Δ_2 is equal to the work done by the force P_2 acting through the displacement Δ_1.

Now if the total force $P_1 + P_2 = P_y$, the force causing yielding of fibers of the bar, and if the bar is made from an ideally elastoplastic material, unconfined plastic flow will set in. This must be so since at yielding a fiber can undergo indefinite straining without additional stress being carried. The load-deflection curve will be as shown in Figure 4.3. Additional work, W_3, will now be done since the force $P_1 + P_2$ is being carried through an additional displacement. Let the plastic flow be halted (by some unspecified agent) when an elongation of amount Δ_3 beyond the yield deflection has occurred. The additional work done is then $(P_1 + P_2)\Delta_3$ and the total work done is

$$W_1 + W_2 + W_3 = \tfrac{1}{2}P_1\Delta_1 + P_1\Delta_2 + \tfrac{1}{2}P_2\Delta_2 + (P_1 + P_2)\Delta_3 \tag{6}$$

Again this corresponds to the area under the load deflection curve from $\Delta = 0$ to $\Delta = \Delta_1 + \Delta_2 + \Delta_3$.

If we divide all ordinates of the P-Δ curve by A (the area of the cross section of the bar) and all abscissas by L (the length of the bar) we have the stress-strain curve for the material in the bar. The area under a stress-strain curve gives us an indication of the amount of work that can be done

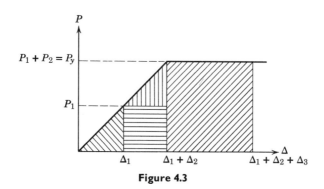

Figure 4.3

to any fiber of our bar. More specifically, the *law of conservation of energy*, which states that in the absence of dissipative elements the total energy can neither be created nor destroyed but can be transformed from one kind to another, requires that the external work done be balanced by energy stored in the member. This stored energy we call *internal strain energy*. In this light, we see that the area under the stress-strain curve gives an indication of the total energy that can be stored in the member.

For the axially loaded bar, all fibers are subjected to the same stress on any given cross section. For a bar of constant area throughout, the stress is the same at all cross sections. Thus, when the yield stress is reached for one fiber it is reached for all fibers and plastic flow of the entire section begins.

In a statically determinate truss, we note that as soon as one member is incapable of carrying additional load the structure as a whole becomes incapable of carrying additional load. In Figure 4.4, for example, if the applied load P causes member AB to be stressed to yielding, no additional load can be placed on the structure without causing it to collapse as shown in Figure 4.5, since member AB is now capable of elongating indefinitely without increasing its axial force. In this statically determinate truss

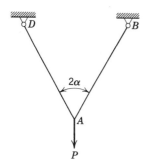

Figure 4.4

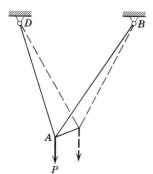

Figure 4.5

there is no reserve of strength left once the first member yields. Additional energy must be absorbed (in this case in member AB) without any adjustment in the bar forces present in the various members.

From this discussion we might define *collapse* as the state wherein it becomes possible to absorb additional strain energy without changing the stress resultants (i.e., the internal forces and moments) present in the members.

The indeterminate truss of Figure 4.6 tells an entirely different story. If a load P_1 causes member AB, for example, to reach its yield stress while all other members remain stressed within the elastic range, collapse does not occur. The structure will still be stable since member CA may still carry additional stress. Only when two bars of this structure have reached their yield stress levels does collapse occur. This indeterminate structure is thus seen to have a reserve of strength left after the first bar yields. The reserve is used up when the second bar yields. Between the yieldings of the first bar and the second bar there is an increase in the strain energy stored in the structure accompanied by changes in the bar forces present. Since member AB had already reached its yield stress, we have plastic flow occurring in that member during this stage; however, it is a *confined*

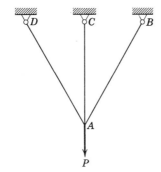

Figure 4.6

plastic flow. It only becomes unconfined when the structure itself is in a state of collapse.

Methods of design that take into account the ability of a structure to absorb large amounts of strain energy prior to failure are now receiving serious consideration by engineers.

Within the elastic range we have from Hooke's Law

$$s_n = E\epsilon_n \tag{7}$$

For the axially loaded member

$$s_n = \frac{N}{A} \tag{8}$$

For a length ds of the bar we have

$$\epsilon_n = \frac{du}{ds} \tag{9}$$

by definition of normal strain. Substituting s_n from 4.1.8 and ϵ_n from 4.1.9 into 4.1.7, we find

$$du = \frac{N}{AE} ds \tag{10}$$

The strain energy stored due to the gradually applied force N being displaced an amount du is

$$dU = \frac{N^2}{2AE} ds \tag{11}$$

The total strain energy stored in a bar of length L is thus

$$U = \int_0^L \frac{N^2 \, ds}{2AE} \tag{12}$$

When N, A, and E are all constant along the length of the bar, this yields

$$U = \frac{N^2 L}{2AE} \tag{13}$$

as the total strain energy stored. If N, A, or E are not constant along the length of the bar, the integral form 4.1.12 must be used instead of 4.1.13.

Example 4.1.1 Find the deflection under the load for the truss of Figure 4.4, when all stresses are within the elastic range. From symmetry we have each bar force equal to $P/\cos \alpha$. These are axial forces that are constants throughout the length of the bars. Let the areas also be constant and of magnitudes A. Let E be the same for both bars. The total energy stored due to the presence of load P is

$$U = 2\left(\frac{P^2 L}{2AE \cos^2 \alpha}\right) = \left(\frac{P^2 L}{AE \cos^2 \alpha}\right) \tag{14}$$

Now the energy stored as elastic strain energy must equal the external work performed. Taking Δ as positive downward, we find

$$W = \tfrac{1}{2}P\Delta \tag{15}$$

Equating 4.1.14 and 4.1.15, we find

$$\Delta = \frac{2PL}{AE \cos^2 \alpha} \tag{16}$$

So long as all stresses are within the elastic range, the deflection Δ will be related to the load P as given previously. When first yielding is reached for one fiber in this symmetrical structure, it will be reached in all fibers and collapse will immediately occur. The unconfined plastic flow ceases only by an actual rupturing of the bars. This occurs when the strain energy absorbed equals the maximum area possible under the $P\Delta$ diagrams.

4.2   Strain Energy in Bars Subject to Bending

Let a ds length of bar be acted on by the positive bending moments M as shown in Figure 4.7. The application of such moments causes a change in slope to occur over the length ds of amount $d\theta$ as shown. The ratio $d\theta/ds$ is called the *curvature* and is given the symbol K. Experimental results indicate that the bending moment is related to the curvature as indicated in Figure 4.8. Whereas all fibers are stressed within the elastic range, the relation between M and K is linear and is given by the derived expression from Chapter 3, equation 3.3.5

$$M = -EIK = -EI\frac{d\theta}{ds} = -EI\frac{d^2y}{ds^2} \tag{1}$$

After first yielding of the cross section occurs, the curve begins to level

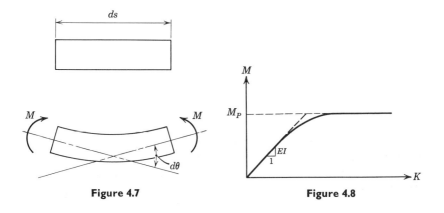

Figure 4.7   Figure 4.8

out approaching the value of the plastic moment M_p as an asymptote. As explained in Chapter 2, this moment can never actually be reached but is approached very closely even for relatively small values of K.

The work done by a couple depends on the rotation associated with the plane on which it acts. Within the elastic range a gradually applied couple M will do an amount of work

$$dU = -\tfrac{1}{2}M \, d\theta \qquad (2)$$

when rotated through an angle $d\theta$. The negative sign is required since, according to our sign convention, a positive moment is associated with a negative change in slope. The work done on the length ds of the bar in Figure 4.7 when in the elastic range is given by

$$dU = -\frac{M \, d\theta}{2 \, ds} ds = -\frac{MK \, ds}{2} \qquad (3)$$

Taking $K = -(M/EI)$ from 4.2.1, we find

$$dU = \frac{M^2}{2EI} ds \qquad (4)$$

This represents the strain energy stored in the ds length of the bar. For the entire length L of the member the energy stored will be

$$U = \int_0^L \frac{M^2}{2EI} ds \qquad (5)$$

When E, I, and M are constant over the length, L, of the bar (pure bending) this reduces to

$$U = \frac{M^2 L}{2EI} \qquad (6)$$

For other bars the proper expressions are introduced into 4.2.5 and the energy is found by performing the required integration.

In 4.2.3 the quantity $MK/2$ is seen to represent the area under the M-K curve within the elastic range. This area is thus a measure of the energy absorbed due to bending. As the member is bent beyond the point of first yielding, the energy absorbed continues to be represented by the area under the M-K curve up to the value of K in question.

As a close approximation to the curve of Figure 4.8, we choose the bilinear curve of Figure 4.9. Its adoption implies certain physical approximations which must be explained. First, the bending moment on every section is assumed to be linearly related to the curvature as long as $M < M_p$, and that upon reaching the value $M = M_p$, the section is able to

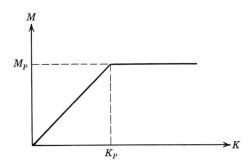

Figure 4.9

sustain unlimited changes in K with no increase in M. This flowing of the section is similar to the action at a hinge section, since abrupt changes in slope, corresponding to large values of K, can occur. Secondly, when $M < M_p$ the section is assumed to be perfectly elastic. Thus plastification is assumed to be total over the cross section or not to exist at all. The partial plastification of Figure 4.10 is assumed never to occur. The fact that a beam can carry bending moments greater than the moment causing first yielding is indicated by the large area under the curve beyond the value of K_p.

Example 4.2.1 Find the free end deflection of the cantilever beam of Figure 4.11. The axis is horizontal; hence, ds becomes dx. Measuring x from the free end we find M given by

$$M = -Px \tag{7}$$

Letting EI be constant, we find the total energy stored to be

$$U = \frac{1}{2EI} \int_0^L (-Px)^2 \, dx \tag{8}$$

or

$$U = \frac{P^2 L^3}{6EI} \tag{9}$$

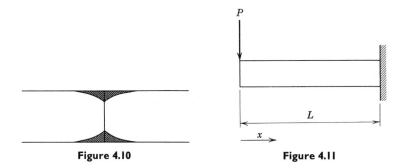

Figure 4.10   **Figure 4.11**

The external work performed is equal to the strain energy stored. Thus

$$W = \frac{P\Delta}{2} = \frac{P^2 L^3}{6EI} \tag{10}$$

or

$$\Delta = \frac{PL^3}{3EI} \tag{11}$$

The positive result indicates a downward deflection. A quick check shows this to be the same value as found by using the conjugate beam method discussed earlier.

If this load is increased beyond that necessary to cause $M = M_p$ at the wall (the section of maximum moment), the beam will collapse.

The calculation of collapse loads for statically indeterminate beams is discussed in Chapter 5.

4.3   Strain Energy Stored Due to Shear Force

On any element of length ds of a rod, the work done by the shear forces within the elastic range is given by

$$dU = \frac{V}{2}\frac{dy_s}{ds}\,ds \tag{1}$$

where (dy_s/ds) is the slope *due to shear* and by 3.6.7 is equal to the shear strain ϵ_s. From 3.6.4,

$$V = \mu AG\epsilon_s \quad \text{or} \quad \epsilon_s = \frac{V}{\mu AG} = \frac{dy_s}{ds} \tag{2}$$

in 4.3.1 we find

$$dU = \frac{V^2\,ds}{2\mu AG} \tag{3}$$

where μ is the shape factor in shear. The work done by the shear force V is equal to the strain energy stored due to shear (see Figure 4.12).

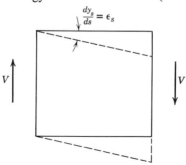

Figure 4.12

Example 4.3.1 Study the contribution of shear to the deflection of the cantilever beam of Figure 4.11. The bending moment and shear force equations are

$$M = -Px \tag{4}$$

$$V = -P \tag{5}$$

The total energy stored due to shear and bending is

$$U = + \frac{1}{2EI} \int_0^L (-Px)^2 \, dx + \frac{1}{2\mu AG} \int_0^L (-P)^2 \, dx \tag{6}$$

$$U = \frac{P^2 L^3}{6EI} + \frac{P^2 L}{2\mu AG} \tag{7}$$

For a rectangle of proportions b and d with $\mu = \frac{2}{3}$, $I = \frac{1}{12}bd^3$, $A = bd$, and taking $G = \frac{2}{5}E$, we find

$$U = \frac{2P^2 L^3}{Ebd^3} + \frac{15P^2 L}{8bdE} = \frac{P^2 L}{bdE} \left[2\left(\frac{L}{d}\right)^2 + \frac{15}{8} \right] \tag{8}$$

Equating this to the external work done in moving the load P through the distance Δ, we find

$$\Delta = \frac{PL}{bdE} \left[4\left(\frac{L}{d}\right)^2 + \frac{15}{4} \right] \tag{9}$$

As the ratio L/d becomes smaller and smaller, the contribution of shear (represented by the second term) to the deflection increases very rapidly. This contribution is one percent of the total when

$$0.01 \left[4\left(\frac{L}{d}\right)^2 + \frac{15}{4} \right] = \frac{15}{4}$$

or

$$4\left(\frac{L}{d}\right)^2 = \frac{1500}{4} - \frac{15}{4}(100 - 1) = 371 \tag{10}$$

and

$$\frac{L}{d} \approx 10 \tag{11}$$

Thus, if L is greater than $10d$ we may say that the effect of shear will be negligible. Since most of the bars with which we shall be concerned have ratios of L/d greater than 10 we shall assume in all of our work that deflection is dependent on bending moment only.

The value of the shape factor μ used in the foregoing example is based on the relation given in 3.6.3; namely,

$$s_{s_{\text{avg}}} = \mu \bar{s}_s \tag{12}$$

where $\bar{s}_s$ is the shear stress at the centroid. An alternate and more exact means of computing μ is based on energy considerations. We saw that the area under the elastic portion of the stress-strain curve for simple tension was given by $\frac{1}{2}s_s\epsilon_s$ and that s_s and ϵ_s represented in terms of the cross sectional area A and elemental length ds became

$$s_s = \frac{N}{A} \qquad \epsilon_s = \frac{N}{AE}\,ds \tag{13}$$

The area under the curve is then the strain energy per unit volume. Integrating over the cross section we get the strain energy per unit length

$$dU = \frac{N^2\,ds}{2AE} \tag{14}$$

as given in § 4.1. In a similar manner the strain energy due to shear over the length ds can be related to the area under the shear stress-shear strain curve. Thus

$$dU = \frac{s_s\epsilon_s}{2}\,dA\,ds \tag{15}$$

For a rectangle,

$$s_s = \frac{V}{2I}\left(\frac{d^2}{4} - \zeta^2\right) \tag{16}$$

where ζ is the distance from the centroid of the cross section to any fiber.
Using Hooke's law

$$s_s = G\epsilon_s \tag{17}$$

and 4.3.15 we get the relation

$$dU = \frac{V^2\,ds}{2(0.833)GA} \tag{18}$$

Comparing this with 4.3.3 we see that μ now has taken on the value of 0.833 or

$$\mu = \tfrac{5}{6} \tag{19}$$

Introducing this value in 4.3.7 we obtain instead of 4.3.9 the expression

$$\Delta = \frac{PL}{b\,dE}\left[4\left(\frac{L}{d}\right)^2 + 3\right] \tag{20}$$

By these figures, the shear accounts for one percent of the total deflection when $L/d \approx 8.5$.

For our purposes we shall make use of the first means of computing μ because of its greater simplicity.

4.4 Strain Energy Stored Due to Twisting Moment

Let an element of length ds of a bar be acted on by the twisting moments T. If the rate of change of angle of twist φ per unit of length is given by $d\varphi/ds$, the work done by the twisting moments will be

$$dU = \tfrac{1}{2}T\frac{d\varphi}{ds}\,ds \tag{1}$$

We found in § 3.7 that the angle of twist is related to the twisting moment in elastic bars through the relation

$$d\varphi = \frac{T}{GC}\,ds \qquad (2)$$

where C is a *torsion shape factor*. Substituting this into 4.4.1 we find

$$dU = \frac{T^2\,ds}{2GC} \qquad (3)$$

This represents the strain energy stored due to torsion over the length ds.

Example 4.4.1 Find the angle of twist for a bar of length L of constant circular cross section and subjected to end torques T. The external work done in twisting the bar through an angle φ will be

$$W = \frac{T\varphi}{2} \qquad (4)$$

Equating this to the integral of 4.4.3 we find

$$\varphi = \frac{1}{T}\int_0^L \frac{T^2\,ds}{2GC} \qquad (5)$$

Since $\bar{T}$, G, and C are constant throughout,

$$\varphi = \frac{TL}{2GC} \qquad (6)$$

For a circular cross section, C is equal to the polar moment of inertia I_p. For rectangular cross sections, C is given by 3.7.11.

4.5 Total Strain Energy

When bending moments, twisting moments, axial forces, and shear forces all act on an elastic bar of length L, the total strain energy stored is equal to the sum of the strain energies associated with the various stress resultants. Thus

$$U = \frac{1}{2}\int_0^L \left(\frac{M^2}{EI} + \frac{T^2}{GC} + \frac{N^2}{AE} + \frac{V^2}{\mu AG}\right) ds \qquad (1)$$

The superposition of strain energies follows from the linear nature of the stress-strain relation. In the usual problem only one of the terms may have a particular bearing on the final result.

Example 4.5.1 Find the vertical deflection at the load point of the space structure of Figure 4.13. The structure is of constant circular section throughout and is made from a single material. We shall choose our coordinates as shown. A free body diagram is given in Figure 4.14. We have for bar AB

$$M = Px_1 - Pb$$
$$V = P \qquad (2)$$
$$T = Pa$$

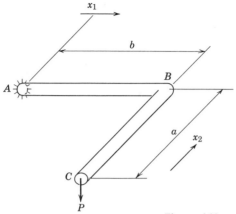

Figure 4.13

For bar BC

$$M = -Px_2$$

$$V = -P \qquad (3)$$

The total external work done is given by

$$W = \frac{P\Delta}{2} \qquad (4)$$

where Δ is the vertical deflection at the load point. Equating external work and strain energy stored we get

$$\frac{P\Delta}{2} = \frac{1}{2} \int_0^b \left[\frac{(Px_1 - Pb)^2}{EI} + \frac{(Pa)^2}{GI_p} + \frac{P^2}{\mu AG} \right] dx_1$$
$$+ \frac{1}{2} \int_0^a \left[\frac{(-Px_2)^2}{EI} + \frac{(-P)^2}{\mu AG} \right] dx_2 \qquad (5)$$

By setting prescribed values for E, I, G, I_p, μ, and A and integrating, we solve for Δ.

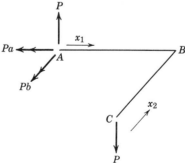

Figure 4.14

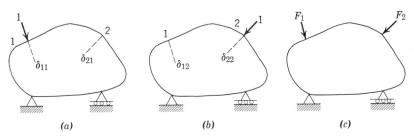

(a)   *(b)*   *(c)*

Figure 4.15

4.6 Betti's Law and Maxwell's Law

Several reciprocal relations between loads and deflections will now be developed for the general elastic body. Consider the body in Figure 4.15. In Figure 4.15a the body is acted on by a single concentrated unit force acting at point 1. This causes a deflection of point 1 in the direction of the force of amount δ_{11} (reading deflection at point 1 due to unit load placed at point 1) and a deflection of point 2 in the direction shown of amount δ_{21} (reading deflection at point 2 due to unit force at point 1). Now if instead of a unit force at point 1 we have a force F_1 these deflections will be $F_1\delta_{11}$ and $F_1\delta_{21}$ since superposition is permissible. In Figure 4.15b a single concentrated unit force acts at point 2, causing a deflection in the direction of the force of amount δ_{22} and the deflection at point 1 in the direction indicated earlier of amount δ_{12}. In general we let δ_{ij} represent the deflection at position i in some prescribed direction due to a unit force acting in some prescribed direction at position j. In Figure 4.15c is shown the body acted on by forces F_1 and F_2. By using the superposition principle, we see that the total deflections at points 1 and 2 are given by

$$\Delta_1 = F_1\,\delta_{11} + F_2\,\delta_{12} \tag{1}$$

$$\Delta_2 = F_1\,\delta_{21} + F_2\,\delta_{22} \tag{2}$$

When a force F is gradually applied to an elastic structure and undergoes a deflection Δ in its direction, work will be done in the amount $W = F\Delta/2$. In Figure 4.15c, for example, if the force F_1 is applied first it will immediately do an amount of work equal to

$$W = \tfrac{1}{2}F_1(F_1\,\delta_{11}) = \frac{F_1^{\,2}\,\delta_{11}}{2} \tag{3}$$

If force F_2 is applied now it causes force F_1 to undergo an additional deflection $F_2\,\delta_{12}$ and thus F_1 does an additional amount of work

$$W = F_1(F_2\,\delta_{12}) = F_1 F_2\,\delta_{12} \tag{4}$$

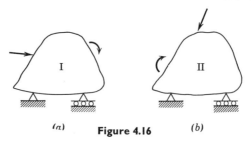

Force F_2, itself, has also done work in moving through the deflection $F_2\,\delta_{22}$. This amounts to

$$W = \tfrac{1}{2}F_2(F_2\,\delta_{22}) = \tfrac{1}{2}F_2{}^2\,\delta_{22} \qquad (5)$$

The total amount of work done by these two forces is, therefore,

$$W = \frac{F_1{}^2\,\delta_{11}}{2} + F_1F_2\,\delta_{12} + \frac{F_2{}^2\,\delta_{22}}{2} \qquad (6)$$

The left support of the body in Figure 4.15 does not move. Hence, the reactive forces at that support do no work. The right reaction may move only horizontally. Since the reactive force at that support is vertical, it does no work. W in 4.6.6 represents the total external work done. By the law of conservation of energy, it likewise represents the total strain energy stored due to the forces.

If we were to place the force F_2 on the body first and then place F_1 on the body, the external work done would be given, not by 4.6.6, but by

$$W = \tfrac{1}{2}F_2{}^2\,\delta_{22} + F_2F_1\,\delta_{21} + \tfrac{1}{2}F_1{}^2\,\delta_{11} \qquad (7)$$

The work done is independent of order of placement if superposition is to be valid. Hence 4.6.7 must equal 4.6.6. This can be true only if

$$F_1(F_2\,\delta_{12}) = F_2(F_1\,\delta_{21}) \qquad (8)$$

This gives us the first reciprocal theorem. It states that the work done by force F_1 on the deflection associated with the force F_2 equals the work done by force F_2 on the deflection associated with force F_1.

This may be easily extended to include general sets of forces and couples where the forces do work in moving through deflections and couples do work in moving through rotations. If we have a body loaded with one set (called system I) of forces and couples in Figure 4.16a and the same body loaded with another set (called system II) of forces and couples in Figure 4.16b, we may say that the work done by the forces and couples of system I on the deflections and rotations of system II equals the work done by the forces and couples of system II on the deflections and rotations of system I.

If we let W_{12} be the work done by the external forces of set I on the displacements of set II and W_{21} be the work done by the external forces of set II on the displacements of set I, we have corresponding to 4.6.6 and 4.6.7

$$W = W_{11} + W_{12} + W_{22} \tag{9}$$

$$W = W_{22} + W_{21} + W_{11} \tag{10}$$

Since these must be equal we find

$$W_{12} = W_{21} \tag{11}$$

This is perfectly general and thus includes work done by forces as well as couples. This is usually known as *Betti's law* and states that the total external work done by a system of forces I on the set of displacements of a system II equals the total external work done by the forces of system II on the displacements of system I provided systems I and II are equilibrium sets.

A special form of Betti's law is obtained by letting $F_1 = F_2 = 1$ in equation 4.6.8. This reads

$$\delta_{12} = \delta_{21} \tag{12}$$

and states that the displacement at point 1 due to a unit force at point 2 equals the displacement at point 2 due to a unit force at point 1 where displacement and force at a given point are chosen in the same direction. This special statement is called *Maxwell's law.**

4.7 Applications of Betti's Law in Finding Reactions

Betti's law is especially useful in finding reactions and in describing influence diagrams. These will now be discussed.

Example 4.7.1 Find the right reaction of the beam shown in Figure 4.17a. The set of forces applied will be considered to be system I. Now take the same beam and apply a force upward at the right end, causing a displacement Δ; (sometimes called a virtual displacement) this will be system II. The deflections in system II corresponding to the load points of system I are $2\Delta/3$, 0, $-\Delta/3$, $-2\Delta/3$, and $-\Delta$. The deflections in system I corresponding to the load points of system II are 0 and 0. Betti's law now gives

$$(P)\left(\frac{2\Delta}{3}\right) - (R_L)(0) + (P)\left(\frac{-\Delta}{3}\right) + (P)\left(\frac{-2\Delta}{3}\right) - (R_R)(\Delta) = -(R_L)(0) - F(0)$$

or

$$R_R = -\frac{P}{3} \tag{1}$$

---

* Clerk Maxwell developed the simple law bearing his name; however, E. Betti developed the more general proof in Italy sometime later. Betti's law is sometimes called the *generalized Maxwell law*.

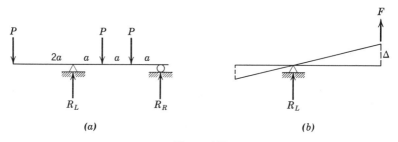

(a)   (b)

Figure 4.17

This indicates that the right reaction acts upward since a force or deflection acting down was considered as positive.

Note that we chose system II so that only one of the reactions would work. Now to find the left reaction we would choose as system II one that would give a deflection Δ at the location of the left support but no deflection at the right support.

Example 4.7.2   Find the moment reaction at the wall of the structure shown in Figure 4.18a. The given forces comprise system I. Since we want to find M we choose a second set of forces (or displacements) that consists of a rotation θ at the left (since moments do work only on a rotation), and no displacement at the left end (so that the force R_L does no work). A rigid body rotation of the beam as shown in Figure 4.18b meets these requirements. The deflections corresponding to the load points of Figure 4.18a are 0, $a\theta$, $2a\theta$. The use of Betti's law gives

$$(-M_L)(\theta) + R_L(0) + (P)(a\theta) - (P)(2a\theta) = M(0) + R(0)$$

or

$$M_L = -Pa \tag{2}$$

This indicates that the moment reaction acts in an opposite sense to that assumed.

Example 4.7.3   Find all reactions of the statically determinate beam in Figure 4.19a. Figures 4.19b, 4.19c, 4.19d, and 4.19e show the choices for system

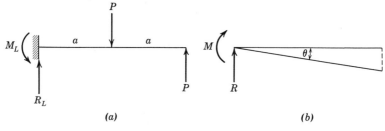

(a)   (b)

Figure 4.18

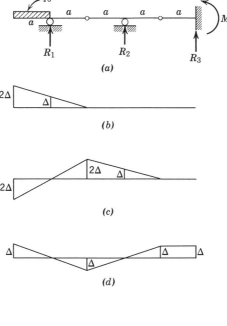

Figure 4.19

II in finding the reactions R_1, R_2, R_3, and M_3. From Figures 4.19b and 4.19a we find

$$(q_0a)\left(\frac{3\Delta}{2}\right) + (-R_1)(-\Delta) = 0, \qquad R_1 = \frac{3q_0a}{2} \tag{3}$$

where the work done by the uniformly distributed load is equal to the work done by a single concentrated load of q_0a acting a distance $a/2$ from the free end. From Figures 4.19c and 4.19a we find

$$(q_0a)(\Delta) + (-R_2)(-\Delta) = 0, \qquad R_2 = q_0a \tag{4}$$

From Figures 4.19d and 4.19a we find

$$(q_0a)\left(\frac{-\Delta}{2}\right) + (R_3)(-\Delta) = 0, \qquad R_3 = \frac{q_0a}{2} \tag{5}$$

From Figures 4.19e and 4.19a we find

$$(q_0a)\left(\frac{+a\theta}{2}\right) + M_3\theta = 0, \qquad M_3 = \frac{-q_0a^2}{2} \tag{6}$$

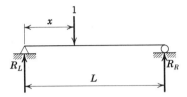

Figure 4.20

4.8   Application of Betti's Law in Finding Reaction Influence Diagrams

In the beam of Figure 4.20, the right reaction is given by

$$R_R = \frac{x}{L} \tag{1}$$

As the position of the unit load varies from $x = 0$ to $x = L$, the right reaction varies from 0 to 1. In Figure 4.21, R_R is plotted against x, and since this diagram shows the influence of a moving unit load on the reaction we speak of it as a *reaction influence diagram.** This is an example of cause and effect, since the diagram shows the effect on the right reaction of a unit load placed anywhere on the beam.

For more complicated structures, Betti's law leads to a simple and systematic method of drawing influence diagrams. Consider the beam of Figure 4.22a. We wish to know the shape and size of the influence diagram for the reaction R_2. Let a unit load be placed at any location as shown. Now since we are interested in the center reaction we choose system II so that there is a displacement at the location of R_2 but no displacement at other supports. This is accomplished by lifting the beam at R_2 to cause a rigid body rotation about R_1 and an upward deflection at R_2 of amount Δ as shown in Figure 4.22b. Let the displacement at the position of the unit load be designated by y. Applying Betti's law, we obtain

$$(1)(-y) + (-R_2)(-\Delta) = 0$$

or

$$R_2 = \frac{y}{\Delta} \tag{2}$$

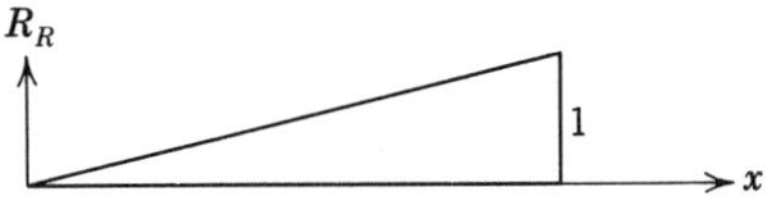

R_R

1

x

Figure 4.21

---

* The determination of influence lines using the method described in this chapter is usually credited to the German engineer H. Mueler-Breslau, who contributed extensively to the theory of structures.

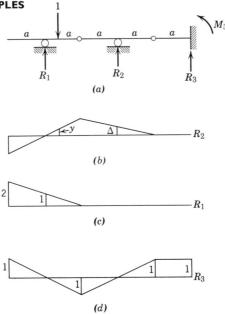

Figure 4.22

This indicates that whatever the position of the unit load, the reaction R_2 is given by the ordinate of the deflection diagram in Figure 4.22b divided by Δ. If the deflection diagram were chosen so that Δ were a unit amount, the deflection diagram would be identical to the influence diagram for R_2.

In general, we may say that the influence diagram for a reactive force is given by the deflection diagram of the structure when a unit upward displacement is given to the reaction point. In a similar manner we would find the influence diagram for R_1 to be as given in Figure 4.22c. For the reaction R_3 we must use as a second system one that will cause M_3 to do no work. Hence, we give the right end an upward unit deflection but retain the same slope we started with. This is shown in Figure 4.22d.

For a moment reaction, we give a rotation θ to the support as in Figure 4.23a and again let y be the deflection at the unit load. Betti's law gives

$$(+1)(-y) + (M_3)(\theta) = 0$$

or

$$M_3 = \frac{y}{\theta} \tag{3}$$

Again we choose $\theta = 1$ and get a deflection diagram to be an influence diagram. Since it is inconvenient to choose a unit angle, as such, what

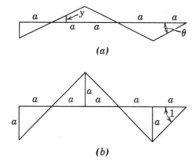

(a)

(b)

Figure 4.23

we shall do is choose θ so that $\tan \theta = \theta = 1$. This is permissible since we are really working with a very small deflection on a greatly enlarged scale. Thus in Figure 4.23a, a unit angle is obtained if we let the deflection at the right hinge be given the magnitude a. Finally, the influence diagram for moment at the wall is as given in Figure 4.23b. We can observe that a positive ordinate to an influence diagram at any particular location is to be interpreted as indicating that a 1-kip downward load at that location causes a positive stress resultant equal in magnitude to the ordinate to scale.

Example 4.8.1 Use influence lines to find the reactions of the beam in Figure 4.24. If we wish to know the value of the reaction R_1, we employ the influence diagram of Figure 4.22c. A 1-kip load at the free end causes a positive reaction of 2 kips according to the influence line. A 10-kip load will therefore cause a reaction of 20 kips upward. A 1-kip load at the position of the 20-kip load would cause an upward reaction of $\frac{3}{5}$ kips; if the 20-kip load is negative, there will be a downward reaction of 12 kips. A 1-kip load at the location of the 30-kip load contributes nothing to R_1. Therefore, the 30-kip load contributes nothing. Thus the reaction R_1 is given by

$$R_1 = (+10)(+2) + (-20)(+\tfrac{1}{2}) + (+30)(0) = 10 \text{ kips} \uparrow$$

Similarly we find M_3 using Figure 4.23b.

$$M_3 = (+10)(-a) + (-20)\left(\frac{+2a}{5}\right) + (+30)\left(\frac{-3a}{5}\right) \tag{4}$$

$$M_3 = -36(5) = -180 \text{ ft-kip} \tag{5}$$

We imagine a uniformly distributed load such as $q(x)$ to be divided into a series of concentrated loads acting over infinitesimal lengths dx of the beam. Each such load will be $q(x)\,dx$ where the value $q(x)$ varies with position. Letting the ordinate of the influence diagram at the location

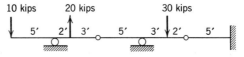

Figure 4.24

of one of these loads be denoted by y, the contribution of one such load will then be $[q(x)\,dx]y$. If the distributed load acts over the distance from $x = a$ to $x = b$, we have the total contribution given by $\int_a^b q(x)y\,dx$. Now if the load is uniformly distributed with $q(x) = q_0$, we find the integral becomes $q_0 \int_a^b y\,dx$. The integral itself represents the area under the influence diagram over that length of the beam carrying the distributed load. If a uniformly distributed load of 10 kips per ft. acts over the cantilevered 5 feet of the beam in Figure 4.24, the contribution of this load to the reactions will be

$$R_1 = [(\tfrac{1}{2})(2)(2a) - (\tfrac{1}{2})(1)(a)](10) = 15a = 75 \text{ kips } \uparrow$$

$$R_2 = -(\tfrac{1}{2})(2)(a)(10) = -10a = 50 \text{ kips } \downarrow$$

$$R_3 = +(\tfrac{1}{2})(1)(a)(10) = 5a = 25 \text{ kips } \uparrow$$

$$M_3 = -(\tfrac{1}{2})(a)(a)(10) = -5a^2 = -125 \text{ ft-kips } \rangle$$

Example 4.8.2 Find the influence lines for all reactions of the beams shown in Figure 4.25a.

We begin by making the observation that the deflection curve for any structure containing a shear connector may show a discontinuity in deflection at the shear connector, and the slopes just to the right and just to the left of the connector will be equal. The influence lines for the three reactions are shown in Figures 4.25b, 4.25c, and 4.25d.

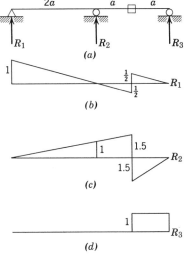

Figure 4.25

4.9 Application of Betti's Law in Finding Influence Diagrams for Bending Moment

In finding the influence diagram for the bending moment at any section, say section A of Figure 4.26a, we begin by recognizing that the structure will be stressed and will deflect in a manner exactly similar to the structure with a hinge at section A and externally applied couples just to the left and just to the right equal to the bending moment present at A in the first case. In Figure 4.26a, for example, we have a beam acted upon by a unit load at B which causes a bending moment at A of M_A. We assume this moment to be positive. Now an equivalent beam would be that shown in Figure 4.26b. Consider this as system I. For system II we take the hinged structure of Figure 4.26b and apply equal and opposite couples m_A just to the left and just to the right as shown. The deflected structure is shown in Figure 4.26c.

Applying Betti's law, we find

$$+(1)(-y) + (M_A)(\alpha) + (M_A)(\beta) = (m_A)(+\theta) + (m_A)(-\theta) = 0$$

Since $\alpha + \beta = \varphi$, we find

$$M_A = \frac{y}{\varphi} \qquad (1)$$

If we choose φ so as to be a unit angle, we may conclude that the deflected structure of system II is the influence diagram for bending moment at A.

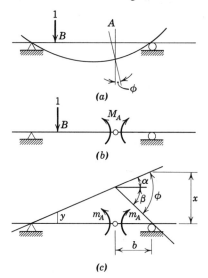

(a)

(b)

(c)

Figure 4.26

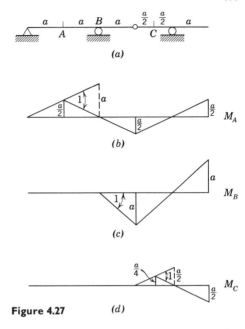

Figure 4.27   (d)

Since we are dealing with very small angles we may establish a scale for the drawing by setting

$$x = b\varphi = b(1) = b \qquad (2)$$

From the foregoing discussion we conclude that the influence diagram for bending moment at any section may be found by introducing a hinge at the section and applying equal and opposite couples such as would act internally for a positive bending moment. Let the change in slope at the hinge be unity. The deflected structure will then be the influence diagram to scale.

Example 4.9.1 Find the bending moment influence diagram for sections A, B, and C of the beam in Figure 4.27a. For section A we have the diagram given in Figure 4.27b. At section B we introduce the hinge and restrain it from any vertical displacement (so that the reaction there will do no work) and get the diagram of Figure 4.27c. For section C we introduce the hinge and note that the deflected structure will be as shown in Figure 4.27d.

Example 4.9.2 Find the influence diagram for bending moment at positions A, B, C, D, E, and F of Figure 4.28a. These are shown in Figures 4.28b–g. It should be noted that in finding the influence line for bending moment at the shear connector, we insert a hinge as usual. This now permits us to have a change in slope as well as a change in deflection at that location.

Since the structures considered thus far have all been statically determinate, it must follow that the influence diagrams will be the same regardless of the material from which the structures are made. For an infinitely

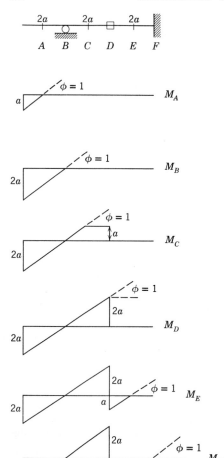

Figure 4.28

rigid material the *influence diagrams will consist only of straight lines.*
Since the material is of no importance, influence lines may be concluded
to consist only of straight line segments for any material.

4.10 Application of Betti's Law in Finding Influence Diagrams for Shear Force

In using Betti's law for determining shear force influence diagrams,
we begin by inserting a shear connector at the section in question and
applying equal and opposite vertical forces such as would be associated
with a positive shear. These forces will have magnitudes V_A corresponding

to the actual shear force in the section. Figure 4.29*a* shows a given beam and its equivalent, Figure 4.29*b*, acted on by a unit load. We call this system I. For system II we choose this same structure acted on by equal and opposite shear forces of magnitude v_A at the connector. It will deflect as shown in Figure 4.29*d*. Applying Betti's law to the two systems, we find

$$V_A \delta_1 + V_A \delta_2 + (1)(-y) = v_a \Delta - v_a \Delta = 0 \qquad (1)$$

Setting $\delta_1 + \delta_2 = \delta$ we have

$$V_A = \frac{y}{\delta} \qquad (2)$$

If we choose $\delta = 1$, the deflected structure in Figure 4.29*d* will be the influence diagram to scale for the shear force at section A.

Example 4.10.1 Draw the influence diagrams for shear force at sections A and C of the beam in Figure 4.27*a*. These are given in Figure 4.30. Note that the lines entering and leaving the section in question must remain parallel. The scale is found as indicated.

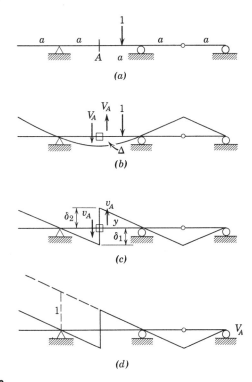

Figure 4.29

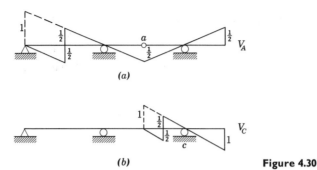

(a)

(b)   Figure 4.30

4.11 Application of Betti's Law in Finding Influence Diagrams for Axial Force

In reviewing the material in previous sections, we notice a common pattern in using Betti's law in determining influence diagrams. In every problem, we began by destroying the resistance to the variable we wished to measure. For bending moment we inserted a hinge; for shear force we inserted a shear connector; for reaction we lifted the support. In seeking the influence diagrams for axial force, we begin by cutting the member to permit a relative axial displacement of the adjacent cut sections.

In this section we concern ourselves with the preparation of influence diagrams for forces in plane trusses. Consider, for example, the truss shown in Figure 4.31. If we wish to discuss the force N_{EF} in bar EF, we begin by observing that the truss in Figure 4.31 is identical to the truss in Figure 4.32a, where bar EF has been cut and tensile forces of magnitude N_{EF} are externally applied to the cut sections. Similarly, if we wish to discuss the force N_{BC} in bar BC, we note that the truss in Figure 4.31 is identical to the truss in Figure 4.32b, where bar BC has been cut and tensile forces of magnitude N_{BC} are externally applied to the cut sections. Finally, when discussing a diagonal such as FD, we proceed in the same manner to find that the truss of Figure 4.31 is identical to the truss of Figure 4.32c. In considering any of the three bar forces mentioned, we take the corresponding diagram in 4.32a, 4.32b or 4.32c as system I and apply Betti's law. As system II for bar force N_{EF}, we choose the structure and loading of Figure 4.33a. Similarly, as system II for bar force N_{BC}, we choose the structure and loading of Figure 4.33b; as system II for bar force N_{FD}, we choose the structure and loading of Figure 4.33c. These are chosen so that in the computation of W_{21}, only the bar force in question will do work. The reactions will do no work.

Influence diagrams for trusses are of special importance in the design of bridges. The loading for such trusses will be on the lower chord for a

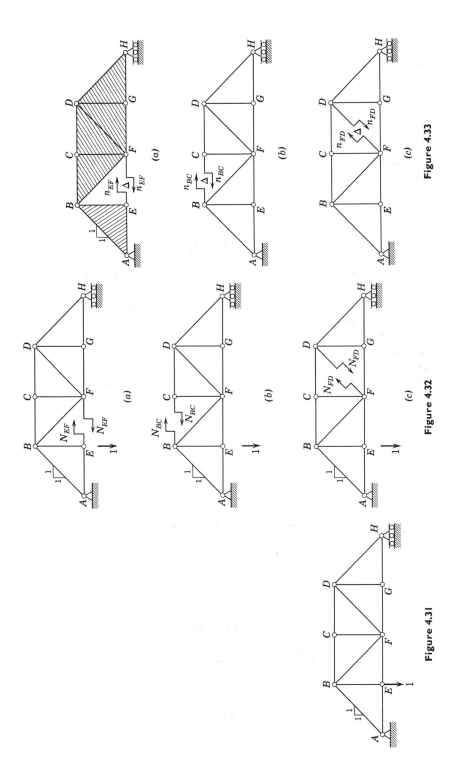

Figure 4.33

Figure 4.32

Figure 4.3l

175

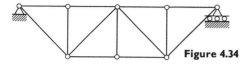

Figure 4.34

structure such as shown in Figure 4.31 or on the upper chord for a structure such as shown in Figure 4.34. The general approach is the same for
either structure. For the loading on the structure of Figure 4.31, it is
important for us to consider the displacement only of the lower chord in
system II. The displacement of the lower chord of Figure 4.33a is shown
in Figure 4.35a. The shaded areas of Figure 4.33a move as rigid bodies
with joint B acting as a hinge.

The presence of the forces n_{EF} causes the distance between joints E
and F to be shortened by an amount Δ. The displacements of all joints
due to this shortening might be readily found using the Williot-Mohr
construction of § 3.2. It will be observed that the displacements of E, F,
and G are $\frac{3}{4}$, $\frac{2}{4}$, and $\frac{1}{4}$ respectively. This indicates that the lower chord will
experience vertical deflections as illustrated in Figure 4.35a. Note that
the displacement varies linearly from A to E and also linearly along the
entire distance from E to H. There is no change in slope of the displacement diagram at F. In a similar manner we find the displacement diagram
for the figure shown in 4.33b to be as shown in 4.35b. In Figure 4.33c the
shortening of member FD will be associated with a lengthening of diagonal

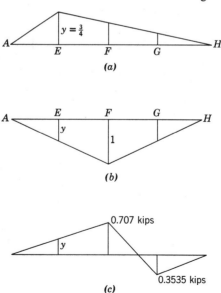

Figure 4.35

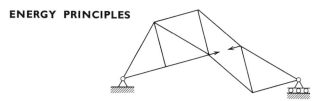

Figure 4.36

distance CG. The panel $CDFG$ will deform to a shape as shown in 4.36. The displacement diagram for the lower chord will be as shown in Figure 4.35c. We now apply Betti's law to system I of 4.32a and system II of 4.33a. This gives

$$(N_{EF})(\Delta_{EF}) + (1)(-y) = 0 \tag{1}$$

or

$$N_{EF} = \frac{y}{\Delta_{EF}} \tag{2}$$

The displacement diagram in 4.35a is thus seen to represent to some scale the influence diagram for member EF. Similarly, applying Betti's law to 4.32b and 4.33b, we find

$$N_{BC} = -\frac{y}{\Delta_{BC}} \tag{3}$$

Since we assumed the given load to give a tensile force in member BC, the negative sign must be interpreted to mean that downward loads will produce compressive forces in member BC. This is illustrated clearly in Figure 4.35b. Finally, applying Betti's law to Figure 4.32c and Figure 4.35c, we find

$$N_{FD} = \frac{y}{\Delta_{FD}} \tag{4}$$

Again the displacement diagram shown in Figure 4.35c is to some scale the influence diagram for force in member FD.

In drawing influence diagrams for trusses, the scale can be determined best by making a few computations. For example, a 1-kip load at joint E causes a bar force N_{EF} equal to 0.75 kips. This gives the ordinate at E in Figure 4.35a and thus fixes the scale for the diagram. A 1-kip load at F gives N_{BC} equal to 1 kip and thus fixes the scale of the diagram in Figure 4.35b. That same 1-kip load gives a force in FD equal to 0.707 kips and a 1-kip load at G gives a force in FD equal to -0.3535 kips.

To summarize, we may say that the influence diagram to some scale for a member of a plane truss is given by the displacement diagram of the loaded chord when the distance between the joints at the ends of the member in question is caused to shorten. The scale is easily found by calculating significant ordinates in the diagram.

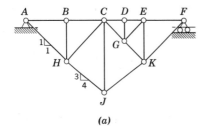

(a)

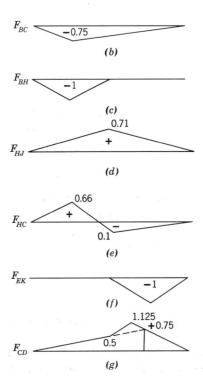

Figure 4.37

Example 4.11.1 Draw the influence diagrams for the bar forces in members *BC, BH, HJ, HC, EK,* and *CD* of the truss in Figure 4.37a. These are shown in Figure 4.37b–g. We note that the dotted line in Figure 4.37g represents the bar force in F_{CD} when the members *DG* and *GE* are absent.

4.12 General Reciprocal Theorems

The development of Betti's law in § 4.6 related exclusively to considerations of work done by external forces on external displacements. We calculated the work done by the external forces of a system I on the displacements of a system II, and found it equal to the work done by the external forces of system II on the displacements of system I. In symbolic form we express this as

$$W_{12} = W_{21} \tag{1}$$

By the law of conservation of energy we equate the work done by external forces in a body to the strain energy stored in the body. This gives in general $W = U$, or in terms of systems I and II

$$W_{11} = U_{11} \qquad W_{22} = U_{22} \tag{2}$$

By proceeding in the same fashion as used to obtain 4.12.1 we can first apply the forces of system I to the body, followed by the application of the forces of system II to get the total strain energy stored of

$$U = U_{11} + U_{12} + U_{22} \tag{3}$$

By reversing the order of application of forces we find

$$U = U_{22} + U_{21} + U_{11} \tag{4}$$

Equating these two we find

$$U_{12} = U_{21} \tag{5}$$

This states that the strain energy associated with the action of the internal forces of system I on the internal displacements of system II equals that associated with the action of the internal forces of system II on the internal displacements of system I.

Comparing 4.12.1, 4.12.2, 4.12.3, and 4.12.4, we conclude also that

$$W_{12} = U_{21} \tag{6}$$

and

$$W_{21} = U_{12} \tag{7}$$

We thus have a wide variety of reciprocal relations at our disposal. The last two expressions are especially useful in finding displacements in statically determinate structures and redundants in statically indeterminate structures as is explained in Chapter 5. In words, 4.12.7 states that "the work done by the external forces of a system II on the corresponding displacements of a system I equals the strain energy associated with the action of internal forces of system I on the displacements of system II." Sometimes the displacements associated with system II are called *virtual displacements* and the work thus performed is called *virtual work*. These terms have become so familiar in the literature on structural analysis that we shall let 4.12.6 or 4.12.7 be referred to as the virtual work relations or the *principle of virtual work*.* It is one of the most versatile and useful tools in the analysis of elastic structures.

---

* The first statement of the principle of virtual work appears to have been made by John Bernoulli (1667–1748); however, it was left to engineers of a later generation to apply it in the manner given in this chapter.

In a truss with all external loads applied at the joints, there are only axial forces present in the members. For variables A, E, and L, the quantity U_{12} associated with a given bar of one system of internal forces N and another system of internal forces n becomes

$$U_{12} = \int_0^L \frac{Nn \, ds}{2AE} \tag{8}$$

When A and E are constant, this becomes

$$U_{12} = \frac{NnL}{2AE} \tag{9}$$

If there are r bars in the truss the total strain energy U_{12} is given by

$$U_{12} = \sum_r \frac{NnL}{2AE} \tag{10}$$

In a member subjected to bending, shear, torsion, and axial force, we find

$$U_{12} = \int_0^L \frac{Nn \, dx}{2AE} + \int_0^L \frac{Mm \, dx}{2EI} + \int_0^L \frac{Vv \, dx}{2\mu AG} + \int_0^L \frac{Tt \, dx}{2GC} \tag{11}$$

where N, M, V, and T relate to system I and n, m, v, and t relate to system II.

The principle of virtual work gives us the means of finding displacements in any elastic structure and also serves as a very useful tool in deriving important general formulas.

4.13 Displacements in Trusses

The displacements in elastic trusses may be found quite readily by the principle of virtual work. When all loads are applied at the joints of the truss, the stresses in the various members will be due to axial forces only. Bending moments, shear forces, and twisting moments will all be zero. Only strain energy associated with the axial forces will be stored.

Now the exact approach to be followed in solving a given problem may vary considerably from one to another. Referring to equations 4.12.5, 4.12.8, and 4.12.9, we find the following relation most useful for our present purpose.

$$U_{12} = W_{21} \tag{1}$$

We shall choose the given set of forces as system I. If we wish to find the deflection in a given direction at a given joint, we choose a set of forces for system II so that the expression for W_{21} contains that deflection as the only unknown.

Consider the truss of Figure 4.38, for example. Suppose we wish to know, for some unspecified reason, the amount of deflection, Δ, experienced

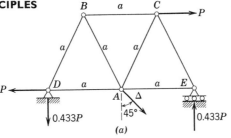

(a)

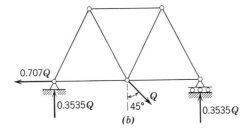

(b)

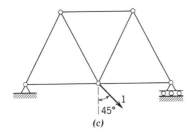

(c)

Figure 4.38

at joint A in the direction shown due to the given load. As system II we choose the loading shown in Figure 4.38b and find

$$W_{21} = \frac{(-0.707Q)(0)}{2} + \frac{(-0.3535Q)(0)}{2}$$
$$+ \frac{(-0.3535Q)(0)}{2} + \frac{Q\Delta}{2} = \frac{Q\Delta}{2} \qquad (2)$$

Our choice for system II is seen to be justified since the only unknown on the right hand side of 4.13.1 will be the desired deflection Δ.

Let the bar forces in the first system be denoted by N and in the second system by N_Q. The left hand side of 4.13.1 will become

$$U_{12} = \sum \frac{N}{2} \left(\frac{N_Q L}{AE} \right) \qquad (3)$$

where the summation is taken over all members of the truss. If we note that the bar forces N_Q due to Q are equal to Q times the bar forces due to a unit load in the direction of Q, we may write in 4.13.3

$$N_Q = Qn \qquad (4)$$

where n is a bar force due to a unit load. Now equating 4.13.2 and 4.13.3 and using 4.13.4 we find

$$Q \sum \frac{NnL}{2AE} = \frac{Q}{2} \Delta \qquad \text{or} \qquad \Delta = \sum \frac{NnL}{AE} \qquad (5)$$

This indicates that the most convenient set of forces for system II includes a unit force at A as shown in Figure 4.38c. A tabular form will be found most useful in applying 4.13.5. In Table 4.1 we begin by listing the bars. We

TABLE 4.I

Bar	L/AE	N	n	NnL/AE
DA	—	—	—	—
AE	—	—	—	—
BC	—	—	—	—
DB	—	—	—	—
BA	—	—	—	—
AC	—	—	—	—
CE	—	—	—	—
				$\sum \dfrac{NnL}{AE} = \Delta$

then tabulate the ratio L/AE for each bar. Next the bar forces in system I and in system II are recorded. The product of the three entries in each row is computed and recorded. The sum of all entries in the last column gives the desired deflection Δ at joint A.

Example 4.13.1 Find the vertical displacement of joint E of the truss shown in Figure 4.39a. As system II we choose the loading shown in Figure 4.39b. Let L/AE be the same for all members. The tabulated results will be as given in Table 4.2 on page 183. We find

$$W_{21} = (1)\Delta_E = U_{12} = \frac{5PL}{AE} \qquad (6)$$

where the deflection at E is taken as positive when downward. Thus

$$\Delta_E = 5PL/AE \qquad (7)$$

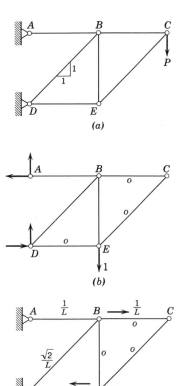

Figure 4.39

TABLE 4.2

Bar	L/AE	N	n	NnL/AE
AB	L/AE	$+2P$	$+1$	$2P\dfrac{L}{AE}$
BC	L/AE	$+P$	0	0
DE	L/AE	$-P$	0	0
DB	L/AE	$-P\sqrt{2}$	$-\sqrt{2}$	$2P\dfrac{L}{AE}$
BE	L/AE	$+P$	$+1$	$P\dfrac{L}{AE}$
EC	L/AE	$-P\sqrt{2}$	0	0
				$\dfrac{5PL}{AE} = U_{12}$

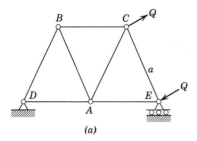

(a)

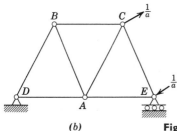

(b)   **Figure 4.40**

Now if the rotation of a certain member due to the given load is desired, we choose a set of forces for system II such that only the rotation will appear as an unknown in W_{21}. For example, if we wish to know θ_{CE} in Figure 4.38a we might choose the forces in Figure 4.40a as system II. The work W_{21} done will clearly be that due only to the couple Qa and thus

$$W_{21} = Qa\theta_{CE} \tag{8}$$

where θ_{CE} is the desired value. As before, it will simplify matters if we have simply

$$W_{21} = \theta_{CE} \tag{9}$$

This is accomplished by setting

$$Qa = 1 \quad \text{or} \quad Q = \frac{1}{a} \tag{10}$$

as shown in Figure 4.39b. If we let n denote the bar forces in system II, and N the bar forces in system I, we get

$$\theta_{CE} = \sum \frac{NnL}{AE} \tag{11}$$

which is similar to the expression found in 4.13.5. The numerical calculations follow as before.

Example 4.13.2   Find the amount of rotation of bar BE due to the loading on the truss in Figure 4.39a. Here we choose as our system II that shown in Figure 4.39c (see Table 4.3). Also

$$W_{21} = \frac{1}{L}\Delta_B - \frac{1}{L}\Delta_E = \frac{1}{L}(\Delta_B - \Delta_E) = \theta_{BE}$$

TABLE 4.3

Bar	L/AE	N	n	NnL/AE
AB	L/AE	$+2P$	$\dfrac{1}{L}$	$\dfrac{2P}{AE}$
BC	L/AE	$+P$	0	0
DE	L/AE	$-P$	$-\dfrac{1}{L}$	$\dfrac{P}{AE}$
DB	L/AE	$-P\sqrt{2}$	0	0
BE	L/AE	$+P$	0	0
EC	L/AE	$-P\sqrt{2}$	0	0
				$\dfrac{3P}{AE} = U_{12}$

Thus

$$\theta_{BE} = \frac{3P}{AE} \tag{12}$$

Example 4.13.3 For the space truss of Figure 4.41a, determine the vertical displacement Δ of the joint B due to the fact that member AB is cut δ inches shorter than planned. We choose the unit load shown in Figure 4.41b as system II and find

$$W_{21} = \Delta \tag{13}$$

where Δ is the only unknown. To find U_{12} we first find U_{21} and then employ 4.12.5. For this statically determinate space truss the shortening of one member (whether by accident or design in fabrication or by application of a turnbuckle) causes the various joints to be displaced but causes no bar stresses in the members. The quantity U_{21} thus gets a contribution only from bar AB equal to

$$U_{21} = n_{AB}\, \delta \tag{14}$$

and we find

$$\Delta = n_{AB}\, \delta \tag{15}$$

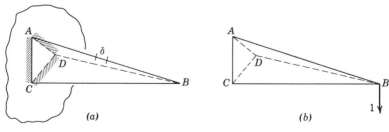

(a) (b)

Figure 4.41

The energy stored by all other bars is zero since the associated members in system I do not change in length.

Comparing the example in § 4.1 with the examples of this section we note that the direct application of the law of conservation of energy in § 4.1 yields useful results when there is a single force (or couple) acting and when the deflection of that force (or rotation of that couple) in the direction of the force is required. The examples of § 4.13 indicate the usefulness of a method that yields results when a single deflection or rotation is desired due to any set of loads. Consequently, it is a much more general method, and is valid in two or three dimensions.

When deflections at all joints of a plane truss are required, the Williot-Mohr graphical solution of Chapter 3 is most useful since the total amount of labor required is much smaller than that required by the foregoing method.

4.14 Displacements in Beams and Simple Frames

In studying the displacements in a beam, we assume that the contribution of shear force to displacements is small compared to that due to bending. The approach to be followed is very similar to that given for trusses in § 4.13. We begin by using the expression

$$U_{12} = W_{21} \tag{1}$$

Let the given set of loads be system I and choose system II so that W_{21} will contain the desired displacement as the only unknown.

Example 4.14.1 Find the vertical displacement Δ and the slope θ at the free end of the beam shown in Figure 4.42a. As system II we choose the loading of Figure 4.42b. For these two systems we have

$$W_{21} = \frac{Q\Delta}{2} \tag{2}$$

$$U_{12} = \int_0^L \tfrac{1}{2}\left(\frac{q_0 x^2}{2}\right)(Qx)\frac{dx}{EI} \tag{3}$$

We note in equating these that the bending moments in Figure 4.42b are exactly Q times the bending moments due to the unit load in Figure 4.42c. Thus

$$U_{12} = Q\int_0^L \frac{q_0 x^3}{4}\frac{dx}{EI} \tag{4}$$

and

$$\Delta = \int_0^L \frac{q_0 x^3}{2}\frac{dx}{EI} = \left[\frac{q_0 x^4}{8EI}\right]_0^L = \frac{q_0 L^4}{8EI} \tag{5}$$

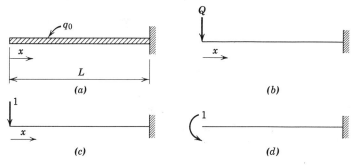

Figure 4.42

In general we denote the bending moments in system II due to the unit load by m, and find

$$\Delta = \int_0^L \frac{Mm\,dx}{EI} \tag{6}$$

When the rotation of a given section is desired (the change in slope of the elastic curve at that section), system II is conveniently chosen as a couple acting at the section. To find the slope at the free end of the cantilever beam in Figure 4.42a, we choose the loading of Figure 4.42d as system II and write

$$W_{21} = -\tfrac{1}{2}(1)(\theta) \tag{7}$$

$$U_{12} = \int_0^L \frac{1}{2}\left(q_0\frac{x}{2}\right)^2(-1)\frac{dx}{EI} = \left[-\frac{q_0 x^3}{12EI}\right]_0^L = -\frac{q_0 L^3}{12EI} \tag{8}$$

and equate these to find

$$\theta = +\frac{q_0 L^3}{6EI} \tag{9}$$

The positive sign indicates that the slope is indeed in the direction of the couple as assumed.

Example 4.14.2 Find the magnitude of the force R necessary to cause a unit upward deflection at the free end of the overhanging beam shown in Figure 4.43. Also, find the magnitude of the couple necessary to cause a clockwise unit rotation at the right end. For each problem we choose the loading shown in Figure 4.43a as system I. The moment diagram will be as shown in Figure 4.43b. The bending moment at any section is given by the following:

$$0 \le x_1 \le a$$

$$M = Rx_1 \tag{10}$$

$$0 \le x_2 \le a$$

$$M = R(a - x_2) \tag{11}$$

The system II to be used in discussing deflection will be that shown in Figure 4.43c. The bending moment equations for this system are as follows:

$$0 \le x_1 \le a$$
$$m = -x_1 \tag{12}$$
$$0 \le x_2 \le a$$
$$m = -(a - x_2) \tag{13}$$

Applying the principle of virtual work, we have

$$U_{12} = \frac{1}{2} \int_0^{x_1} \frac{Mm \, dx_1}{EI} + \frac{1}{2} \int_0^{x_2} \frac{Mm \, dx_2}{EI}$$

$$= \frac{1}{2} \frac{R}{EI} \int_0^a (x_1)(-x_1) \, dx_1 + \frac{1}{2} \frac{R}{EI} \int_0^a (a - x_2)(-)(a - x_2) \, dx_2 = -\frac{Ra^3}{3EI} \tag{14}$$

We are given a unit upward deflection at C. Hence,

$$W_{21} = \tfrac{1}{2}(1)(-1) = -\tfrac{1}{2} \tag{15}$$

Equating U_{12} and W_{21} we find

$$R = \frac{3EI}{2a^3} \tag{16}$$

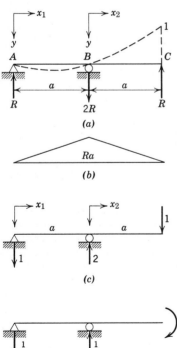

(a)

(b)

(c)

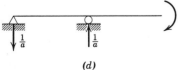

(d)   **Figure 4.43**

The positive value indicates that we assumed the direction of R correctly in Figure 4.43a.

To find the reaction necessary to cause a unit clockwise rotation at C, we use the structure of Figure 4.43d as system II. The bending moments for this system will be as follows:

$$0 \le x_1 \le a$$

$$m = -\frac{x_1}{a} \tag{17}$$

$$0 \le x_2 \le a$$

$$m = -1 \tag{18}$$

Here we find

$$U_{12} = \frac{1}{2}\int_0^a (Rx_1)\left(-\frac{x_1}{a}\right)\left(\frac{dx_1}{EI}\right) + \frac{1}{2}\int_0^a R(a - x_2)(-1)\left(\frac{dx_2}{EI}\right) = -\frac{5Ra^2}{12EI} \tag{19}$$

Since we are interested in a unit rotation at C, we find that

$$W_{21} = \frac{1}{2}(+1)(+1) = \frac{1}{2} \tag{11}$$

Equating U_{12} and W_{21}, we find

$$R = -\frac{6EI}{5a^2} \tag{12}$$

The negative sign indicates the assumed direction of R is incorrect for this problem. A unit clockwise rotation is given only when R acts downward.

Example 4.14.3 The cross section of the frame in Figure 4.44a is circular and constant throughout. Determine the vertical deflection at joint A. Let the structure as loaded be system I. The stress resultants will be

$$CB: M = -Px_1 \qquad BA: M = -Px_2 \qquad AO: M_1 = +Pa$$
$$V = -P \qquad\qquad V = -P \qquad\qquad M_2 = +Pa$$
$$T = 0 \qquad\qquad T = -Pa \qquad\qquad V = 0$$
$$N = 0 \qquad\qquad N = 0 \qquad\qquad T = 0$$
$$N = +P \tag{20}$$

where M_1 and M_2 for member AO represent the bending moments about horizontal and vertical axes.

Although it makes no difference in treating system I of this particular problem, it is well to point out that when axis x_3 is directed as shown, the reader must be very attentive to his sign convention on shear forces. The correct sign is given by imagining himself so placed that the axis x_3 will be pointed to his right. Thus, a load Q acting vertically downward at C, for example, will cause a shear force $-Q$ in member AO with x_3 chosen as shown. The sign on bending moment will not be affected by reversing the direction of the axis.

Since we wish to know the vertical deflection at A we choose as system II the loading in Figure 4.41b. It is evident that for this system there are no stress resultants along members CB and BA and that along AO we have

$$M = -(1)(x_3)$$

$$V = -1 \tag{21}$$

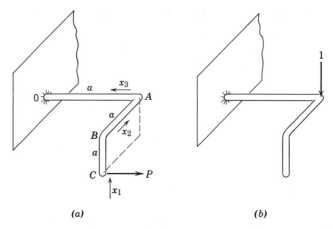

(a)   (b)

Figure 4.44

For this problem,

$$W_{21} = \tfrac{1}{2}(1)\Delta \tag{22}$$

In finding U_{12} we note that the products of moments Mm are zero along CB and BA. The products of normal force Nn are zero for all members since for those members where $N \neq 0$ for system I, $n = 0$ for system II, and vice versa. Similarly when twist occurs in a member in system I it does not occur in that member for system II. Finally, if we neglect the contribution of shear, we find

$$U_{12} = -\int_0^a \tfrac{1}{2}(Pa)(x_3)\,\frac{dx_3}{EI} = -\frac{Pa^3}{4EI} \tag{23}$$

Equating W_{21} and U_{12} we find

$$\Delta = -\frac{Pa^3}{2EI} \tag{24}$$

indicating that the deflection at A is upward.

4.15   Castigliano's Theorem

Our discussion in previous sections has been confined to relations between total external work performed and total internal strain energy stored. In particular, we were able to set these quantities equal to one another by using the law of conservation of energy. Thus

$$W = U \tag{1}$$

Similarly, we may say that a differential change in W must equal a differential change in U. Or,

$$dW = dU \tag{2}$$

Now dU for bending, axial force, shear force, and twisting moment is found from 4.5.1 to be

$$dU = \left(\frac{M^2}{2EI} + \frac{T^2}{2GC} + \frac{N^2}{2AE} + \frac{V^2}{2\mu AG}\right) ds \qquad (3)$$

If this change in strain energy stored is due to an increase dP in a single concentrated force, that additional force is displaced an amount Δ and we find

$$dW = dP(\Delta) \qquad (4)$$

Equating 4.15.2 and 4.15.4 and clearing we find the theorem first derived by Castigliano*

$$\Delta = \frac{dU}{dP} \qquad (5)$$

where the direction is positive in the direction of the force. The deflection Δ at the site of the load P is thus given by the rate of change of the total strain energy with respect to that load. When more than one load is present, the differentiation, being only with respect to one particular load, must be partial in nature. Hence,

$$\Delta = \frac{\partial U}{\partial P} \qquad (6)$$

In making use of this theorem, the strain energy stored is expressed in terms of the force P and takes its derivative with respect to P. Since the energy itself is an integral expression, this amounts to taking the derivative of an integral. When the limits on the integral are not functions of the independent variable, the order may be interchanged, permitting us to differentiate first and then integrate. This greatly reduces the time required to carry out a particular computation.

When only bending energy is considered, we have

$$\Delta = \frac{\partial}{\partial P} \int \frac{M^2 \, dx}{2EI} = \int \frac{M}{EI} \left(\frac{\partial M}{\partial P}\right) dx \qquad (7)$$

Example 4.15.1 Find the deflection of the end of the cantilever beam of Figure 4.45. We have

$$M = Px \qquad (8)$$

$$U = \int_0^L \frac{P^2 x^2 \, dx}{2EI} = \frac{P^2 L^3}{6EI} \qquad (9)$$

Applying 4.15.6, we have

$$\Delta = \frac{\partial U}{\partial P} = \frac{PL^3}{3EI} \qquad (10)$$

---

* Alberto Castigliano (1847–1884) of Italy gave the first acceptable proof of this theorem although it had been stated earlier for the case of $\Delta = 0$ by L. F. Menabrea.

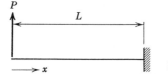

Figure 4.45

By reversing the order of differentiation and integration, we find

$$\frac{\partial M}{\partial P} = x \tag{11}$$

and from 4.15.7

$$\Delta = \int_0^L \frac{Px}{EI}(x)\, dx = \frac{PL^3}{3EI} \tag{12}$$

The ratio $\partial M/\partial P$ in 4.15.7 is the rate of change of bending moment with respect to P, or may be interpreted as being the bending moment expression for a unit load at the position of P. Letting $\partial M/\partial P$ be given the symbol m, we find

$$\Delta = \int \frac{Mm\, dx}{EI} \tag{13}$$

which is the virtual work expression found in §4.14.

Castigliano's theorem, as described here, is of little computational value since it is less general than the methods already discussed.

4.16 Complementary Energy

The curve relating axial load to longitudinal deflection for a straight member is shown in Figure 4.46a. The particular one shown is linear up to a value of Δ_0 and nonlinear beyond that point. The strain energy stored when Δ is a given value is given by the area under the curve up to that value. A small change in strain energy stored accompanies each small

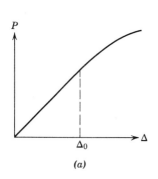

(a)

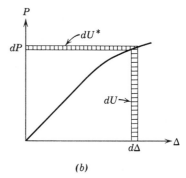

(b)

Figure 4.46

change in deflection as represented by the elemental vertical area in Figure 4.46b. We write for this case

$$dU = P \, d\Delta \tag{1}$$

The total area above the curve up to a certain deflection is called the *complementary energy*.† We give it the symbol U^*. Now an elemental area representing a horizontal strip gives an elemental change dU^* in complementary energy.

$$dU^* = \Delta \, dP \tag{2}$$

Dividing 4.16.2 through by dP we get

$$\frac{dU^*}{dP} = \Delta \tag{3}$$

The rate of change of the complementary energy with respect to load is thus equal to the deflection under the load in the direction of the load.

Within the elastic range, the strain energy equals the complementary energy and 4.16.3 reduces to Castigliano's theorem.

For general use we write 4.16.3 by using partial derivatives as follows:

$$\Delta = \frac{\partial U^*}{\partial P} \tag{4}$$

If slopes and couples are involved we get

$$\theta = \frac{\partial U^*}{\partial M} \tag{5}$$

The theorem of complementary energy is more general than Castigliano's theorem since it pertains to the elastic and post elastic ranges.

Problems

4.1.1 Find the actual elongation of the elastic bar of variable section shown. Let $a = b = 10$ in., $P_0 = 100$ lb., $E = 10^7$ psi, and $A_0 = 5$ in.². Compare the strain energy stored with the external work performed, as well as with the area under the load-deflection diagram.

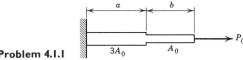

Problem 4.1.1

4.1.2 An elastoplastic steel bar of uniform area, 5 in.², is axially loaded, giving a total elongation of 0.03 in. The yield stress is 15 ksi and the bar is 40 in. long. Calculate the yield load, yield deflection, and strain energy stored and compare with the area under the load-deflection diagram.

† F. Engesser of Germany introduced the concept of complementary energy in 1889. H. M. Westergaard brought it to the attention of modern engineers in 1941.

4.1.3 A uniform bar of length L hangs vertically downward from a fixed support. If its weight is w lb. per ft., what will be the total amount of elastic strain energy stored? Express in terms of w, A, E, and L.

4.1.4 Calculate the amount of elastic strain energy stored in the simple steel truss. Use the law of conservation of energy to find the deflection of the applied load. The length of each bar in feet equals its area in square inches.

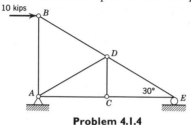

Problem 4.1.4

4.1.5 Determine the elongation of the following bar if $P_0 = 100$ kips, $E = 10^7$ ksi, $A_0 = 100$ in.^{2}, $L = 100$ in.

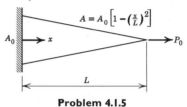

$$A = A_0\left[1 - \left(\tfrac{x}{L}\right)^2\right]$$

Problem 4.1.5

4.2.1 A straight elastic bar is subjected to positive pure bending by couples M_0 applied at the ends. The bar is of length $2a$ and modulus of elasticity E. With x measured from the left end, the value of I is given by $I = I_0[1 - (x/2a)^2]$. Write the expression for the energy stored and the change in slope between the end points.

4.2.2 A straight, elastic bar is acted on by axially applied compressive end forces of 10 kips and positive end moments of 30 in. kips. The bar is square of side dimension d and of length 30 in. What is the ratio of bending energy stored to axial compressive energy stored? For what value of d will (a) these energies be equal; (b) the bending energy be ten times the axial compressive energy; (c) the axial compressive energy be 10% of the total energy?

4.2.3 Find the energy stored in the elastic bar shown. Choose $E = 10^7$ psi, $I = 300$ in.^{4}. How much rotation of the cross section occurs at midspan?

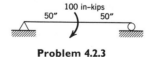

Problem 4.2.3

4.2.4 What value of a single concentrated load at midspan of the beam in the previous problem would produce an equal amount of energy stored? What would then be the midspan deflection?

4.2.5 Find the deflection at the free end of the following uniform beam.

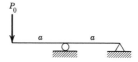

Problem 4.2.5

4.3.1 Calculate the shear shape factor for a circular cross section of radius R. Use the simplified computation.

4.3.2 Compare values of the shear shape factor computed for the cross section shown using the two methods of computation.

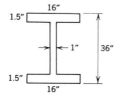

Problem 4.3.2

4.3.3 Compare the energies stored due to bending and shear for a simply supported beam of length L loaded by a force of 15 kips at midspan. Let $G = 0.4E$, $E = 10^4$ ksi, $b = d = 6$ in. For what length will these energies be equal? For what length will the shear energy be 10% of the bending energy?

4.3.4 Find the midspan deflection for the beam in the previous problem (*a*) considering only bending and (*b*) considering bending and shear deflections. Compare the accuracies obtained by neglecting shear in the two specific cases.

4.4.1 Given a bar of circular cross section. What must the ratio of E to G be such that the energy stored when subject to pure bending equals that stored when subject to pure torsion?

4.4.2 A bar of square cross section is of length L and subjected to torques as shown. Write an expression for the strain energy stored.

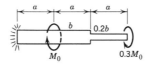

Problem 4.4.2

4.4.3 The side dimension of a bar having a square cross section varies linearly from a value of b at the left end to a value of $3b$ at the right end. If this bar is subjected to equal and opposite twisting couples, T_0, applied at its ends, find the angle of twist of one end relative to the other.

4.5.1 Prepare a percentage breakdown of the energy stored in the following uniform bars due to bending, twisting, axial forces, and shear forces. $E = 1.2G$, $C = 2I$, $\mu = 0.3$.

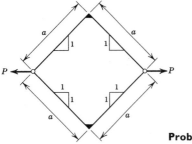

Problem 4.5.1

4.5.2   A circular bar of radius 3 in. is loaded as shown. $G = 0.4E = 12 \times 10^6$ psi, $a = 6$ in., and $P = 40$ kips. Does bending or twisting contribute most to the total energy stored? The left support offers no resistance to twisting.

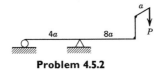

Problem 4.5.2

4.6.1   Verify Betti's law for the following systems.

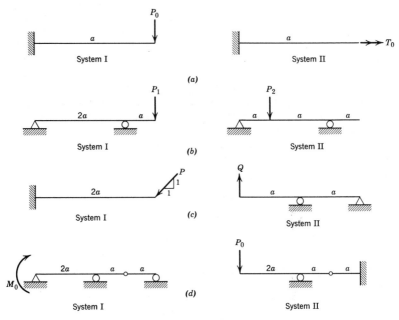

Problem 4.6.1

4.7.1   Find the reactions of the following beams using Betti's law.

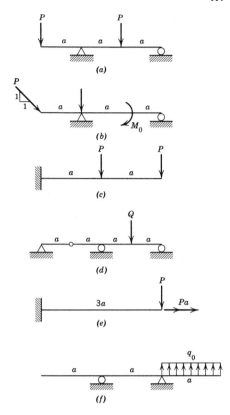

Problem 4.7.1

4.8.1 Find the influence diagrams for all reactions of the following beams.

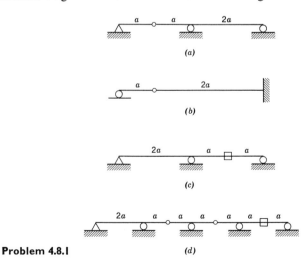

Problem 4.8.1

4.8.2   Draw appropriate influence diagrams.   From these diagrams find all reactions due to the given loads.

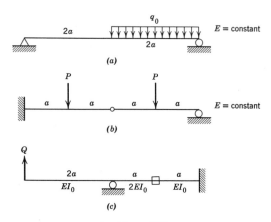

(a)

(b)

(c)

Problem 4.8.2

4.8.3   Can influence diagrams, as treated in this section, be used to find reactions when couples are applied to the structure? Explain your answer.

4.8.4   Sketch and label the influence diagrams for the reactions of the following structures.

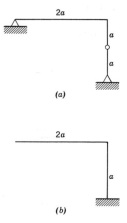

(a)

(b)

Problem 4.8.4

4.9.1   Find the influence diagrams for bending moments at sections A and B in the beams given.

(a)

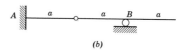

(b)

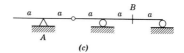

(c)

Problem 4.9.1

4.9.2 Use influence diagrams to find the bending moment at section *A* in the beams below.

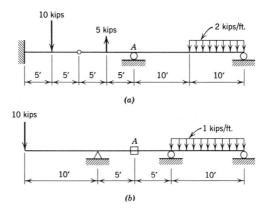

(a)

Problem 4.9.2   *(b)*

4.9.3 Find the influence diagrams for bending moments at sections *A* and *B* in the structures shown.

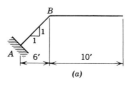

(a)

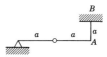

Problem 4.9.3   *(b)*

4.10.1   Find the shear force influence diagrams for sections *A* and *B* of the given beams.

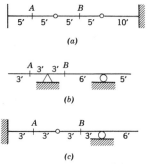

Problem 4.10.1

4.10.2   Use influence diagrams to find the shear force at section *A* in each of the given beams.

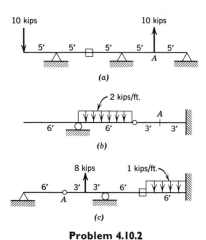

Problem 4.10.2

4.10.3 Draw the shear force influence diagrams for sections A and B of the following structures.

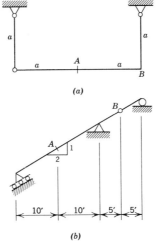

(a)

(b)

Problem 4.10.3

4.11.1 Draw influence diagrams for the bars labeled X and Y in the trusses shown. Load acts only at lower chord joints.

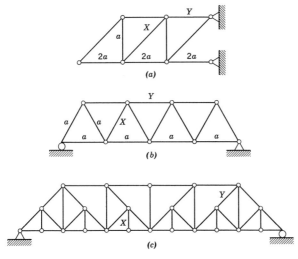

(a)

(b)

(c)

Problem 4.11.1

4.12.1   Verify equation 4.12.5 and 4.12.6 for each of the following.

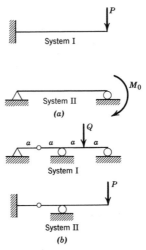

Problem 4.12.1

4.13.1   The steel truss shown below is composed of vertical members each of 1 sq. in. area, inclined members 0.5 sq. in. area, and horizontal members each 1.5 sq. in. area. Find the deflection at joint A in (a) a vertical direction and (b) in a horizontal direction.

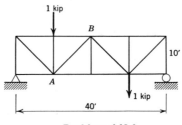

Problem 4.13.1

4.13.2   Find the amount of rotation experienced by bar AB in problem 4.13.1.

4.14.1 Find the deflections of points A and B on the following beams.

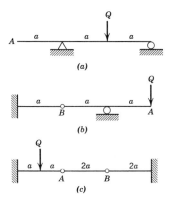

Problem 4.14.1

4.14.2 Find the slope at point A of the following structures.

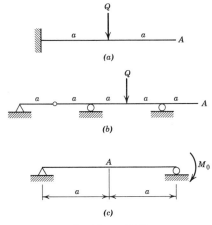

Problem 4.14.2

4.15.1 Find the deflection (or rotation) at the load point in each part of Problem 4.14.2.

5 STATICALLY INDETERMINATE STRESS RESULTANTS

5.1 Superposition

In our work thus far we have dealt with stress resultants that could be determined by a straightforward application of the equations of static equilibrium. We have also discussed means of finding slopes and deflections in these statically determinate structures. This knowledge will now be employed in finding statically indeterminate stress resultants.

The primary tool available to us in considering elastic structures is the *principle of superposition*. For our purpose we may state it in the following manner. The deflections, slopes, shear forces, and bending moments caused by a set of loads acting on a structure are equal to the sum of the deflections, shear forces, and bending moments due to the various loads acting singly on the structure. For the structure of Figure 5.1*a*, for example, the forces acting are those shown in the free body diagram of Figure 5.1*b*. Since there is one more unknown stress resultant than available equations of equilibrium, this structure is statically indeterminate to the first degree; it follows that one of the reactions can

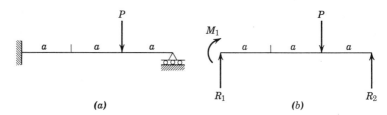

(a)   *(b)*

Figure 5.1

204

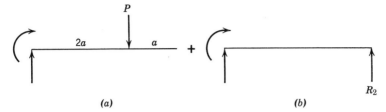

Figure 5.2

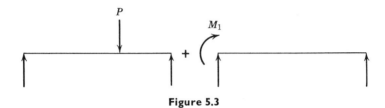

Figure 5.3

be considered redundant. Letting R_2 be redundant and using the super-position principle, we may say that the deflections, slopes, shear forces, and bending moments in the structure of Figure 5.1a equal the sum of these quantities in the two structures 5.2a and 5.2b where R_2 is chosen so that the sum of deflections at the right support equals to zero.

We could equally well have chosen M_1 as the redundant and considered the sum of Figures 5.3a and 5.3b with M_1 so chosen that the slope sum is zero at the left end.

5.2 Stress Resultants Found by Using the Conjugate Beam

The application of the conjugate beam method in finding reactions will now be considered.

Example 5.2.1 Find the reactions for the beam of Figure 5.1a. We begin by choosing R_2 as the redundant and drawing the bending moment diagram for the structure in terms of R_2. Corresponding to the free body diagrams in Figure 5.2 we have the bending moment diagrams of Figure 5.4. Using this information,

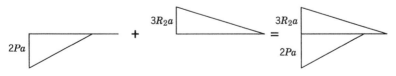

Figure 5.4

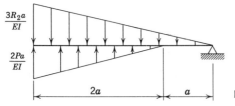

$\dfrac{3R_2a}{EI}$

$\dfrac{2Pa}{EI}$

$2a$ a **Figure 5.5**

we proceed to sketch and load the conjugate beam corresponding to Figure 5.1a, which is shown in Figure 5.5. Now if the conjugate beam is in equilibrium, the sum of moments about the right end must be zero. This yields

$$-\left(\frac{2Pa}{EI}\right)\left(\frac{2a}{2}\right)[a + (\tfrac{2}{3})(2a)] + \left(\frac{3R_2a}{EI}\right)\left(\frac{3a}{2}\right)(\tfrac{2}{3})(3a) = 0$$

or

$$R_2 = \tfrac{14}{27}P \tag{1}$$

The direction of R_2 was assumed correctly since the value in 5.2.1 came out positive. Now that we know R_2, we find from statics

$$R_1 = \tfrac{13}{27}P \tag{2}$$

$$M_1 = -\frac{4Pa}{9} \tag{3}$$

If we choose M_1 as the redundant we find the bending moment diagrams associated with the free body diagrams of Figure 5.3 to be as shown in Figure 5.6. The conjugate beam is given in Figure 5.7. Again, we sum moments about the right support to give

$$-\left(\frac{M_1}{EI}\right)\left(\frac{3a}{2}\right)(\tfrac{2}{3})(3a) - \left(\frac{2Pa}{3EI}\right)\left(\frac{2a}{2}\right)[a + (\tfrac{1}{3})(2a)] - \left(\frac{2Pa}{3EI}\right)\left(\frac{a}{2}\right)(\tfrac{2}{3}a) = 0$$

or

$$M_1 = -\frac{4Pa}{9} \tag{4}$$

as found before.

Of all the ways to break down a given structure, one is usually superior to the others. In the present instance, choosing R_2 as the redundant is best. If R_1 were chosen as the redundant we would have the free body diagrams of Figure 5.8 and the moment diagrams of Figure 5.9.

Example 5.2.2 Find the reactions of the beam of Figure 5.10 whose center support is caused to settle an amount Δ vertically downward. Here we recognize that the effect of settlement is similar to the effect of a force of amount R acting vertically downward on a simply supported beam of length $2a$ and causing a deflection at mid-span of Δ as shown in Figure 5.11a. The associated moment

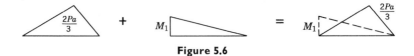

$\dfrac{2Pa}{3}$ $+$ M_1 $=$ M_1 $\dfrac{2Pa}{3}$

Figure 5.6

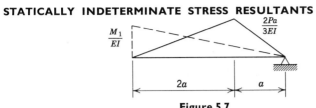

Figure 5.7

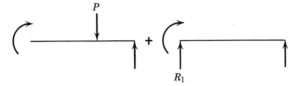

Figure 5.8

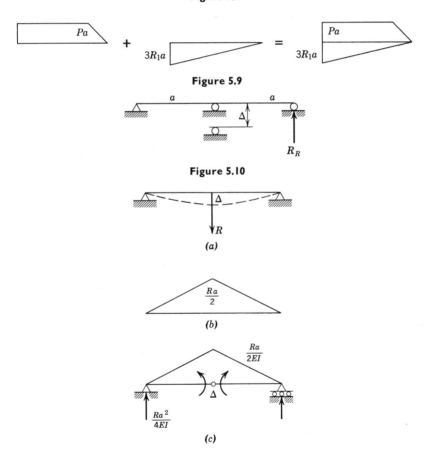

Figure 5.9

Figure 5.10

Figure 5.11

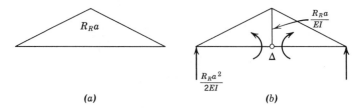

(a)   (b)

Figure 5.12

diagram expressed in terms of R is shown in Figure 5.11b. For the conjugate beam we have simple supports at the ends. In the real beam at mid-span, the deflection is Δ and the slope is the same a small distance to the right as it is to the left. Thus in the conjugate beam at mid-span, the bending moment must be Δ and the shear force must be the same to the left and right. This is provided by a hinge and externally applied couples of Δ as shown in Figure 5.11c. The left conjugate beam reaction is found to be $Ra^2/4EI$ when the sum of moments about the right end is set equal to zero. Now by requiring the moment to be Δ at mid-span we obtain

$$-\left(\frac{Ra^2}{4EI}\right)a + \left(\frac{Ra}{2EI}\right)\left(\frac{a}{2}\right)\left(\frac{a}{3}\right) - \Delta = 0$$

or

$$R = \frac{6EI\,\Delta}{a^3} \tag{5}$$

If we choose the right support R_R in Figure 5.10 as the redundant we have the moment diagram of Figure 5.12a and the conjugate beam of Figure 5.12b. This yields

$$R_R = \frac{3EI\,\Delta}{a^3} \tag{6}$$

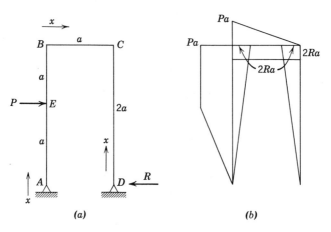

(a)   (b)

Figure 5.13

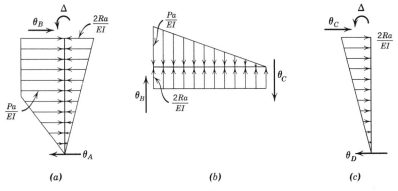

(a)   (b)   (c)

Figure 5.14

Example 5.2.3   Find the reactions of the bent of Figure 5.13a. This structure is indeterminate to the first degree. We choose the horizontal right reaction as the redundant and find the moment diagrams of Figure 5.13b. Free body diagrams for the conjugates of members AB, BC, and CD are shown in Figure 5.14. From the free body of 5.14a we find

$$\theta_B = \frac{\Delta}{2a} + \frac{4Ra^2}{3EI} - \frac{11Pa^2}{12EI} \tag{7}$$

From the free body of Figure 5.14c we find

$$\theta_C = -\frac{4Ra^2}{3EI} + \frac{\Delta}{2a} \tag{8}$$

From the free body of Figure 5.14b we find

$$\theta_B - \theta_C = \frac{Pa^2}{2EI} - \frac{2Ra^2}{EI} \tag{9}$$

Substituting θ_B and θ_C from 5.2.7 and 5.2.8 into 5.2.9, we find

$$R = +\tfrac{17}{56}P \tag{10}$$

With R determined, all other reactions can be found from statics. The slopes may be found by again, considering the free body of Figure 5.14b. Taking moments about B we find

$$\theta_C = +\frac{23Pa^2}{168EI} \tag{11}$$

$$\theta_B = +\frac{5Pa^2}{168EI} \tag{12}$$

From 5.2.8 we find Δ to be

$$\Delta = \frac{13Pa^3}{12EI} \tag{13}$$

An alternate approach to this problem, which is the basis for the work of the following section, will now be given. We again choose the right horizontal

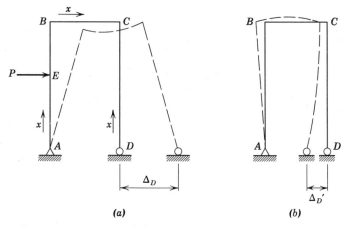

(a)   **(b)**

Figure 5.15

reaction as the redundant and find the horizontal displacement Δ_D present when R is removed. We then determine the value of Δ_D' in terms of R that would be present if only R were acting. We equate these two values and solve for R. See Figures 5.15a and 5.15b. The associated conjugates are shown in Figures 5.16 and 5.17. By considering the free body of Figure 5.16b, we find

$$\theta_B = +\frac{Pa^2}{3EI} \quad \text{and} \quad \theta_C = -\frac{Pa^2}{6EI} \tag{14}$$

Considering the free body of Figure 5.16a, we now find

$$\Delta_B = \frac{5Pa^3}{2EI} \tag{15}$$

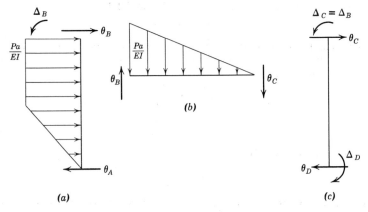

(a)   **(c)**

Figure 5.16

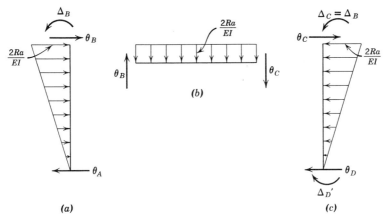

Figure 5.17

Considering the free body of Figure 5.16c, we now find

$$\Delta_D = \frac{17Pa^3}{6EI} \tag{16}$$

The free body of Figure 5.17b yields

$$\theta_B = +\frac{Ra^2}{EI} \qquad \theta_C = -\frac{Ra^2}{EI} \tag{17}$$

The free body diagram of Figure 5.17a yields

$$\Delta_B = \frac{14Ra^3}{3EI} \tag{18}$$

Using a free body of Figure 5.17c, we now find

$$\Delta_D' = \frac{28Ra^3}{3EI} \tag{19}$$

Now noting that $\Delta_D' = \Delta_D$ in the actual problem, we find

$$R = \tfrac{17}{56}P \tag{20}$$

as found before.

Example 5.2.4 Find the reactions for the beam of Figure 5.18, which is statically indeterminate to the second degree. Let the two right reactions be

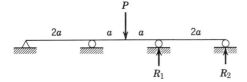

Figure 5.18

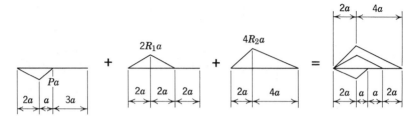

Figure 5.19

taken as the redundants. The bending moment diagrams in terms of R_1 and R_2 are shown in Figure 5.19. The loaded conjugate beam is shown in Figure 5.20. Note that the conjugate beam is statically determinate. There are two equations of statics, two equations of condition (for the hinges), and four unknowns (end reactions of the conjugate beam plus R_1 and R_2). The shear force at B in the conjugate beam is found by summing moments about the left reaction of forces acting on the left third of the span. This gives

$$\theta_B = -\frac{2a^2}{3EI}(4R_2 + 2R_1 - P) \tag{21}$$

The summing of the moments about the right reaction of forces acting on the right third yields

$$\theta_C = \frac{4R_2a^2}{3EI} \tag{22}$$

Summing the forces in the vertical direction on the middle third gives

$$20R_1 + 60R_2 - 7P = 0 \tag{23}$$

By summing moments about the left end of the middle third, we get

$$8R_1 + 48R_2 - P = 0 \tag{24}$$

We solve 5.2.23 and 5.2.24 simultaneously to find

$$R_1 = \tfrac{23}{40}P \quad \text{and} \quad R_2 = -\tfrac{3}{40}P \tag{25}$$

All other reactions may now be found using statics.

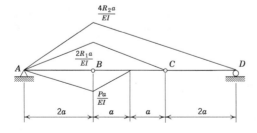

Figure 5.20

5.3 Stress Resultants Found by Using Energy Principles

In § 4.14, displacements in beams were treated by the energy method. This method is equally useful in finding statically indeterminate stress resultants.

Example 5.3.1 Find the reactions for the beam of Figure 5.1a that is indeterminate to the first degree. We choose the right reaction as the redundant. When this reaction is removed the right end will deflect vertically an amount Δ_1. The correct value of R is the value necessary to bring the end of the beam back to a position of zero deflection. Using the energy method we take the beams of Figure 5.21 as the first system and the beam loaded as shown in Figure 5.22 as the second system. We choose our origin at the right support and measure x positive to the left as shown. We set W_{21} equal to U_{12} to find

$$\Delta_1 = \int_a^{3a} \frac{Mm\,dx}{EI} = \int_a^{3a} \frac{(-P)(x-a)(-x)\,dx}{EI} = \frac{14Pa^3}{3EI} \tag{1}$$

Δ_2 is given by

$$\Delta_2 = \int_0^{3a} \frac{(R_2 x)(-x)\,dx}{EI} = -\frac{9Ra^3}{EI} \tag{2}$$

and since $\Delta_1 + \Delta_2 = 0$, we find

$$R_2 = \frac{14Pa^3}{27EI} \tag{3}$$

as found before.

Example 5.3.2 Determine the center reaction of the structure shown in Figure 5.23a due to a vertical settlement of Δ downward at the center support using the principle of virtual work. A free body diagram of the structure that will be used as system I is shown in Figure 5.23b. As system II we choose the structure as loaded in Figure 5.23c. The symmetry of this structure and its loading make possible the writing of a single set of equations that will be valid for both halves of the structure.

$$x \le a: \quad M = \frac{Rx}{2} \quad \text{and} \quad m = \frac{x}{2} \tag{4}$$

Equating W_{21} to U_{12}, we find

$$\frac{(1)(\Delta)}{2} = \frac{2}{2EI} \int_0^a \left(\frac{Rx}{2}\right)\left(\frac{x}{2}\right) dx = \frac{Ra^3}{6EI} \tag{5}$$

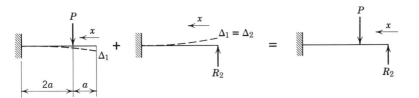

Figure 5.21

Figure 5.22

Δ being given, we find

$$R = \frac{6EI\,\Delta}{a^3} \tag{6}$$

Example 5.3.3 Find the horizontal reaction at D in the bent of Figure 5.13 using $P = 40$ kips and $a = 10$ ft. In order to use the principle of superposition, we first calculate the deflection Δ_D of Figure 5.15a and then calculate the deflection $\Delta_D{}'$ (in terms of R) of Figure 5.15b. The deflections Δ_D and $\Delta_D{}'$ may

TABLE 5.1

Member	Limits	Figure 5.15a	Figure 5.15b	Figure 5.24
AE	$0 \le x \le 10$	$M = 40x$	$M = -Rx$	$m = -x$
EB	$10 \le x \le 20$	$M = 400$	$M = -Rx$	$m = -x$
BC	$0 \le x \le 10$	$M = 400 - 40x$	$M = -20R$	$m = -20$
DC	$0 \le x \le 20$	$M = 0$	$M = +Rx$	$m = +x$

be found by choosing the structures of 5.15a and 5.15b in turn as system I, and choosing the structure as loaded in Figure 5.24 as system II for each case. We denote the bending moments in systems I by M and the bending moments in systems II by m; we choose our x axes as shown. All bending moments are given in Table 5.1.

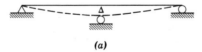

(a)

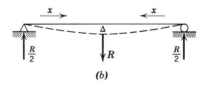

(b)

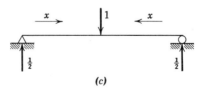

(c)

Figure 5.23

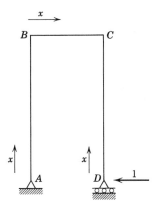

Figure 5.24

We use Figures 5.15a and 5.24 to write

$$W_{21} = -(\tfrac{1}{2})(1)(\Delta_D) \tag{7}$$

$$U_{12} = \frac{1}{2EI} \int_0^{10} -(40x)(x) \, dx + \frac{1}{2EI} \int_{10}^{20} -(400)(x) \, (dx)$$

$$+ \frac{1}{2EI} \int_0^{10} -(400 - 40x)(20) \, dx = \frac{-113,300}{2EI} \tag{8}$$

Equating 5.3.7 to 5.3.8, we have

$$\Delta_D = \frac{113,300}{EI} \tag{9}$$

We use Figures 5.15b and 5.24 to write

$$W_{21} = (\tfrac{1}{2})(1)(\Delta_D') \tag{10}$$

$$U_{12} = \frac{1}{2EI} \int_0^{20} (Rx)(x) \, (dx) + \frac{1}{2EI} \int_0^{10} (20R)(20) \, (dx)$$

$$+ \frac{1}{2EI} \int_0^{20} (Rx)(x) \, dx = \frac{4670}{EI} R \tag{11}$$

These are equated to yield

$$\Delta_D' = \frac{9330}{EI} R \tag{12}$$

The principle of superposition requires that $\Delta_D = \Delta_D'$. Using the foregoing values, we obtain

$$R = -\frac{113,300}{9330} = -12.1 \text{ kips} \tag{13}$$

Example 5.3.4   Use Castigliano's principle to find R_2 in Figure 5.1a. Accordinging to Castigliano's principle we may find the deflection in the direction of any load by taking the derivative of the total strain energy with respect to that load.

If we treat the reaction R_2 in Figure 5.1a as a load, and note that the deflection in the direction of R_2 is zero, we may write

$$\frac{\partial U}{\partial R_2} = 0 \tag{14}$$

This requires that the energy be a minimum and is a mathematical statement of a *principle of least work*. The bending moment equations with x measured from the right support positive to the left are

$$0 \le x \le a \qquad M = R_2 x$$
$$a \le x \le 3a \qquad M = R_2 x - P(x - a) \tag{15}$$

The energy stored is

$$U = \int_0^a \frac{(R_2 x)^2\, dx}{2EI} + \int_a^{3a} \frac{(R_2 x - Px + Pa)^2\, dx}{2EI} \tag{16}$$

Thus

$$\frac{\partial U}{\partial R_2} = 0 = \int_0^a \frac{R_2 x^2\, dx}{EI} + \int_a^{3a} \frac{(R_2 x - Px + Pa)x\, dx}{EI} \tag{17}$$

and

$$\frac{R_2 a^3}{3} + \left[\frac{R_2 x^3}{3} - \frac{Px^3}{3} + \frac{Pax^2}{2} \right]_a^{3a} = 0 \tag{18}$$

or

$$R_2 = \frac{14P}{27} \tag{19}$$

as found in Example 5.2.1.

Example 5.3.5 Find the right horizontal reaction of the truss of Figure 5.25a. We let the right horizontal reaction component be the redundant, and use the superposition principle, insisting that the deflection of the right support be zero. The right support will move a distance δ_0 in the absence of reaction R as indicated in Figure 5.25b. A unit horizontal force acting alone at the right support will cause a deflection δ_1 as shown in Figure 5.26. The reaction R acting alone will thus cause a deflection $R \delta_1$ as shown in Figure 5.25c. As the system II used in finding the deflections, we also choose that shown in Figure 5.26 and write

$$\delta_0 + R \delta_1 = 0 \tag{20}$$

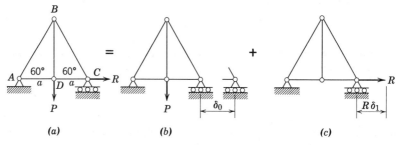

(a)   (b)   (c)

Figure 5.25

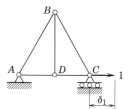

Figure 5.26

where according to § 4.13

$$\delta_0 = \sum \frac{NnL}{AE} = \frac{N_{AD}n_{AD}L_{AD}}{A_{AD}E_{AD}} + \frac{N_{DC}n_{DC}L_{DC}}{A_{DC}E_{DC}} \tag{21}$$

and

$$\delta_1 = \frac{n_{AD}^2 L_{AD}}{A_{AD}E_{AD}} + \frac{n_{DC}^2 L_{DC}}{A_{DC}E_{DC}} \tag{22}$$

since $n_{AB} = n_{BC} = n_{BD} = 0$. Taking $L_{AD} = L_{DC} = L$, $A_{AD} = A_{DC} = A$, and $E_{AD} = E_{DC} = E$, and noting that $n_{AD} = n_{DC} = +1$ and $N_{AD} = N_{DC} = P/2\sqrt{3}$, we find

$$\delta_0 = \frac{PL}{\sqrt{3}\,AE} \quad \text{and} \quad \delta_1 = \frac{2L}{AE} \tag{23}$$

and from 5.3.20,

$$R = -\frac{\delta_0}{\delta_1} = -\frac{P}{2\sqrt{3}} \tag{24}$$

where the minus sign indicates that R was assumed to act in the wrong direction.

Example 5.3.6 Determine the force in DC of the truss in Figure 5.27. We begin by noting that internally this structure is statically indeterminate to the first degree. The bar DC will be considered redundant. Just as in determining redundant reactions, we now make use of the principle of superposition in determining this redundant bar force. The displacements of the truss in Figure 5.27 will be equal to the sum of the corresponding displacements of Figures 5.28*a* and 5.28*b*. At any cross section *a–a* of bar DC in Figure 5.27, the displacement to the left will be exactly equal to the displacement to the right of the section. If we now cut bar DC at section *a–a* as shown in Figure 5.28*a*, the structure will become statically determinate and there will be a relative displacement δ_0 of the two sides of the section. This displacement is given by

$$\delta_0 = \sum \frac{N'nL}{AE} \tag{25}$$

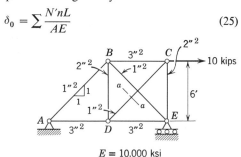

$E = 10{,}000$ ksi

Figure 5.27

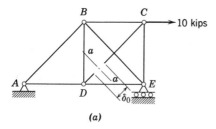

(a)

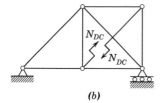

(b)

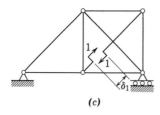

(c)

Figure 5.28

where the N' represents the bar forces in 5.28a and the n represents the bar forces in the same structure shown in 5.28c, but with unit tensile forces acting on the cut sections. The bar force N_{DC} is acting in the absence of externally applied loads as shown in Figure 5.28b and will induce forces in the bars of magnitude $N_{DC}n$. The relative displacement of the two sides of the cut section for this structure will be denoted by $N_{DC}\delta_1$ where

$$\delta_1 = \sum \frac{n^2 L}{AE} \qquad (26)$$

The principle of superposition now requires that the relative displacement of the two sides of section a–a in Figure 5.27 be equal to the relative displacement of 5.28a plus the relative displacement in Figure 5.28b. Stated mathematically this gives

$$\delta_0 + N_{DC}\delta_1 = 0 \qquad (27)$$

where δ_0 and δ_1 can be readily determined from 5.3.25 and 5.3.26. For convenience many of the computations are displayed in Table 5.2.

Substituting values from Table 5.2 into 5.3.27 we find

$$(-804.6 \times 10^{-4}) + N_{DC}(263.6 \times 10^{-4}) = 0 \qquad (28)$$

$$N_{DC} = 3.05 \text{ kips} \qquad (29)$$

All other bar forces are now given by

$$N = N' + N_{DC}n$$

TABLE 5.2

Member	L/AE	N'	n	$N'nL/AE$	n^2L/AE
AB	101.8×10^{-4}	$+7.07$	0	0	0
BC	24×10^{-4}	$+10$	-0.707	-169.7×10^{-4}	12×10^{-4}
AD	24×10^{-4}	$+5$	0	0	0
DE	24×10^{-4}	-5	-0.707	84.8×10^{-4}	12×10^{-4}
BD	36×10^{-4}	0	-0.707	0	18×10^{-4}
BE	101.8×10^{-4}	-7.07	$+1$	-719.7×10^{-4}	101.8×10^{-4}
DC	101.8×10^{-4}	0	$+1$	0	101.8×10^{-4}
CE	36×10^{-4}	0	-0.707	0	18×10^{-4}
Σ				-804.6×10^{-4}	263.6×10^{-4}

5.4 Higher Order Indeterminateness

The structure that is indeterminate to the first degree is solved by a straightforward application of the superposition theorem. For higher order indeterminateness, this same approach leads to a set of n simultaneous algebraic equations where n is the number of redundants considered. In every structure we begin by removing the redundants and thus leaving a stable and statically determinate structure called the *auxiliary structure*. Let the redundants be $R_1, R_2 \cdots R_n$, where R may be a redundant force or a redundant couple. Let δ_{11} be the displacement in the direction of the redundant due to a unit force acting on the auxiliary structure. Similarly, let $\delta_{22}, \delta_{33} \cdots \delta_{nn}$ be the displacement (deflection or rotation) associated with a unit load (force or couple) acting at the point of application of the redundant $R_2, R_3 \cdots R_n$ on the auxiliary structure. Let δ_{10} be the displacement in the auxiliary structure associated with the point of application of redundant R_1. Similarly, let $\delta_{20}, \delta_{30} \cdots \delta_{n0}$ be displacements associated with points of application $R_2, R_3 \cdots R_n$. Let δ_{12}, for example, be the displacement at position 1 in the structure due to a unit load acting at position 2. Similarly, let δ_{ij} be the displacement at position i due to a unit load at position j.

Example 5.4.1 Find the δ values for the indeterminate beam of Figure 5.29. This beam is statically indeterminate to the second degree since there are two unknown vertical force reactions and two unknown couple reactions with only two useful equations of statics available. Two possible choices for the auxiliary structure are shown in Figures 5.30a and 5.30b. We shall choose the cantilevered beam of Figure 5.30a. The delta terms, δ_{10} and δ_{20}, are indicated in Figure 5.31a. Note that since R_1 is a force, δ_{10} must be the deflection in the direction of R_1 acting at the position of R_1 in the auxiliary structure. Similarly δ_{20}, corresponding to R_2, a couple, must be the rotation at the position of R_2 in the

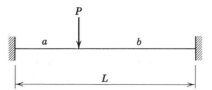

Figure 5.29

auxiliary structure. Figure 5.31b illustrates the meaning of δ_{11} and δ_{21}, which are the displacements associated with the positions of R_1 and R_2 due to a unit load at the position of R_1. Finally, Figure 5.31c illustrates δ_{22} and δ_{12}. We may calculate these δ values very quickly by the conjugate beam method and find

$$\delta_{10} = \frac{Pa^2(3b + 2a)}{6EI} \qquad \delta_{20} = \frac{Pa^2}{2EI}$$

$$\delta_{11} = -\frac{L^3}{3EI} \qquad \delta_{21} = -\frac{L^2}{2EI} \tag{1}$$

$$\delta_{12} = -\frac{L^2}{2EI} \qquad \delta_{22} = -\frac{L}{EI}$$

Note that if we speak of Figure 5.31b as system I and Figure 5.31c as system II, we have $W_{12} = W_{21}$ in accordance with Betti's law. Now let $\delta_1, \delta_2, \delta_3 \cdots \delta_n$ be the actual displacements that occur in the original structure. These may be due to settlement of supports, for example. Such a displacement must be equal to the sum of displacements at that position due to auxiliary loads and all redundant loads. Thus, we state for position 1

$$\delta_1 = \delta_{10} + R_1 \delta_{11} + R_2 \delta_{12} + \cdots R_n \delta_{1n} \tag{2}$$

where $R_1 \delta_{11}$, for example, is the displacement due to R_1 since δ_{11} was the displacement due to a unit load in the direction of R_1. Similarly, for position n, we have

$$\delta_n = \delta_{n0} + R_1 \delta_{n1} + R_2 \delta_{n2} + \cdots R_n \delta_{nn} \tag{3}$$

With n redundants, it then results that we have n simultaneous equations in n unknowns since all δ_{ij} values may be determined and the δ_n values are known.

Example 5.4.2 Set up and solve the set of simultaneous equations associated with the problem of Example 5.4.1. Here we have but two redundants and write

$$\delta_1 = \delta_{10} + R_1 \delta_{11} + R_2 \delta_{12} \tag{4}$$

$$\delta_2 = \delta_{20} + R_1 \delta_{21} + R_2 \delta_{22} \tag{5}$$

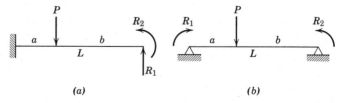

(a)   (b)

Figure 5.30

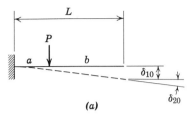

(a)

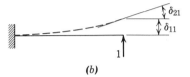

(b)

Figure 5.31   (c)

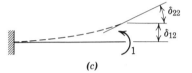

Since there is no displacement at positions 1 and 2 in the given structure, $\delta_1 = \delta_2 = 0$. We use all δ values found in Example 5.4.1 to write

$$Pa^2(3b + 2a) - 2R_1L^3 - 3R_2L^2 = 0 \tag{6}$$

$$Pa^2 - R_1L^2 - 2R_2L = 0$$

These are now solved for R_1 and R_2 to yield

$$R_1 = +\frac{Pa^2}{L^3}(L + 2b) \tag{7}$$

$$R_2 = -\frac{Pa^2b}{L^2} \tag{8}$$

The reaction R_1 is in the same direction as assumed and the reaction R_2 is opposite to the direction assumed. We see that regardless of the values of δ_n and δ_0, the values δ_{ij} will be the same for any given loading. We call these *influence coefficients*. For numerous redundants we may solve the set of simultaneous algebraic equations by the methods described in § 1.5.

5.5 Three-Moment Equation

A particularly useful tool for solving multispan beams is presented in this section. Consider a continuous beam as shown in Figure 5.32. Let some interior support be the nth support; let the remaining supports be designated as shown in the figure. Let the given structure be designated as system I. As system II consider the same structure subjected to the

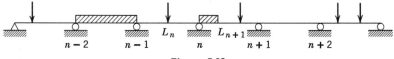

Figure 5.32

loads shown in Figure 5.33. The reciprocal theorem dictates now that the work done by the external forces in II on the corresponding displacements in I must equal the work done by the internal forces in I on the corresponding displacements in II.

We let M be the bending moment at any section of the first system and m be the bending moment at any section of the system II. Note that $m = 0$ to the right of support $n + 1$ and to the left of support $n - 1$. Thus we have

$$-(1)(0) + (2)(0) - (1)(0) = \int_{n-1}^{n+1} \frac{Mm\, dx}{EI} = 0 \qquad (1)$$

where the integration is performed from support $n - 1$ to $n + 1$. For the span $(n - 1, n)$ we let x be measured from support $n - 1$. In span $(n, n + 1)$ we let x be measured from support $n + 1$. Thus, we have $m = x$ for each span and

$$\int_0^{L_n} \frac{Mx\, dx}{EI} + \int_0^{L_{n+1}} \frac{Mx\, dx}{EI} = 0 \qquad (2)$$

as the appropriate equation. The left integral may be interpreted as the first moment of the area under the M/EI diagram for the $(n - 1, n)$ span taken about the $n - 1$ support. The second integral is the first moment of the area under the M/EI diagram for the $(n, n + 1)$ span taken about the $n + 1$ support. To simplify the results somewhat we consider the M/EI diagrams for the two spans as shown in Figure 5.34 where the value of EI may vary from span to span but is taken as constant within a given span. Figure 5.34b represents the contributions from the end bending moments when assumed positive. Figure 5.34a represents the contributions from the applied loads in the absence of end bending moments. Let the areas under the curves in Figure 5.34a be A_n/EI_n and A_{n+1}/EI_{n+1}. Let

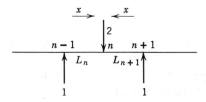

Figure 5.33

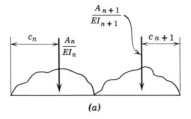

(a)

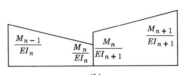

(b)
Figure 5.34

their centroids be c_n and c_{n+1} measured from the left and right ends, respectively. We now rewrite 5.5.2 as

$$\frac{A_n}{EI_n} c_n + \frac{A_{n+1}}{EI_{n+1}} c_{n+1} + \frac{M_n}{EI_n} L_n \frac{L_n}{2} + \frac{M_{n-1} - M_n}{EI_n} \frac{L_n}{2} \frac{L_n}{3}$$

$$+ \frac{M_n}{EI_{n+1}} L_{n+1} \frac{L_{n+1}}{2} + \frac{M_{n+1} - M_n}{EI_{n+1}} \frac{L_{n+1}}{2} \frac{L_{n+1}}{3} = 0 \quad (3)$$

or

$$\frac{M_{n-1}L_n^2}{6EI_n} + \frac{M_n}{3}\left(\frac{L_n^2}{EI_n} + \frac{L_{n+1}^2}{EI_{n+1}}\right) + \frac{M_{n+1}L_{n+1}^2}{6EI_n} = -\frac{A_n c_n}{EI_n} - \frac{A_{n+1} c_{n+1}}{EI_{n+1}} \quad (4)$$

For a given continuous beam A_n, A_{n+1}, c_{n+1}, and c_n are known for any two adjacent spans. Equation 5.5.4 is thus an equation in the three unknown end bending moments. When $EI_n = EI_{n+1}$ and $L_n = L_{n+1}$, it reduces to

$$M_{n-1} + 4M_n + M_{n+1} = -\frac{6A_n c_n}{L^2} - \frac{6A_{n+1} c_{n+1}}{L^2} \quad (5)$$

Two particular loadings and the associated products Ac are given below.

(1) Uniformly distributed load q_0 acting over beam of span L.

$$Ac = +\frac{q_0 L^4}{24} \quad (6)$$

(2) Single concentrated load P acting at distance a from end about which the area moments are taken.

$$Ac = +\frac{Pa}{6}(L^2 - a^2) \quad (7)$$

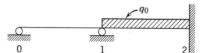

$L_1 = \alpha L_2 \qquad L_2 \qquad L_3 = \beta L_2$

EI constant   **Figure 5.35**

Example 5.5.1 Find the bending moment at support 2 for the beam of Figure 5.35. In this case we write the three moment equation twice: for stations 0, 1, 2, and for stations 1, 2, 3. Note that $M_0 = M_3 = 0$. Let *EI* be constant throughout. We find

$$\frac{M_1}{3}(L_1^2 + L_2^2) + \frac{M_2}{6}L_2^2 = -\frac{q_0L_2^4}{24} \tag{8}$$

$$\frac{M_1L_2^2}{6} + \frac{M_2}{3}(L_2^2 + L_3^2) = -\frac{q_0L_2^4}{24}$$

The introduction of α and β reduces these to

$$8M_1(\alpha^2 + 1) + 4M_2 = -q_0L_2^2$$

$$4M_1 + 8M_2(1 + \beta^2) = -q_0L_2^2 \tag{9}$$

where $\alpha = L_1/L_2$ and $\beta = L_3/L_2$.

Solving simultaneously, we find

$$M_2 = \frac{q_0L^2}{4}\frac{1 + 2\alpha^2}{1 - 4(1 + \alpha^2)(1 + \beta^2)} \tag{10}$$

As the value of β goes to infinity, $M_2 \to 0$, which is logical since a right span infinite in length will have little or no rigidity and hence will offer no resistance to rotation at support 2. The action is equivalent to that at a simple support. If α and β both go to infinity, we will have what is equivalent to a simply supported beam. As β decreases, we have a right span that gets more and more rigid until in the limit ($\beta = 0$) the support 2 is equivalent to a fixed support, and

$$M_2 = -\frac{q_0L^2}{4}\frac{1 + 2\alpha^2}{3 + 4\alpha^2} \tag{11}$$

This corresponds to the beam of Figure 5.36. Finally, when α and β both approach zero, the loaded span becomes a fixed end beam, and

$$M_2 = -\frac{q_0L^2}{12} \tag{12}$$

The problem considered in Example 5.5.1 gives us a clue as to how we solve a beam such as that shown in Figure 5.37. This structure is indeterminate to the third degree. We can write the three-moment equation for

0   1   2   **Figure 5.36**

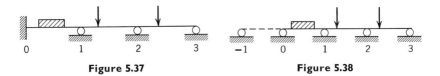

| Figure 5.37 | Figure 5.38 |

0, 1, 2, and 1, 2, 3 but we still need a third equation in order to find all values of the bending moment. To meet this need we imagine a fictitious rigid span to the left as shown by the dotted line of Figure 5.38. We may let the length of $(-1, 0)$ be zero or let the rigidity EI be infinitely large. Either way, we will be able to write a third equation for $(-1, 0, +1)$ and proceed to a solution for the problem.

Once again we see a set of simultaneous algebraic equations coming into the picture, which may be solved by the method of § 1.5.

5.6 Indeterminate Stress Resultants beyond the Elastic Range

In § 2.5 the normal stresses associated with bending moments were discussed. It was shown that the strain at the outer fiber of the cross section varies linearly with moment as long as all fibers are strained less than the yield strain ϵ_0. When the yield moment M_0 was exceeded the moment-strain curve (given in Figure 2.22) assumed a curved shape with the value of ϵ going to infinity as the bending moment asymptotically approached the fully plastic value M_p.

If we consider the relation between bending moment M and curvature K, $d\theta/ds$, we find a linear relation in the elastic range given by 3.3.5 to be

$$M = -EIK \tag{1}$$

Since outer fiber strain increases with curvature, it is not surprising to find that the shape of the moment-strain curve of Figure 2.22 is the same as the experimentally determined moment-curvature curve given in Figure 5.39.

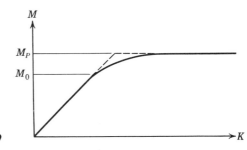

Figure 5.39

 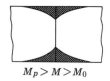 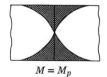

$M \le M_0$ $M_p > M > M_0$ $M = M_p$

Figure 5.40

The difficulties involved in solving problems of post-elastic bending are problems that arise from this nonlinear relation between M and K.

As an expedient in treating such problems, we approximate the M-K curve by the dotted bilinear curve indicated in Figure 5.39. Errors involved in making this approximation are very small as far as most practical situations are concerned. As far as local strain variations (which are not apt to be of serious practical significance) are concerned, however, the errors introduced may be appreciable. In Figure 5.40 we have illustrations of the growth of the plastic range as it actually occurs. The shaded area represents the area in which stresses have reached yield values and strains have exceeded yield values. When $M = M_p$ the elastic core finally disappears, giving plastic strains over the entire cross section.

The bilinear relation indicates a linear relation between M and K until $M = M_p$. Thus the cross section passes rapidly from a perfect elastic stress to a state of complete plastic stress. M_p is assumed to be reached at a finite value of K rather than only approached asymptotically. This suggests the action of a hinge, for after the moment reaches M_p no additional moment can be carried. Additional changes in slope occur with no increase in moment. We may say that when M reaches the value M_p (increasing linearly from zero with the elastic ratio $M/K = -EI$), a *plastic hinge* is formed. The presence of a sufficient number of such plastic hinges causes the structure to be unstable (or to become a *mechanism*) and collapse will follow. The determination of collapse loads is a particular concern of structural designers and is treated in § 5.7.

When the moment-curvature relation is bilinear, we conclude that the indeterminate stress resultants will be the same as those for a perfectly elastic structure so long as the bending moment at no section reaches M_p. When M becomes equal to M_p at a given section, that section will carry no additional moment and will behave as a hinge as the loads continue to increase.

5.7 Collapse Loads Based on Equilibrium Analysis

The simplest example of collapse is that of a uniformly loaded, simply supported beam such as shown in Figure 5.41a. Its bending moment diagram is shown in Figure 5.41b. It is evident that if M_p is the maximum

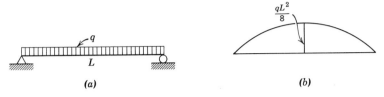

Figure 5.41

moment the section can withstand, the maximum load q_c that the beam can carry is the value that will give

$$\frac{q_c L^2}{8} = M_p \tag{1}$$

or

$$q_c = \frac{8 M_p}{L^2} \tag{2}$$

At this loading the cross section at midspan is no longer capable of supporting additional moment. This means that an increase in curvature is now possible without additional load. Since curvature is rate of change of slope, we conclude that over a dx length of beam at midspan, the value of $d\theta$ will continue to increase. The structure is thus unstable and collapse is imminent. In Figure 5.42 various stages are shown for the beam as collapse occurs. Note the continually increasing rate of $d\theta/dx$ at midspan and the constancy of $d\theta/dx$ at all other locations.

As a general rule, we can say that a statically determinate structure will collapse whenever the load is large enough to cause the bending moment at any section to reach its plastic value M_p. This is not to imply that the entire structure will necessarily collapse, since only a portion of the structure may be effected. In Figure 5.43a, for example, we have an overhanging beam and its bending moment diagram given in Figure 5.43b. It is evident in this structure that the plastic hinge will form at the right support when the load reaches the value P_c given by

$$P_c = \frac{M_p}{a} \tag{3}$$

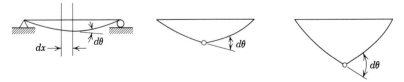

Figure 5.42

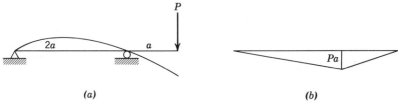

(a)   (b)

Figure 5.43

Here the cantilevered arm will collapse, leaving the main span intact and capable of supporting additional downward load along its length. We designate this as *partial collapse*. When the entire structure becomes unstable we speak of *total collapse*. It is interesting to note in the latter that for a single load Q acting at the center of the main span, collapse will occur when that load reaches the value

$$Q_c = \frac{2M_p}{a} \tag{4}$$

and a hinge forms at mid-span. Now by placing an additional load at the free end, we reduce the moments at mid-span below the value of M_p. As long as the load at mid-span is less than three times the size of the load at the free end, a partial collapse will occur with a hinge formed at the right support as shown in Figure 5.44. When the mid-span load is three times the free end load, total collapse will occur with hinges forming at mid-span and the right support as shown in Figure 5.45. When $Q > 3P$, partial collapse occurs with a hinge forming at mid-span as shown in Figure 5.46.

Since the structural integrity of the system is impaired whether collapse is partial or total, it would be appropriate in the foregoing example to select a cross section over the right support that is different from the cross section chosen for the remainder of the span so that total collapse would be likely to occur. In this way we would be making most efficient

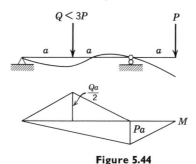

Figure 5.44

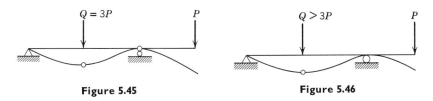

| Figure 5.45 | Figure 5.46 |

use of the material provided in the structure. For example, if the load Q at mid-span is equal to $4P$, the moments at mid-span and right support are $1.5Pa$ and Pa respectively. We would choose a section for the main span with a value of M_p that is 50% greater than the value provided over the support.

When a structure is statically indeterminate, the number of hinges necessary to cause collapse is usually equal to $n + 1$ where n is the degree of indeterminateness. This is not a fast rule but is a useful guide. Several examples illustrate the method of calculating collapse loads using an equilibrium analysis.

Example 5.7.1 Find the collapse load for the beam of Figure 5.47a. Within the elastic range the end bending moments are equal to $Pa/4$ and the moment diagram is as shown in Figure 5.47b. By "folding" the negative area up and over the positive area we get the composite diagram of Figure 5.47c. The maximum moment of $Pa/4$ is reached simultaneously at the end supports and mid-span. This means that as the load is increased, plastic hinges can be expected to form simultaneously at these points. If the value of the plastic moment is M_p throughout the beam, we find the collapse load given by

$$P_c = \frac{4M_P}{a} \tag{5}$$

If, on the other hand, the end quarters of the beam have plastic moments that are twice that of the middle portion of the beam as indicated in Figure 5.47d, a hinge will form at mid-span at a value of

$$P = \frac{4M_p}{a} \tag{6}$$

Hinges will not form at the ends until P becomes much larger. Free-body diagrams of the two halves of the beam at collapse show, as in Figure 5.47e, moments equal to $-2M_P$ at the supports and $+M_P$ at mid-span. Equilibrium will require shear forces as shown equal to $3M_P/a$. At the load point this gives

$$P_c = \frac{6M_P}{a} \tag{7}$$

Due to the haunching of the supported ends, the strength of the beam has thus been increased by 50% as seen by comparing 5.7.6 and 5.7.7. The bending moment diagram at collapse is shown in Figure 5.47f.

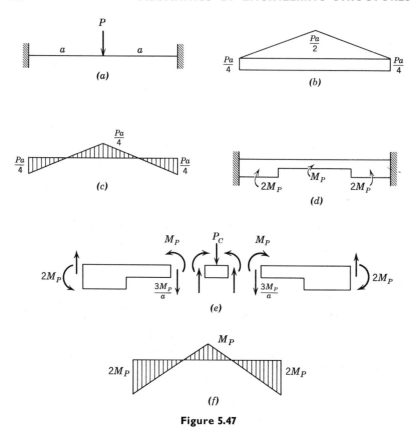

Figure 5.47

In Example 5.7.1 we recognize a procedure for finding collapse loads that can be generalized. We begin by sketching a bending moment diagram for the beam as associated with elastic behavior. From this diagram, we guess at the locations of a sufficient number of plastic hinges to cause collapse. We then draw free body diagrams such as might be associated with collapse and from these determine a collapse load. Having calculated the collapse load we now draw final bending moment diagrams for the collapse condition. If at every section of the beam we read off a value of bending moment that is equal to or less than the plastic moment for that section, we conclude that the locations assumed for the plastic hinges are indeed the correct ones.

In general, when the bending moment at every section is equal to or less than the plastic bending moment for the section, the loading is said to be *safe*. When enough plastic hinges have been formed to cause the structure to become unstable, collapse is imminent and we say the structure has become a *mechanism*. The following very useful *statical theorem* may now be stated.

For a given structure and a given loading, if there exists a safe distribution of bending moment, the given load will be equal to or less than the collapse load. If, in addition, enough plastic hinges are formed to create a mechanism, the load will be equal to the collapse load.

Example 5.7.2 Use the statical method of analysis to find the value of P necessary to cause collapse of the beam in Figure 5.48. As a first step we sketch the relevant bending moment diagram for the elastic range and recognize from it that the likely places for hinges to occur are at the center support and at either or both of the load points. Two modes of partial collapse and one of total collapse are possible. We first assume local collapse in the left span as shown in Figure 5.48c. From the associated free body diagrams in Figure 5.48d we find $P_c = 3M_p/a$. The final moment diagram consistent with this value of P_c is as shown in Figure 5.48e. Since this is not a safe distribution of bending moment the mechanism assumed must be incorrect.

Now we assume partial collapse in the right span to be the proper mode. The collapse mechanism is shown in Figure 5.49a. Here we calculate $2P_c = 3M_P/a$ or $P_c = 3M_P/2a$. The final moment diagram will be as shown in Figure 5.49b. All bending moments are safe ($M \leq M_P$), and since a mechanism is indicated this must be the correct mechanism. The collapse load is therefore as previously calculated.

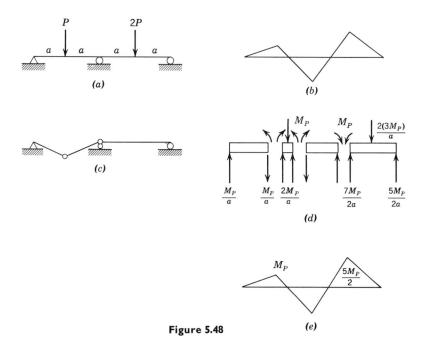

Figure 5.48

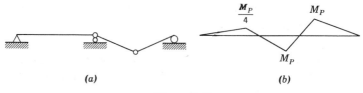

(a)   (b)

Figure 5.49

It is evident that this statical method of analysis is very good as long as there are not too many possible modes of collapse. For more complicated cases the kinematic method described in the next section may be preferred.

5.8 Collapse Loads Based on a Kinematic Analysis

The calculation of collapse loads may be easily handled through the use of the energy principles of Chapter 4. As system I, we take the structure in its mode of collapse. As system II, we take the chosen mechanism with an impressed displacement. We then equate, as before, the work done by external forces of I on the displacements of II and the work done by internal forces of I on the displacements of II. Thus $W_{12} = U_{12}$. In the structure of Example 5.7.7 we have system I as shown in Figure 5.50a and system II as shown in Figure 5.50c where an impressed rotation of θ has been chosen. Now $W_{12} = P_c a \theta$. U_{12} is the total internal work done

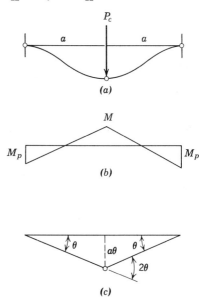

Figure 5.50

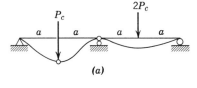

(a)

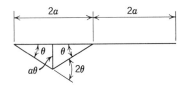

(b)
Figure 5.51

by bending moments in system I on the values of $d\theta$ in system II. Values of $d\theta$ over any dx length between the hinges in Figure 5.50c are zero. There is thus no contribution to U_{12} by the bending moments in Figure 5.50a between the hinges. Values of $d\theta$ at the hinges, however, will be θ, 2θ, and θ as shown in Figure 5.50c. Bending moments in Figure 5.50a in these locations all equal M_p. U_{12} is thus given by

$$U_{12} = (M_P)(\theta) + M_P(2\theta) + M_P(\theta) \qquad (1)$$

Equating W_{12} and U_{12} we find

$$P_c = \frac{4M_P}{a} \qquad (2)$$

as found in 5.7.6. Similarly, for the structure of Example 5.7.2, we study the possibility of partial collapse of the left span and have the systems I and II of Figures 5.51a and 5.51b. We find

$$W_{12} = P_c a\theta \qquad U_{12} = 3M_P\theta \qquad P_c = \frac{3M_P}{a} \qquad (3)$$

Taking the partial collapse of the right span as the correct mode we have systems I and II of Figures 5.52a and 5.52b.

$$W_{12} = 2P_c a\theta \qquad U_{12} = 3M_P\theta \qquad P_c = \frac{3M_P}{2a} \qquad (4)$$

Finally, we test the possibility of total collapse using systems I and II of Figures 5.53a and 5.53b. We find

$$W_{12} = P_c a\theta + 2P_c a\theta$$
$$U_{12} = 3M_P\theta + 3M_P\theta = 6M_P \qquad (5)$$

or

$$P_c = \frac{2M_P}{a}$$

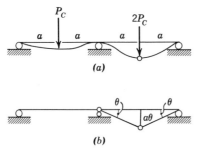

(a)

(b)   Figure 5.52

Note that we chose the reference angles of the left span in 5.53b to be the same as the reference angle in the right span as a convenience.

Now the three possible mode shapes yielded values of $P_c = 3M_P/2a$, $P_c = 3M_P/a$, and $P_c = 2M_P/a$. Quite logically we must conclude that if all mode shapes have been considered, the least value of P_c must be the correct value of the collapse load. In general, we may state the following *kinematic theorem*.

When a possible mechanism is checked to find the corresponding value of P_c, the value found must be equal to or greater than the correct collapse load. If, in addition, a statical check yields a final moment diagram that is everywhere safe, the load calculated must be equal to the collapse load.

Example 5.8.1 Indicate the possible mechanisms for the bent of Figure 5.54a and determine the collapse load using the kinematic method. First, we recognize the mechanism associated with partial collapse of the left column shown in Figure 5.54b. The collapse load is $P_{c1} = 4M_P/a$. A general sidesway mechanism is indicated in Figure 5.54c giving $P_{c2} = 3M_P/a$. The combined mechanism giving total collapse is shown in Figure 5.54d which yields $P_{c3} = 2.5M_P/a$. No other modes of collapse are possible. According to the kinematical theorem we conclude that P_{c3}, since it is the smallest, must represent the true collapse load for the structure.

Example 5.8.2 Determine the collapse load for the structure in Figure 5.55a using the kinematic theorem. We know that two plastic hinges will be necessary

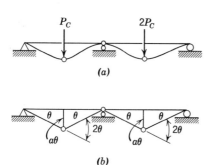

(a)

(b)   Figure 5.53

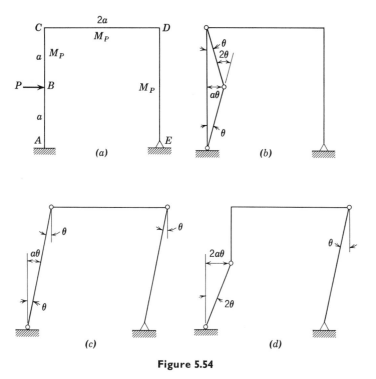

Figure 5.54

for collapse of this structure: one at the center support and one at some position, yet undetermined, in the left span. We use a trial and error procedure for determining the location of this second hinge by first assuming it to be at midspan and then correcting that assumption. With the second hinge at midspan we use as our system II the structure shown in Figure 5.55b with an impressed rotation of θ at the left support. The value of W_{12} corresponding to the uniform load can be readily found by treating the load on the left half of the span and the load on the right half of the span in terms of their resultants as shown in Figure 5.55b. The values of W_{12} and U_{12} will be

$$W_{12} = \frac{1}{2} \frac{q_0 a}{2} \frac{a\theta}{4} 2 \qquad (6)$$

$$U_{12} = \tfrac{1}{2} 3M_p\theta \qquad (7)$$

Equating 5.8.6. and 5.8.7 we find

$$q_0 = \frac{12M_p}{a^2} \qquad (8)$$

Using this value and considering the free-body diagram as shown in Figure 5.55c, we find the left reaction to be $5M_p/a$. The shear force in that span will be

$$V = \frac{5M_p}{a} - \frac{12M_p}{a^2}(x) \qquad (9)$$

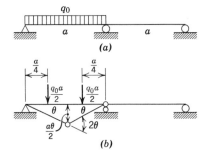

(a)

(b)

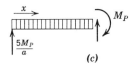

(c)

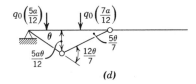

(d)   **Figure 5.55**

and equals zero when

$$x = \frac{5a}{12} \tag{10}$$

This indicates that the correct position of the hinge is not at midspan. As a second approximation we now assume it to be located at $x = 5a/12$ and repeat the computation until such time as the assumed value of x equals the value found using statics. Using $x = 5a/12$ and the appropriate values given on Figure 5.55c we find that

$$q_c = \frac{11.7 M_p}{a^2} \tag{11}$$

Example 5.8.3 Solve the problem of 5.8.2 using a semigraphical approach. If we consider our redundant as the moment at the center support, the moment diagram may be drawn as Figure 5.56a. We now lay off the parabolic portion of the diagram to scale and imagine the diagram due to M_2 to be folded up and shown as the dotted line in Figure 5.56b. At collapse, the positive ordinates at the two hinges will each be equal to M_p as shown. Denoting the distance from the left end to the hinge by x, we note

$$M_A = M_p + \frac{x M_p}{a} = \left(\frac{x + a}{a}\right) M_p \tag{12}$$

or

$$M_p = M_A \left(\frac{a}{x + a}\right) \tag{13}$$

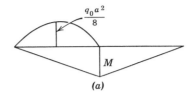

(a)

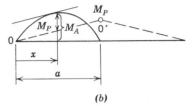

Figure 5.56   (b)

where M_A is the ordinate at position x of the parabolic diagram of Figure 5.56a. We begin by measuring the distance x to an assumed hinge location and the corresponding value of M_A and substitute into 5.8.13 to find M_p. This value of M_p is laid off to scale at the middle support to locate point $0'$. A line parallel to $00'$ in Figure 5.56b is now drawn tangent to the parabola. If the point of tangency is located at the assumed value of x, the hinge will have been located correctly and the collapse load can be found from the calculated value of M_p. If the point of tangency is at a position other than the assumed value of x, we repeat the process, taking as the new location of the hinge the position given by the point of tangency in the previous cycle.

5.9 Influence Lines for Statically Indeterminate Stress Resultants

Chapter 4 discusses the construction of influence lines for statically determinate stress resultants. Because of the statical determinacy of the structure, we note that the actual stiffness of the members has no effect on the shape of the influence diagrams. Consequently, all line segments of the diagrams are straight. For the indeterminate case the stiffness of members is very important and the influence diagram consists of curved line segments. The same method of construction is possible and is used in the following examples.

Example 5.9.1   Sketch the influence lines for the reactions of the beam shown in Figure 5.57 and calculate a few ordinates for the diagram corresponding to R_1. We recall that the influence line for a reaction is identical in shape to the deflected structure associated with an upward displacement of the reaction in question. The scale is given by letting the upward displacement be equal to unity. The diagrams for the three reactions are shown in Figures 5.57b–d.
    In order to get a quantitative understanding of the influence diagram we shall compute the ordinates at the midpoints of the two spans in Figure 5.57b. We begin by determining the force necessary to cause the unit displacement. Figure

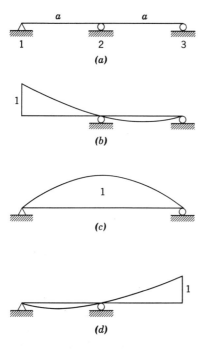

Figure 5.57

5.58a shows the conjugate beam corresponding to the beam in Figure 5.57b. Note that the upward deflection of unity in 5.57b dictates a negative moment of unity at the left end in Figure 5.58a. In Figure 5.58b we see that the shear force at the center of the conjugate beam must be $R_1 a^2/3EI$ in order to have equilibrium of the right half of the conjugate beam. From this we find that equilibrium of the left half requires $R_1 = 3EI/2a^3$. This then is the upward force necessary to give a unit upward deflection at the left end of the given beam. The loading on the conjugate beam (Figure 5.58a) is completely known when R_1 is known. The reactions of the conjugate beam are shown in Figure 5.58c. We sum moments in the conjugate beam to get the deflections in the given beam which in turn are the influence ordinates in the original beam for R_1. Final values are shown in Figure 5.58d.

Example 5.9.2   Calculate several ordinates of the influence diagram for the bending moment at the midpoint of the left span of the beam shown in Figure 5.57a. Here we assume a hinge to be present at the midpoint of the left span and equal and opposite external couples applied to cause a unit change in slope at the hinge as shown in Figure 5.59a. The associated conjugate beam is shown in Figure 5.59b. The value of the couple m is now chosen to give a change in slope of unity in the given beam or a change in shear (a reaction in this case) of unity in the conjugate beam. Equilibrium of the conjugate beam requires m to have the value $3EI/8a$. The reactions of the conjugate beam are shown in Figure 5.59b. The final mid-span ordinates for the influence line correspond to the midspan bending moments in the conjugate beam. They are shown in Figure 5.59c.

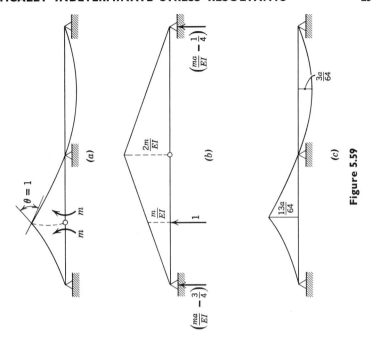

Figure 5.59

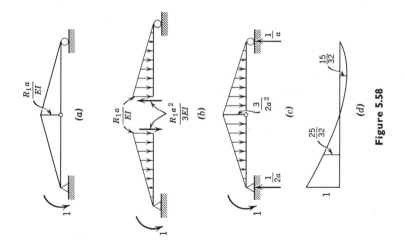

Figure 5.58

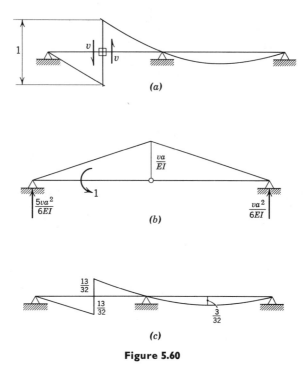

Figure 5.60

Example 5.9.3   Calculate several ordinates of the influence diagram for the shear force at the midpoint of the left span of Figure 5.57a. In this diagram we assume a shear connector to be present at the midpoint of the left span and that equal and opposite external vertical forces act at that location as shown in Figure 5.60a. We choose these forces so that the change in deflection at the point in the beam equals unity. The loaded conjugate beam is shown in Figure 5.60b. Note that the negative change in deflection of unity in the given beam corresponds to a negative change in bending moment of unity in the conjugate beam. The value of v consistent with equilibrium is found to be equal to $3EI/2a^3$. The reactions of the conjugate beam are shown in Figure 5.60b. The desired ordinates of the influence line are shown in Figure 5.60c.

Problems

5.1.1   The structure shown is supported by springs which provide resistance in amounts indicated in the figure. The F-Δ diagrams represent the relationship between force on a given spring and deflection on the spring. The structure is loaded with a 1-kip load and a couple, M, of variable magnitude. What is the maximum value of M consistent with the principle of superposition?

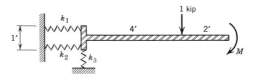

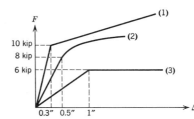

Problem 5.1.1

5.1.2 A slender bar is acted on by axial forces and lateral loads. Discuss the applicability of the superposition principle as regards bending moments in the bar.

5.2.1 Using the conjugate beam method, find the reactions of the structure shown, first using the left reaction as redundant and then using the center reaction as redundant.

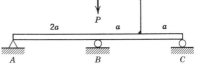

Problem 5.2.1

5.2.2 Find the reactions associated with the prescribed loading and a clockwise rotation of 0.02 radian.

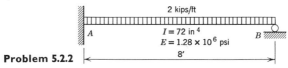

Problem 5.2.2

5.2.3 Find the reactions for the frame shown.

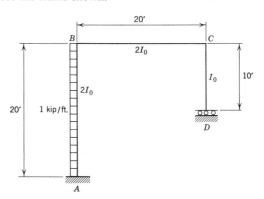

Problem 5.2.3

5.2.4   Find the bending moments at the ends of the structure shown.

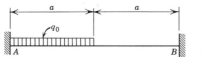

Problem 5.2.4

5.2.5   Find the reactions for the structure shown.

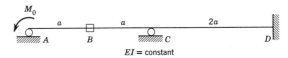

EI = constant

Problem 5.2.5

5.3.1   Repeat Problem 5.2.1 using the principle of virtual work.

5.3.2   Repeat Problem 5.2.2 using Castigliano's principle.

5.3.3   Repeat Problem 5.2.3 using the principle of virtual work.

5.3.4   Find the reactions for the truss shown. L/A for all members is equal to 30.

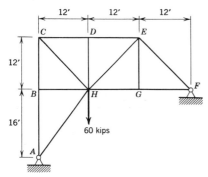

Problem 5.3.4

5.3.5   Find all reactions and bar forces of the structure shown. L/A for all members is equal to 100.

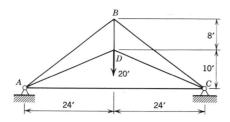

Problem 5.3.5

5.3.6 Use the principle of virtual work to find the reactions of the structure shown, taking due account of all axial bending forces.

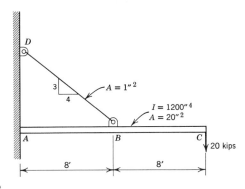

Problem 5.3.6

5.4.1 Use any method you desire to find the reactions of the structure shown.

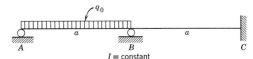

Problem 5.4.1

5.4.2 Use any method you wish to find the reactions of the structure shown.

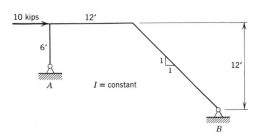

Problem 5.4.2

5.4.3 Use the principle of virtual work to find the reactions of the structure shown.

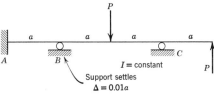

Problem 5.4.3

5.5.1 Find the bending moments at the supports using the three moment equations.

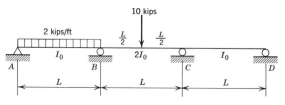

Problem 5.5.1

5.5.2 Repeat Problem 5.5.1 with the right support fixed.

5.5.3 Rederive the three moment equations so as to provide for a vertical settlement Δ at the center support.

5.6.1 A simply supported 20-ft. beam is loaded uniformly with 1 kip per ft. The elastic section modulus, Z, is 15 in.[3], the shape factor, α, is 1.4. Locate the section at which the bending moment is equal to the yield moment, M_0. Determine the bounds of the elastic core of the cross section at mid-span, at the section at which $M = M_0$, and a section halfway between these two points. Sketch the zone of partial plastification similar to Figure 5.6.2.

5.7.1 Determine the value of P as a multiple of Q such that there will be partial collapse of the overhanging position of the structure shown and also such that there will be total collapse.

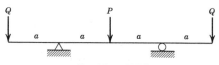

Problem 5.7.1

5.7.2 Determine the collapse load for the structure shown. Note that the plastic section modulus for the left span is one-half that for the right span.

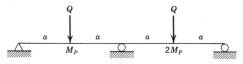

Problem 5.7.2

5.7.3 Find the load necessary to cause collapse.

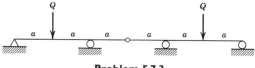

Problem 5.7.3

5.7.4 Compare the collapse load for the structure shown with that for a similar structure with simply supported ends.

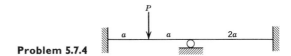

Problem 5.7.4

5.8.1   Repeat Problem 5.7.4 using the kinematic method.

5.8.2   Find the collapse load using the kinematic method.

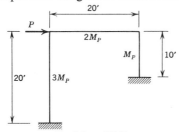

Problem 5.8.2

5.8.3   What effect would a settlement of 1 in. at the center support have on the collapse load in Problem 5.7.2?

5.8.4   Prove that three plastic hinges must form in order to cause collapse of the frame shown regardless of the point of application of the load on the girder.

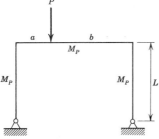

Problem 5.8.4

5.9.1   Given a beam of two equal spans that has EI constant and is simply supported at its ends. Determine the ordinates at midspan and at the center support in the influence diagram for the middle reaction.

5.9.2   Determine at least three ordinates to the influence diagram for bending moment at the left support for a uniform fixed end beam.

5.9.3   Determine the equation for the influence diagram over the overhanging portion of the beam shown for the shear force at section b.

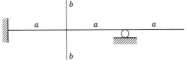

Problem 5.9.3

6 EQUATIONS OF BRESSE AND THE COLUMN ANALOGY

6.1 Equations of Bresse

In this chapter the general analysis of single cell framed structures is discussed, with special attention being given to the problems of plane elastic curved structures. A segment of such a structure subjected to external loads and internal stress resultants is shown in Figure 6.1 where M, N, and V represent the bending moment, axial force, and shear force present on any cross section. The ends of the segment are defined by the end stations 0 and 1 and these numbers are used as subscripts with M, N, and V to indicate clearly which stress resultants are being considered. Stress resultants are positive as shown in the figure.

Let us define the segment of the structure in question by the equation $y = f(x)$ for the axis. We assume, for the present, that the structure is plane and that the axis is taken as the locus of points representing the centroids of the various right cross sections of the structure. The origin

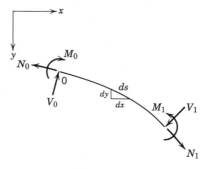

Figure 6.1

246

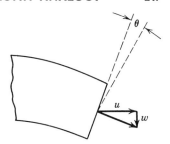

Figure 6.2

of coordinates may be located at any convenient position. We take x and y as positive to the right and downward, respectively. The slope of the axis when unloaded is given by $\alpha = \tan^{-1}(dy/dx)$. The distance s is measured along the axis such that

$$ds^2 = dx^2 + dy^2 \tag{1}$$

When loaded, the centroid of any cross section may suffer a displacement u in the x direction and w in the y direction where these displacements are likewise measured positive to the right and downward, respectively. The right cross section at any location may suffer a rotation θ about an axis taken through the centroid and normal to the plane of the structure. Its sign is positive when the rotation is clockwise. Displacements are illustrated in Figure 6.2. When necessary we shall introduce displacement components normal to the cross section and transverse to the cross section as shown in Figure 6.3. We shall denote these by $\bar{u}$ and $\bar{w}$. They are related to u and w through the expressions

$$u = \bar{u} \cos \alpha - \bar{w} \sin \alpha \tag{2}$$

$$w = \bar{u} \sin \alpha + \bar{w} \cos \alpha \tag{3}$$

and since

$$\tan \alpha = dy/dx, \quad \sin \alpha = dy/ds, \quad \cos \alpha = dx/ds \tag{4}$$

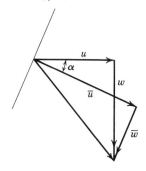

Figure 6.3

we write

$$u = \bar{u}\frac{dx}{ds} - \bar{w}\frac{dy}{ds} \tag{5}$$

$$w = \bar{u}\frac{dy}{ds} + \bar{w}\frac{dx}{ds} \tag{6}$$

In the most general case we shall have six unknown stress resultants and three equations of statics. It remains for us to find three additional equations to obtain a complete solution. In deriving these equations we choose the structure as actually loaded in Figure 6.1 as system I and the structure with another special loading as system II. The most useful energy theorem for use is

$$W_{21} = U_{21} \tag{7}$$

In terms of the internal stress resultants m, v, and n in system II we write

$$U_{21} = -\tfrac{1}{2}\int_0^1 m\, d\theta + \tfrac{1}{2}\int_0^1 n\, d\bar{u} + \tfrac{1}{2}\int_0^1 v\, d\bar{w}_s \tag{8}$$

where $d\theta$ is the change in slope of system I over a length ds due to the applied load, $d\bar{u}$ is the change in axial displacement in system I over a length ds and $d\bar{w}_s$ is the change in transverse displacement over a length ds due to shear in system I. Note that although the total change in transverse displacement is $d\bar{w}$, part of this amount is due to the presence of bending moments and has already been accounted for in the first integral. Thus only that contribution due to shear $d\bar{w}_s$ need be added. The internal stress resultants in Figure 6.4 are at any location

$$m = 1, \qquad n = 0, \qquad v = 0 \tag{9}$$

and will be used in deriving the first required equation. Thus we have here

$$W_{21} = \tfrac{1}{2}(\theta_0 - \theta_1) \tag{10}$$

$$U_{21} = -\tfrac{1}{2}\int_0^1 d\theta \tag{11}$$

or

$$\theta_1 = \theta_0 + \int_0^1 d\theta \tag{12}$$

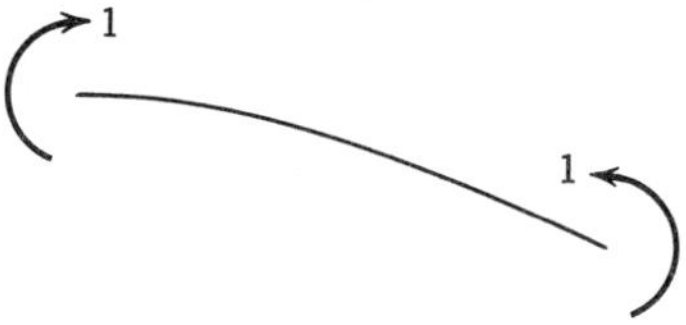

Figure 6.4

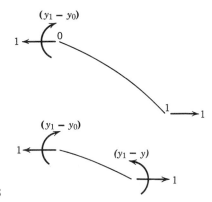

Figure 6.5

As a second expression, consider as system II the structure loaded as shown in Figure 6.5. Here we have

$$m = (y_1 - y), \qquad n = (1) \cos \alpha, \qquad v = -(1) \sin \alpha \qquad (13)$$

Using 6.1.4 we get

$$m = (y_1 - y), \qquad n = \frac{dx}{ds}, \qquad v = -\frac{dy}{ds} \qquad (14)$$

Using 6.1.7 we now find

$$W_{21} = \tfrac{1}{2}[-u_0 + (y_1 - y_0)\theta_0 + u_1] \qquad (15)$$

and using 6.1.8, we get

$$U_{21} = \frac{1}{2}\int_0^1 \frac{d\bar{u}}{ds}\,dx - \frac{1}{2}\int_0^1 \frac{d\bar{w}_s}{ds}\,dy - \frac{1}{2}\int_0^1 (y_1 - y)\,d\theta \qquad (16)$$

or

$$u_1 = u_0 - (y_1 - y_0)\theta_0 + \int_0^1 \frac{d\bar{u}}{ds}\,dx - \int_0^1 \frac{d\bar{w}_s}{ds}\,dy - \int_0^1 (y_1 - y)\,d\theta \qquad (17)$$

Finally, we obtain a third equation using the loaded structure in Figure 6.6 as system II. Here we find

$$m = -(x_1 - x), \qquad n = +\frac{dy}{ds}, \qquad v = \frac{dx}{ds} \qquad (18)$$

$$W_{21} = \tfrac{1}{2}[-w_0 - (x_1 - x_0)\theta_0 + w_1] \qquad (19)$$

$$U_{21} = \frac{1}{2}\int_0^1 d\bar{u}\,\frac{dy}{ds} + \frac{1}{2}\int_0^1 d\bar{w}_s\,\frac{dx}{ds} + \frac{1}{2}\int_0^1 (x_1 - x)\,d\theta \qquad (20)$$

and finally

$$w_1 = w_0 + (x_1 - x_0)\theta_0 + \int_0^1 \frac{d\bar{u}}{ds}\,dy + \int_0^1 \frac{d\bar{w}_s}{ds}\,dx + \int_0^1 (x_1 - x)\,d\theta \qquad (21)$$

In order to evaluate the various integrals we must find useable expressions for $d\bar{u}/ds$, $d\bar{w}_s/ds$, and $d\theta$. For an elastic structure the normal strain

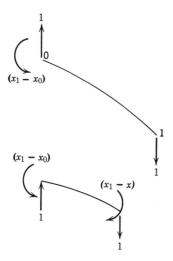

Figure 6.6

at a distance ζ from the centroid is found in the following manner. First we note that an element of length along the axis of the structure in the undeformed state is ds. An elemental fiber length a distance ζ away from the axis* will be designated ds_ζ. In Figure 6.7 we see that these are related through the expression

$$ds_\zeta = ds - \zeta \, d\alpha \tag{22}$$

where $d\alpha$ is the differential change in slope over the length ds. Now upon loading, fibers change in length such that

$$ds \text{ becomes } ds + d\bar{u}$$
$$ds_\zeta \text{ becomes } ds_\zeta + d\bar{u}_\zeta$$
$$d\alpha \text{ becomes } d\alpha + d\theta$$

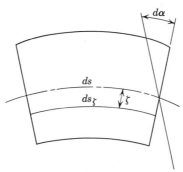

Figure 6.7

* The letter ζ is used instead of the w of § 2.3 to prevent any possible confusion with the displacement in the y direction.

Substituting these into 6.1.22 we obtain

$$ds_\zeta + d\bar{u}_\zeta = ds + d\bar{u} - \zeta\, d\alpha - \zeta\, d\theta \tag{23}$$

Combining 6.1.22 and 6.1.23 we find

$$d\bar{u}_\zeta = d\bar{u} - \zeta\, d\theta \tag{24}$$

The normal strain at fiber ζ is thus

$$\epsilon = \frac{d\bar{u}_\zeta}{ds_\zeta} = \frac{d\bar{u} - \zeta\, d\theta}{ds_\zeta} = \frac{d\bar{u} - \zeta\, d\theta}{ds}\left(\frac{r}{r - \zeta}\right) \tag{25}$$

since

$$ds_\zeta = ds\left(\frac{r - \zeta}{r}\right) \tag{26}$$

as shown in § 2.3. Using Hooke's law, we get

$$s_n = E\frac{d\bar{u}_\zeta}{ds_\zeta} = E\left(\frac{d\bar{u} - \zeta\, d\theta}{ds}\right)\left(\frac{r}{r - \zeta}\right) \tag{27}$$

We now substitute 6.1.27 into the equilibrium equations

$$N = \int_A s_n\, dA = \frac{E\, d\bar{u}}{ds}\int_A \frac{r\, dA}{r - \zeta} - \frac{E\, d\theta}{ds}\int_A \frac{r\zeta\, dA}{r - \zeta} \tag{28}$$

$$M = \int_A s_n\zeta\, dA = \frac{E\, d\bar{u}}{ds}\int_A \frac{r\zeta\, dA}{r - \zeta} - \frac{E\, d\theta}{ds}\int_A \frac{r\zeta^2\, dA}{r - \zeta} \tag{29}$$

These integrals are defined in Chapter 4 as

$$\int_A \frac{r\, dA}{r - \zeta} = A + \frac{J}{r^2} \tag{30}$$

$$\int_A \frac{r\zeta^2\, dA}{r - \zeta} = J \tag{31}$$

$$\int_A \frac{r\zeta\, dA}{r - \zeta} = \frac{J}{r} \tag{32}$$

We thus find upon substituting these identities into 6.1.28 and 6.1.29 and solving simultaneously

$$\frac{d\bar{u}}{ds} = +\frac{N}{AE} - \frac{M}{AEr} \tag{33}$$

$$\frac{d\theta}{ds} = +\frac{N}{AEr} - \frac{M}{EJ} - \frac{M}{AEr^2} \tag{34}$$

The shear expression is given as before

$$\frac{d\bar{w}_s}{ds} \approx \gamma = \frac{V}{\mu AG} \tag{35}$$

Substituting these relations in the three governing equations yields

$$\theta_1 = \theta_0 + \int_0^1 \left[+\frac{N}{AEr} - \frac{M}{EJ} - \frac{M}{AEr^2} \right] ds \tag{36}$$

$$u_1 = u_0 - (y_1 - y_0)\theta_0 + \int_0^1 \left[\frac{N}{AE} - \frac{M}{AEr} \right] dx - \int_0^1 \frac{V\,dy}{\mu AG}$$

$$- \int_0^1 (y_1 - y)\left(\frac{N}{AEr} - \frac{M}{EJ} - \frac{M}{AEr^2} \right) ds \tag{37}$$

$$w_1 = w_0 + (x_1 - x_0)\theta_0 + \int_0^1 \left[\frac{N}{AE} - \frac{M}{AEr} \right] dy + \int_0^1 \frac{V\,dx}{\mu AG}$$

$$+ \int_0^1 (x_1 - x)\left[\frac{N}{AEr} - \frac{M}{EJ} - \frac{M}{AEr^2} \right] ds \tag{38}$$

These three equations will be referred to hereafter as the three *equations of Bresse*.* Their generality is such that they can be used to solve an extraordinarily large variety of problems.

6.2 Some Kinematic Problems

Frequently a structure is caused to move as if it were a rigid body. It performs as a mechanism and all displacements can be found from purely kinematic consideration. The equations of Bresse are applicable to this special class of problems. Since movement of the structure is not associated with deformation, the strain terms $d\bar{u}/ds$, $d\bar{w}_s/ds$, and $d\theta/ds$ become zero, and all integral terms disappear. The governing equations reduce to

$$\theta_1 = \theta_0 \tag{1}$$

$$u_1 = u_0 - (y_1 - y_0)\theta_0 \tag{2}$$

$$w_1 = w_0 + (x_1 - x_0)\theta_0 \tag{3}$$

Kinematic problems are really degenerate in nature as far as the equations of Bresse are concerned. Their consideration here is only to acquaint

---

* Jacques Antoine Charles Bresse (1822–1883) was a distinguished pioneer in structural engineering science who won the Poncelet prize of the French Academy largely on the basis of his investigations of curved bars.

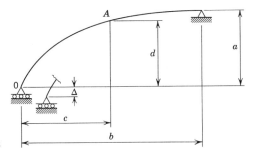

Figure 6.8

the reader with the significance of the rigid body terms in the governing equations. The following examples illustrate such problems.

Example 6.2.1   Determine the amount of horizontal displacement suffered by the left support of the structure in Figure 6.8 due to a vertical settlement of that support of amount Δ. This movement is obviously a rigid body motion. We take station 0 at the left support and station 1 at the right support and note that the following information is known; $w_0 = +\Delta$. $u_1 = w_1 = 0$. From 6.2.3 we find

$$0 = +\Delta + b\theta_0 \tag{4}$$

and

$$\theta_0 = -\frac{\Delta}{b} \tag{5}$$

From 6.2.2 we find

$$0 = u_0 + a\left(-\frac{\Delta}{b}\right) \tag{6}$$

or

$$u_0 = +\frac{a\Delta}{b} \tag{7}$$

We find from 6.2.1

$$\theta_1 = -\frac{\Delta}{b} \tag{8}$$

The displacements at a point A are now found by letting station 1 be at A and station 0 be at the left support. We find from 6.2.1, 6.2.2, and 6.2.3 and 6.2.5 with 6.2.7,

$$\theta_A = -\frac{\Delta}{b} \tag{9}$$

$$u_A = \frac{a\Delta}{b} - d\frac{\Delta}{b} = \Delta\left(\frac{a - d}{b}\right) \tag{10}$$

$$w_A = +\Delta - c\frac{\Delta}{b} = -\Delta\left(\frac{c - b}{b}\right) \tag{11}$$

The cross section at A must therefore rotate counterclockwise.

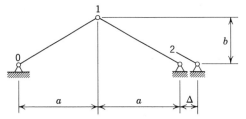

Figure 6.9

Example 6.2.2   Find the amount of rotation suffered at the left support of the structure in Figure 6.9 due to a horizontal movement to the right of amount Δ at the right support. This problem must be considered in two parts. We choose first stations 0 and 1 at the left support and at the central hinge. We then choose stations 1 and 2 at the central hinge and right support. We are given that $u_0 = w_0 = 0$ and $w_2 = 0$ and $u_2 = \Delta$. Using 6.2.2 and 6.2.3 we have

$$u_1 = +b\theta_0 \tag{12}$$

$$w_1 = a\theta_0 \tag{13}$$

$$\Delta = u_1 - b\theta_{1R} \tag{14}$$

$$0 = w_1 + a\theta_{1R} \tag{15}$$

where θ_{1R} represents the rotation just to the right of station 1. Combining these, we find

$$\Delta = +b\theta_0 - b\theta_{1R} \tag{16}$$

$$\theta = a\theta_0 + a\theta_{1R} \tag{17}$$

Solving simultaneously we find

$$\theta_0 = +\frac{\Delta}{2b} \tag{18}$$

as required.

6.3   Straight Beam Problems

While the equations of Bresse are derived primarily for curved structures they are equally well suited for straight structures. In such a case the radius of curvature, r, is infinitely great, J becomes I, and the strain terms reduce to

$$\frac{d\bar{u}}{ds} = \frac{N}{AE} \tag{1}$$

$$\frac{d\bar{w}_s}{ds} = \frac{V}{\mu AG} \tag{2}$$

$$\frac{d\theta}{ds} = -\frac{M}{EI} \tag{3}$$

These are identical to the expressions given in Chapter 4. Substituting into the equations of Bresse, we find

$$\theta_1 = \theta_0 - \int_0^1 \frac{M \, ds}{EI} \tag{4}$$

$$u_1 = u_0 - (y_1 - y_0)\theta_0 + \int_0^1 \frac{N \, dx}{AE} - \int_0^1 \frac{V \, dy}{\mu AG} + \int_0^1 (y_1 - y) \frac{M \, ds}{EI} \tag{5}$$

$$w_1 = w_0 + (x_1 - x_0)\theta_0 + \int_0^1 \frac{N \, dy}{AE} + \int_0^1 \frac{V \, dx}{\mu AG} - \int_0^1 (x_1 - x) \frac{M \, ds}{EI} \tag{6}$$

For a straight beam with the x-axis taken along the axis of the member, we will have $y_1 = y = 0$ at all locations and thus $dy = 0$. These equations then reduce to

$$\theta_1 = \theta_0 - \int_0^1 \frac{M \, dx}{EI} \tag{7}$$

$$u_1 = u_0 + \int_0^1 \frac{N \, dx}{AE} \tag{8}$$

$$w_1 = w_0 + (x_1 - x_0)\theta_0 + \int_0^1 \frac{V \, dx}{\mu AG} - \int_0^1 (x_1 - x) \frac{M \, dx}{EI} \tag{9}$$

They may equally well be written as

$$\theta_1 - \theta_0 = - \int_0^1 \frac{M \, dx}{EI} \tag{10}$$

$$u_1 - u_0 = \int_0^1 \frac{N \, dx}{AE} \tag{11}$$

$$w_1 - w_0 - (x_1 - x_0)\theta_0 = \int_0^1 \frac{V \, dx}{\mu AG} - \int_0^1 (x_1 - x) \frac{M \, dx}{EI} \tag{12}$$

These three expressions may be given interesting interpretations. The first is the familiar *moment-area theorem*. $(\theta_1 - \theta_0)$ represents the change in slope between two stations and $\int_0^1 \frac{M \, dx}{EI}$ represents the area under the M/EI diagram between the stations. The second is less familiar but equally useful. $(u_1 - u_0)$ represents the total change in axial distance between stations 0 and 1 and $\int_0^1 \frac{N \, dx}{AE}$ represents the area under the N/AE diagram between those stations. The third reduces to a *second moment-area theorem*. Note that in Figure 6.10 the quantity $w_1 - w_0 - (x_1 - x_0)\theta_0$ represents the magnitude of the distance from station 1 on the elastic curve

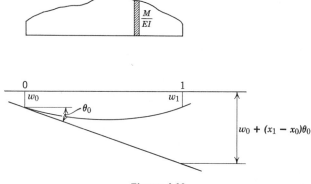

Figure 6.10

to a tangent drawn to station 0 on the elastic curve where the distance is taken perpendicular to the undeformed axis. The integral $\int_0^1 \dfrac{V\,dx}{\mu AG_1}$ represents the area under the $V/\mu AG$ diagram between the stations, and $\int_0^1 (x_1 - x)\,\dfrac{M\,dx}{EI}$ represents the first moment of the area under the M/EI diagram between the two stations taken about station 1. The usual form of the last equation omits the integral containing the shear force V.

6.4　Displacements

In curved beams that have statically determinate stress resultants, the values of M, N, and V can be found for every cross section by statics alone. The equations of Bresse then give a straight forward means of calculating the components of displacement at any desired location. The following example illustrates the method.

Example 6.4.1　Find the rotation components of displacement at the free end of the structure of uniform section shown in Figure 6.11. Since the axis of the structure is a circular arc, it follows that the radius of curvature at every section equals r. Also we see that

$$M = H(b - y) = Hr(\cos \beta - \cos 60°) \qquad (1)$$

$$N = H \cos \beta \qquad (2)$$

$$V = -H \sin \beta \qquad (3)$$

$$ds = r\,d\beta \qquad (4)$$

$$dx = ds \cos \beta = r \cos \beta\,d\beta \qquad (5)$$

$$dy = ds \sin \beta = r \sin \beta\,d\beta \qquad (6)$$

We choose the wall support as station 0 and note that $u_0 = v_0 = \theta_0 = 0$. We

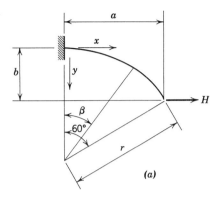

(a)

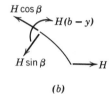

Figure 6.11   (b)

choose the free end as station 1 and wish to know θ_1. Substituting into 6.1.36
we find

$$\theta_1 = \int_0^{\pi/3} \frac{H \cos \beta}{AE} d\beta - \int_0^{\pi/3} \frac{Hr^2(\cos \beta - \cos 60°)}{EJ} d\beta$$

$$- \int_0^{\pi/3} \frac{H(\cos \beta - \cos 60°)}{AE} d\beta \qquad (7)$$

$$\theta_1 = \frac{H}{E}\left[\underbrace{\frac{0.866}{A}}_{\substack{\text{axial} \\ \text{force}}} - \underbrace{\frac{0.343r^2}{J}}_{\substack{\text{bending} \\ \text{moment}}} - \underbrace{\frac{0.343}{A}}_{\substack{\text{curvature} \\ \text{correction}}}\right] \qquad (8)$$

In order to estimate the contributions of axial force, bending moment, and
curvature correction on the value of θ, we now set, as an approximation,

$$J \approx I = A\rho^2 \qquad (9)$$

where ρ is the radius of gyration of the cross section of the member   Thus

$$\theta_1 = \frac{H}{AE}\left[0.866 - 0.343\left(\frac{r}{\rho}\right)^2 - 0.343\right] \qquad (10)$$

To fix ideas, we note that for a rectangular section of depth d, the radius of
gyration is $0.289d$. Thus

$$\theta_1 = \frac{H}{AE}\left[0.866 - 4.11\left(\frac{r}{d}\right)^2 - 0.343\right] \qquad (11)$$

It is evident that when the radius of curvature is as small as the depth ($r = d$),
the contribution of the bending moment is five times the contribution due to
axial force. Also, the contribution due to axial force is about twice that due to

curvature. As the radius of curvature increases, the significance of the term due to bending moment increases rapidly due to the squaring of r/d.

In most problems we can neglect the curvature terms (those containing $1/r$) without appreciably affecting the results. In many instances we may also neglect the terms representing axial force and shear force contributions. This is shown in the next example.

Example 6.4.2   Find the horizontal displacement of the free end of the structure in Figure 6.11, but neglect the curvature correction terms. We make use of the results from the previous example and use equation 6.1.37 in the form

$$u_1 = \int_0^1 \frac{N\,dx}{AE} - \int_0^1 \frac{V\,dy}{\mu AG} + \int_0^1 \frac{M(y_1 - y)}{EJ}\,ds \tag{12}$$

This yields

$$u_1 = \frac{Hr}{AE} \int_0^{\pi/3} \cos^2 \beta\,d\beta + \frac{Hr}{\mu AG} \int_0^{\pi/3} \sin^2 \beta\,d\beta + \frac{Hr^3}{EJ} \int_0^{\pi/3} (\cos\beta - \cos 60°)^2\,d\beta \tag{13}$$

or

$$u_1 = 0.741 \frac{Hr}{AE} + 0.307 \frac{Hr}{\mu AG} + 0.137 \frac{Hr^3}{EJ}$$

Letting $J \approx I = A\rho^2$, we have

$$u_1 = \frac{Hr}{AE}\left[0.741 + 0.307\left(\frac{E}{\mu G}\right) + 0.137\left(\frac{r}{\rho}\right)^2\right] \tag{14}$$

For a rectangular cross section we have $\rho = 0.289d$, $\mu = \frac{2}{3}$ and using $G = 0.4E$, we reduce this to

$$u_1 = \frac{Hr}{AE}\left[\underset{\substack{\text{axial}\\\text{force}}}{0.741} + \underset{\substack{\text{shear}\\\text{force}}}{1.150} + \underset{\substack{\text{bending}\\\text{moment}}}{1.644\left(\frac{r}{d}\right)^2}\right] \tag{15}$$

Here the contribution of shear force is greater than that due to axial force. When $r > 3d$, the contribution of bending moment is more than ten times the contribution of shear or axial forces. When $r > 9d$, the contribution of axial force and shear force amounts to less than one percent of the total. In all but exceptional cases the effects of shear force are neglected in displacement computations.

Example 6.4.3   Find the vertical displacement at the free end of the structure in Figure 6.11, but neglect the curvature correction terms. We substitute into 6.1.38 to find

$$w_1 = \int_0^1 \frac{N\,dy}{AE} + \int_0^1 \frac{V\,dx}{\mu AG} - \int_0^1 \frac{M(x_1 - x)}{EJ}\,ds \tag{16}$$

or

$$w_1 = \left[\frac{Hr}{AE} - \frac{Hr}{\mu AG}\right]\int_0^{\pi/3} \sin\beta\cos\beta\,d\beta$$
$$+ \frac{Hr^3}{EJ}\int_0^{\pi/3} [\sin\beta(\cos\beta - 0.5) + 0.866(0.5 - \cos\beta)]\,d\beta \tag{17}$$

or

$$w_1 = \left[\frac{Hr}{AE} - \frac{Hr}{\mu AG} - \frac{Hr^3}{EJ}\right](0.375) - \frac{Hr^3}{EJ}(0.55) \tag{18}$$

Using again $J \approx I = A\rho^2$ and $\rho = 0.289d$, $\mu = \frac{2}{3}$, $G = 0.4E$, we find

$$w_1 = \frac{Hr}{AE} \left[\underset{\substack{\text{axial} \\ \text{force}}}{0.375} - \underset{\substack{\text{shear} \\ \text{force}}}{1.405} - \underset{\substack{\text{bending} \\ \text{moment}}}{2.100 \left(\frac{r}{d}\right)^2} \right] \tag{19}$$

Again it is evident that bending moment contributes the most to the displacement. The full importance of axial force effects are shown in the next problem.

Example 6.4.4 Find the amount of horizontal movement suffered by the right support of the structure shown in Figure 6.12. Neglect curvature corrections and shear force effects. The axis of the structure is parabolic and has the equation

$$y = -\frac{4b}{a^2} x(a - x) \tag{20}$$

We let the left support be station 0 and the right support be station 1. The displacement u_1 is then given by

$$u_1 = \int_0^1 \frac{N\,dx}{AE} + \int_0^1 \frac{M(y_1 - y)\,ds}{EI} \tag{21}$$

Due to the uniformly distributed load we have

$$M = \frac{q_0 x}{2}(a - x) \tag{22}$$

$$N = q_0 \left(\frac{a}{2} - x\right) \sin \alpha \tag{23}$$

$$V = q_0 \left(\frac{a}{2} - x\right) \cos \alpha \tag{24}$$

where α is the slope of the curve 6.4.20. Here the integrals become exceedingly difficult to evaluate and we are forced to use some method of numerical integration to find an answer. We, therefore, approach the problem by dividing the structure into a number of small units of equal dimension Δx as shown in Figure 6.13. Instead of integrals and dx elements, we now have finite sums Σ and Δx elements. We rewrite 6.4.21 to read

$$u_1 = \Sigma \frac{N\,\Delta x}{AE} + \Sigma \frac{M(y_1 - y)\,\Delta s}{EI} \tag{25}$$

The method is to calculate $N\,\Delta x/AE$ and $M(y_1 - y)\,\Delta s/EI$ for each element and sum the results to find u_1. It is evident that the smaller the value of Δx chosen, the more elements we will have and the more nearly exact will be our result. For convenience we use a tabular form as shown in Table 6.1. Note that values are calculated at the midpoint of each element. Since E, A, and I are constant throughout, they are not introduced in the table but only in the resulting sum.

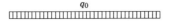

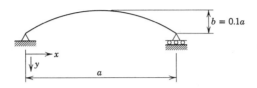

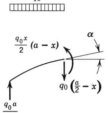

Figure 6.12

Thus we find

$$u_1 = -\frac{0.0630 q_0 a^2}{AE} + \frac{0.0068 q_0 a^2}{EI} \tag{26}$$

or

$$u_1 = \frac{q_0 a^2}{AE}\left[-0.0630 + \frac{0.0068 a^2}{\rho^2}\right] \tag{27}$$

It is clear that in this example the contribution of normal forces to the displacement will be greater than 10% of that due to bending moment only for arches with $a < 10\rho$. This is generally true when *flat arches* are considered. However, for *high arches*, that is, arches with large ratios of rise to span, the effect of normal force is even smaller compared with the effects of bending moment and is usually omitted entirely from consideration.

The effect of the normal forces is to compress the arch. Terms associated with normal forces are therefore called *rib shortening* terms.

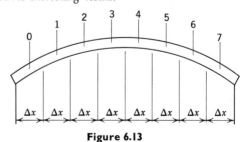

Figure 6.13

TABLE 6.1

Station	Δx	$\sin \alpha$	N	$N \Delta x$	$\tan \alpha$	Δs	M	$(y_1 - y)$	$M(y_1 - y) \Delta s$
0	$0.125a$	-0.331	$-0.1448q_0a$	$-0.0181q_0a^2$	-0.35	$0.132a$	$0.0292q_0a^2$	$0.0234a$	$0.0001q_0a^4$
1	$0.125a$	-0.243	$-0.0759q_0a$	$-0.0095q_0a^2$	-0.25	$0.129a$	$0.0761q_0a^2$	$0.0609a$	$0.0006q_0a^4$
2	$0.125a$	-0.148	$-0.0278q_0a$	$-0.0035q_0a^2$	-0.15	$0.126a$	$0.1074q_0a^2$	$0.0859a$	$0.0012q_0a^4$
3	$0.125a$	-0.050	$-0.0031q_0a$	$-0.0004q_0a^2$	-0.05	$0.125a$	$0.1230q_0a^2$	$0.0984a$	$0.0015q_0a^4$
4	$0.125a$	0.050	$-0.0031q_0a$	$-0.0004q_0a^2$	0.05	$0.125a$	$0.1230q_0a^2$	$0.0984a$	$0.0015q_0a^4$
5	$0.125a$	0.148	$-0.0278q_0a$	$-0.0035q_0a^2$	0.15	$0.126a$	$0.1074q_0a^2$	$0.0859a$	$0.0012q_0a^4$
6	$0.125a$	0.243	$-0.0759q_0a$	$-0.0095q_0a^2$	0.25	$0.129a$	$0.0761q_0a^2$	$0.0609a$	$0.0006q_0a^4$
7	$0.125a$	0.331	$-0.1448q_0a$	$-0.0181q_0a^2$	0.35	$0.132a$	$0.0292q_0a^2$	$0.0234a$	$0.0001q_0a^4$
				$\Sigma = -0.0630q_0a^2$					$\Sigma = 0.0068q_0a^4$

6.5 Indeterminate Stress Resultants

As was pointed out in § 6.4, displacements may be found in a direct manner whenever the stress resultants for any cross section can be determined by the consideration of statics alone. For structures having statically indeterminate stress resultants and a sufficient number of known displacement components, a direct use of the equations of Bresse is still possible.

It will be observed that for the statically determinate case all values of N, M, and V are known, hence the integrals in the equations of Bresse can be evaluated between two stations 0 and 1. Since six displacement components figure in the three equations it follows that if we know any three independent displacement components, the remaining three may be found.

In a similar manner, if we have a structure that is statically indeterminate to the third degree or less, we may use the equations of Bresse to find the indeterminate redundants provided we have information on the six components of displacement.

In the following examples, various typical problems are set up to illustrate the technique. Actual detailed solutions are left to the reader.

Example 6.5.1 Find the stress resultants at any cross section in the proving ring of Figure 6.14. In this example we neglect the curvature correction terms ($1/r$ terms), assuming that the depth of cross section will be small compared to the radius of curvature. From symmetry, we conclude that no shear forces are present on the horizontal axis. Only normal force and bending moment can occur there. The normal force, again from symmetry, will be $N = P/2$. We combine the normal force and bending moment into a single force N having an unknown eccentricity e as shown in Figure 6.15. The normal force, shear force, and bending moment can now be expressed at every cross section in terms of the known value of N and the unknown value of e as shown in Figure 6.16. If we

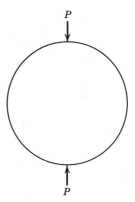

Figure 6.14

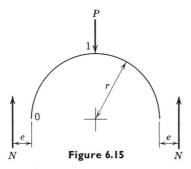

Figure 6.15

choose stations 0 and 1 as indicated on Figure 6.15, we note that $\theta_0 = \theta_1 = 0$ during deformation, and since this structure is indeterminate to the first degree we can get our solution by using only the first of the equations of Bresse. Thus

$$0 = \int_0^1 \frac{M \, ds}{EI} = \frac{N}{EI} \int_0^1 (r + e - r \sin \beta) r \, d\beta \tag{1}$$

After solving this equation for e we will be able to find explicit relations for all stress resultants. It will then be possible to use the remaining two equations of Bresse to find the horizontal and vertical components of displacement at any point.

Example 6.5.2   Find the reactions of the two-hinged bar in Figure 6.17. This is a structure that is also indeterminate to the first degree. We choose the co-ordinates as shown and let stations 0 and 1 be at the supports. Now if the supports were at the same elevation we would have $u_0 = u_1 = y_0 = y_1 = 0$, and neglecting shear and curvature correction terms we would have equation 6.1.37 reducing to

$$0 = \int_0^1 \frac{N \, dx}{AE} - \int_0^1 \frac{My \, ds}{EI} \tag{2}$$

N and M at any section may be expressed in terms of the single redundant and this gives us a single equation for solving the problem. When the supports are at different levels as shown in the figure, we may use the axes x and y as shown

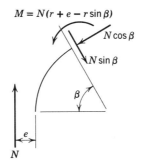

$$M = N(r + e - r \sin \beta)$$

Figure 6.16

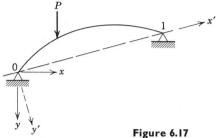

Figure 6.17

and the equations 6.1.37 and 6.1.38. Two unknowns will now be present, the redundant and the value of θ_0, and we may solve simultaneously for both. A much simpler approach, however, would be to rotate the axes so that the x-axis passes through the two supports. In this way a single equation will again suffice to solve the problem.

Example 6.5.3 Find the stress resultants in Figure 6.18. This structure is indeterminate to the second degree. Two redundant reactions must therefore be determined. We have $\theta_0 = u_0 = w_0 = u_1 = w_1 = 0$. The simultaneous solution of equations 6.1.37 and 6.1.38 will yield the solution.

Example 6.5.4 Find the stress resultants induced in the structure in Figure 6.19 due to a horizontal movement Δ at the right support. Again we shall have a single redundant in terms of which N, M, and V at all locations can be expressed. We know $u_0 = w_0 = w_1 = 0$ and $u_1 = +\Delta$. We use equation 6.1.37 to solve for the single redundant in terms of Δ. Note, however, that if there were a vertical settlement of the right support, the structure would rotate as a rigid body about the left support and no stresses would be induced.

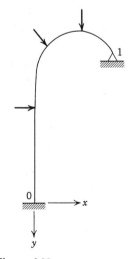

Figure 6.18

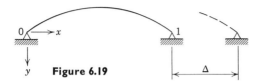

y   **Figure 6.19**

6.6   The Column Analogy—Fixed Members

A useful mathematical analogy, comparable to the conjugate beam used in the analysis of straight members, that leads to an economy of thought when solving curved members can be derived. We begin by considering the special problem of an unsymmetric member fixed at its ends, assuming that bending moments affect displacements far more than shear or normal forces. We also ignore curvature correction terms.

The equations of Bresse then take the form

$$\theta_1 = \theta_0 - \int_0^1 \frac{M \, ds}{EI} \tag{1}$$

$$u_1 = u_0 - (y_1 - y_0)\theta_0 + \int_0^1 \frac{M(y_1 - y) \, ds}{EI} \tag{2}$$

$$w_1 = w_0 + (x_1 - x_0)\theta_0 - \int_0^1 \frac{M(x_1 - x) \, ds}{EI} \tag{3}$$

If we let the fixed ends be stations 0 and 1, we find $\theta_1 = \theta_0 = u_1 = u_0 = w_1 = w_0 = 0$. The foregoing equations then become

$$\int_0^1 \frac{M \, ds}{EI} = 0 \tag{4}$$

$$\int_0^1 \frac{My \, ds}{EI} = 0 \tag{5}$$

$$\int_0^1 \frac{Mx \, ds}{EI} = 0 \tag{6}$$

where x and y are measured from the position of station 0 (the left support). See Figure 6.20(a). Since this is a structure that is indeterminate to the third degree, we may choose three redundant stress resultants and express all others in terms of these. We choose the reactions at the left support as redundants as shown in Figure 6.20(b). At any position on the structure the bending moment is given by

$$M = M_s + M_0 + H_0 y + V_0 x \tag{7}$$

where M_s represents the statical bending moment; that is, the bending

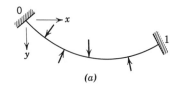

(a)

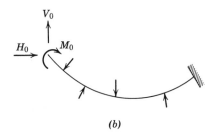

(b)   Figure 6.20

moment when the redundants are taken equal to zero. We substitute this expression into the three previous equations to find

$$\int_0^1 \frac{M_s \, ds}{EI} + M_0 \int_0^1 \frac{ds}{EI} + H_0 \int_0^1 \frac{y \, ds}{EI} + V_0 \int_0^1 \frac{x \, ds}{EI} = 0 \qquad (8)$$

$$\int_0^1 \frac{M_s y \, ds}{EI} + M_0 \int_0^1 \frac{y \, ds}{EI} + H_0 \int_0^1 \frac{y^2 \, ds}{EI} + V_0 \int_0^1 \frac{xy \, ds}{EI} = 0 \qquad (9)$$

$$\int_0^1 \frac{M_s x \, ds}{EI} + M_0 \int_0^1 \frac{x \, ds}{EI} + H_0 \int_0^1 \frac{yx \, ds}{EI} + V_0 \int_0^1 \frac{x^2 \, ds}{EI} = 0 \qquad (10)$$

For convenience let us now consider an area having a middle line that is the shape of the axis of the curved member and a thickness at any location that is equal to the value of $1/EI$ at the corresponding location in the curved member as shown in Figure 6.21. An element of area would then be given by

$$dA = \frac{ds}{EI} \qquad (11)$$

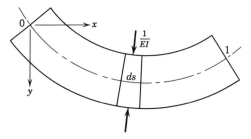

Figure 6.21

The first and second moments of this area with respect to the x and y axes would be

$$dm_x = y \, dA = \frac{y \, ds}{EI} \tag{12}$$

$$dm_y = x \, dA = \frac{x \, ds}{EI} \tag{13}$$

$$dI_x = y^2 \, dA = \frac{y^2 \, ds}{EI} \tag{14}$$

$$dI_y = x^2 \, dA = \frac{x^2 \, ds}{EI} \tag{15}$$

$$dI_{xy} = xy \, dA = \frac{xy \, ds}{EI} \tag{16}$$

When these elemental contributions are summed over the entire area, called the *elastic area*, we obtain

$$A = \int_0^1 \frac{ds}{EI} \tag{17}$$

$$m_x = \int_0^1 \frac{y \, ds}{EI} \tag{18}$$

$$m_y = \int_0^1 \frac{x \, ds}{EI} \tag{19}$$

$$I_x = \int_0^1 \frac{y^2 \, ds}{EI} \tag{20}$$

$$I_y = \int_0^1 \frac{x^2 \, ds}{EI} \tag{21}$$

$$I_{xy} = \int_0^1 \frac{xy \, ds}{EI} \tag{22}$$

Let us further imagine that this area is subjected to a distributed normal pressure. Let the intensity of pressure at any location on the middle line correspond to the value of the statical moment, M_s, at the corresponding location in the curved beam. Then the element load dN and its first moments lead to

$$N = \int_A dN = \int_A M_s \, dA = \int_A \frac{M_s \, ds}{EI} \tag{23}$$

$$M_x = \int_A dM_x = \int_A y \, dN = \int_A M_s y \, dA = \int_A \frac{M_s y \, ds}{EI} \tag{24}$$

$$M_y = \int_A dM_y = \int_A x \, dN = \int_A M_s x \, dA = \int_A \frac{M_s x \, ds}{EI} \tag{25}$$

We introduce these various symbols into 6.6.8, 6.6.9, and 6.6.10 to obtain

$$N + M_0 A + H_0 m_x + V_0 m_y = 0 \tag{26}$$

$$M_x + M_0 m_x + H_0 I_x + V_0 I_{xy} = 0 \tag{27}$$

$$M_y + M_0 m_y + H_0 I_{xy} + V_0 I_y = 0 \tag{28}$$

Now if we shift our origin so as to be at the centroid of the elastic area we find

$$m_x = m_y = 0 \tag{29}$$

and that M_x and M_y remain unchanged since couples may be shifted in their plane or into parallel planes without changing in value. Thus we find

$$N = -M_0 A \tag{30}$$

$$M_x = -H_0 I_x - V_0 I_{xy} \tag{31}$$

$$M_y = -H_0 I_{xy} - V_0 I_y \tag{32}$$

Comparing these with equation 2.2.11 where $a = -M_0$, $b = -H_0$, and $c = -V_0$, and where the z is now replaced by x, we find as was found for 2.2.12

$$M_0 = -\frac{N}{A} \tag{33}$$

$$H_0 = -\frac{M_x I_y - M_y I_{xy}}{I_x I_y - I_{xy}^2} \tag{34}$$

$$V_0 = -\frac{M_y I_x - M_x I_{xy}}{I_x I_y - I_{xy}^2} \tag{35}$$

We may rewrite 6.6.7 as

$$M = M_s - M_i \tag{36}$$

where

$$M_i = -(M_0 + H_0 y + V_0 x) \tag{37}$$

It will be recalled that this expression related to the redundants acting at the origin of coordinates, which was originally considered to be at the supports. When we move the origin to the centroid of the elastic area, we change the values of x and y as well as the values of M_0, H_0, and V_0. However, there will be no change in M_i.

This process is comparable to attaching a rigid ($EI = \infty$) arm to the structure at the left support and extending it to the centroid of the elastic area as shown in Figure 6.22. We see that for equilibrium we must have horizontal and vertical forces at the end of the bracket equal to H_0 and V_0, respectively. We also must have a couple acting that is not equal to the moment at the left support. In terms of these new redundants we see that equation 6.6.37 is still applicable if we consider M_0, H_0, and V_0 to be

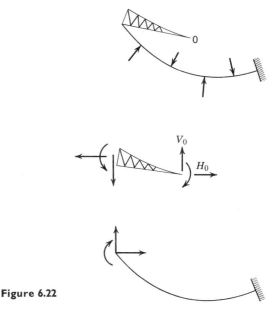

Figure 6.22

redundants acting at the elastic centroid. We substitute 6.6.33, 6.6.34, and
6.6.35 into 6.6.37 to obtain

$$M_i = \frac{N}{A} + \frac{M_x I_y - M_y I_{xy}}{I_x I_y - I_{xy}^2} y + \frac{M_y I_x - M_x I_{xy}}{I_x I_y - I_{xy}^2} x \qquad (38)$$

Term by term this expression is analogous to the expression 2.2.13 which
governs normal stress on a cross section acted on by a normal force and
bending moments about two axes. Since this is the problem encountered
in analyzing short posts, we speak of this method of solution as the
short-post analogy, or more usually the *column analogy*.

Briefly, we construct an elastic area corresponding to any given curved
beam, find its centroid, and load it with the statical moment diagram for
the beam. We then find the normal stress in the analogous column and let
this be M_i. Then from 6.6.36 we can find the bending moment at any location of the given beam.

The method works equally well for a straight horizontal beam or a
simple frame. For the straight beam we have the centroid of the elastic
area always on the x-axis; hence, $y = 0$ for all stations and $M_x = 0$
everywhere. We obtain

$$M_i = \frac{N}{A} + \frac{M_y}{I_y} x \qquad (39)$$

Several examples illustrate the method.

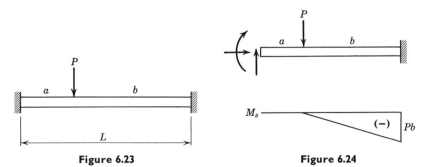

Figure 6.23   **Figure 6.24**

Example 6.6.1 Find the bending moments at the fixed ends of the beam in Figure 6.23. We begin by defining the redundants and determining the statical moment diagram. See Figure 6.24. The analogous column with its loading is now drawn in Figure 6.25. For this rectangular area we have

$$A = \frac{L}{EI}, \qquad I_x \approx 0, \qquad I_y = \frac{L^3}{12EI}$$

Since the moment diagram is negative, the load on the area is negative by 6.6.23.

$$N = -\tfrac{1}{2}(Pb)(b)\left(\frac{1}{EI}\right) = -\frac{Pb^2}{2EI} \tag{40}$$

This gives a negative force at a positive distance along the x-axis; hence a negative moment results.

$$M_y = -\left(\frac{Pb^2}{2EI}\right)\left(\frac{L}{2} - \frac{b}{3}\right) = -\frac{Pb^2(3L - 2b)}{12EI} = -\frac{Pb^2(3a + b)}{12EI} \tag{41}$$

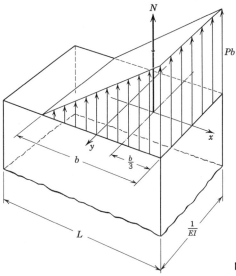

Figure 6.25

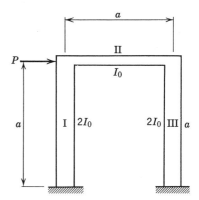

Figure 6.26

We substitute into 6.6.39 to get

$$M_i = -\frac{Pb^2}{2L} - \frac{Pb^2}{L^3}(3a + b)x \qquad (42)$$

At the left edge, $x = -L/2$, we have

$$[M_i]_{x = -L/2} = +\frac{Pb^2a}{L^2}$$

and by 6.6.36

$$[M]_{x = -L/2} = -\frac{Pb^2a}{L^2} \qquad (43)$$

Similarly, at the right edge, $x = +L/2$, we find

$$[M_i]_{x = +L/2} = -\frac{Pb^2}{L^2}(L + a) \qquad \text{and} \qquad [M]_{x = L/2} = -\frac{Pa^2b}{L^2} \qquad (44)$$

Example 6.6.2 Find the bending moments at the fixed ends of the simple bent in Figure 6.26. Here we have a symmetrical structure that gives rise to a symmetrical cross section of the analogous column as shown in Figure 6.27.

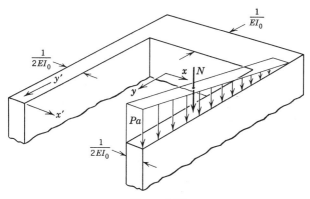

Figure 6.27

We find the centroid of the elastic area and choose the x and y axes as shown. The following tabular form is used to keep the bookkeeping straight in locating the centroid.

Segment	Area A	x'	Ax'	y'	Ay'
I	$\dfrac{a}{2EI_0}$	0	0	$\dfrac{-a}{2}$	$-\dfrac{a^2}{4EI_0}$
II	$\dfrac{a}{EI_0}$	$\dfrac{a}{2}$	$\dfrac{a^2}{2EI_0}$	$-a$	$-\dfrac{a^2}{EI_0}$
III	$\dfrac{a}{2EI_0}$	a	$\dfrac{a^2}{2EI_0}$	$\dfrac{-a}{2}$	$-\dfrac{a^2}{4EI_0}$
Σ	$2a/EI_0$		a^2/EI_0		$-3a^2/2EI_0$

$$\bar{x} = \frac{\Sigma \, Ax'}{\Sigma \, A} = \frac{a}{2}, \qquad \bar{y} = \frac{\Sigma \, Ay'}{\Sigma \, A} = \frac{-3a}{4}, \qquad A = \frac{2a}{EI_0}$$

The moments and products of inertia are conveniently found by using the following table.

Segment	$I_{x(cg)}$	$A'y_{cg}^2$	$I_{x(cg)} + A'y_{cg}^2$	$I_{y(cg)}$	$A'x_{cg}^2$	$I_{y(cg)} + A'x_{cg}^2$
I	$\dfrac{a^3}{24EI_0}$	$\dfrac{a^3}{32EI_0}$	$\dfrac{7a^3}{96EI_0}$	≈ 0	$\dfrac{a^3}{8EI_0}$	$\dfrac{3a^3}{24EI_0}$
II	≈ 0	$\dfrac{a^3}{16EI_0}$	$\dfrac{6a^3}{96EI_0}$	$\dfrac{a^3}{12EI_0}$	0	$\dfrac{2a^3}{24EI_0}$
III	$\dfrac{a^3}{24EI_0}$	$\dfrac{a^3}{32EI_0}$	$\dfrac{7a^3}{96EI_0}$	≈ 0	$\dfrac{a^3}{8EI_0}$	$\dfrac{3a^3}{24EI_0}$
			$I_x = 5a^3/24EI_0$			$I_y = a^3/3EI_0$

From symmetry, $I_{xy} = 0$. The statical moment diagram is found by freeing the left support. See Figure 6.27. The axial force N is the volume under the M diagram and is equal to

$$N = (Pa)(a/2)\left(\frac{1}{2EI_0}\right) = \frac{Pa^2}{4EI_0}$$

Note that the statical bending momei.. is positive; hence, the force N is positive. The center of pressure of the single N force is $x = a/2$, $y = +(3a/4 - a/3) = +5a/12$. Thus

$$M_x = \frac{Pa^2}{4EI_0}\left(+\frac{5a}{12}\right) = +\frac{5Pa^3}{48EI_0}$$

$$M_y = \frac{Pa^2}{4EI_0}\left(\frac{a}{2}\right) = \frac{Pa^3}{8EI_0}$$

The indeterminate moment, M_i, at any location is

$$M_i = \frac{Pa}{8} + \frac{P}{2}y + \frac{3P}{8}x$$

The true moment is given by $M = M_s - M_i$. At the left support we have

$$M = 0 - \left[\frac{Pa}{8} + \left(\frac{P}{2}\right)\left(+\frac{3a}{4}\right) + \left(\frac{3P}{8}\right)\left(-\frac{a}{2}\right)\right] = -\frac{5Pa}{16}$$

At the right support we have

$$M = Pa - \left[\frac{Pa}{8} + \frac{P}{2}\left(+\frac{3a}{4}\right) + \frac{3P}{8}\left(\frac{a}{2}\right)\right] = +\frac{5Pa}{16}$$

Example 6.6.3 Find the bending moment at the crown of the circular arch shown in Figure 6.28a. The moment of inertia of the arch varies from a value of I_0 at the crown to a value of $2I_0$ at the supports. The elastic area likewise has a circular axis. We shall use a numerical method of solving this problem with our results presented in tabular form.

We break the arch into ten segments of equal length Δs; that is, each segment subtends an angle of 18°. The center of the left-most segment is denoted as station 1 with the other segment centers numbered in sequence thereafter. Stations are thus located at θ values of $-81°$, $-63°$, $-45°$, $-27°$, $-9°$, $+9°$,

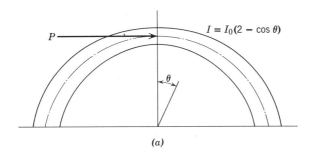

(a)

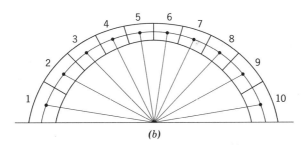

(b)

Figure 6.28

$+27°$, $+45°$, $+63°$, and $+81°$. The total area is given by the sum of the elemental areas. Each has a length $\Delta s = a\theta$ where $\theta = 18° = 0.1\pi$ radian. Thus Δs is a constant, $\Delta s = 0.1\pi a$. E is also a constant so we write

$$A = \sum \frac{\Delta s}{EI} = \frac{\Delta s}{E} \sum \frac{1}{I} = \frac{0.1\pi a}{E} \sum \frac{1}{I} \tag{45}$$

The centroid will be on the symmetry axis and a distance $\bar{y}$ from the base. Each elemental area lies a distance $y = -a \cos \theta$ from the base. The value of $\bar{y}$ is thus given by

$$A\bar{y} = m_x = \sum y' \, \Delta A = \sum \frac{y' \Delta s}{EI} = \frac{\Delta s}{E} \sum \frac{y'}{I} \tag{46}$$

or

$$\bar{y} = \frac{\sum - \dfrac{a \cos \theta}{I}}{\sum \dfrac{1}{I}} \tag{47}$$

These are found from Table 6.2 to be

$$A = 2.4210a/EI_0 \tag{48}$$

$$\bar{y}' = -0.7020a \tag{49}$$

The centroidal coordinates of each station are given as x and y. The moments and products of inertia are given by

$$I_x = \sum y^2 \, \Delta A = \frac{\Delta s}{E} \sum \frac{y^2}{I} \tag{50}$$

$$I_y = \sum x^2 \, \Delta A = \frac{\Delta s}{E} \sum \frac{x^2}{I} \tag{51}$$

$$I_{xy} = \sum xy \, \Delta A = \frac{\Delta s}{E} \sum \frac{xy}{I} \tag{52}$$

Moments of inertia of elemental areas about their own centroidal axes have been neglected. We find

$$I_x = 0.1974a^3/EI_0 \tag{53}$$

$$I_y = 1.0304a^3/EI_0 \tag{54}$$

$$I_{xy} = 0 \tag{55}$$

all from Table 6.2.

Table 6.3 gives the loading characteristics for the analogous column. The given arch is made statically determinate by freeing the left support. The statically determinate bending moment at any station is then given by $Pa(1 - \cos \theta)$ and is positive at every station. The total normal force on the elastic area is thus positive also.

$$N = \sum \frac{M_s \, \Delta s}{EI} = \frac{Pa \, \Delta s}{E} \sum \frac{1 - \cos \theta}{I} \tag{56}$$

TABLE 6.2

Station	θ	$\cos\theta$	I	$\dfrac{1}{I}$	$\dfrac{y'}{I}$	y	x	$\dfrac{y^2}{I}$	$\dfrac{x^2}{I}$
1	-81	0.1564	$1.8436I_0$	$0.5424/I_0$	$-0.0848a/I_0$	$+0.5456a$	$-0.9877a$	$0.1615a^2/I_0$	$0.5292a^2/I_0$
2	-63	0.4540	$1.5460I_0$	$0.6468/I_0$	$-0.2936a/I_0$	$+0.2480a$	$-0.8910a$	$0.0398a^2/I_0$	$0.5135a^2/I_0$
3	-45	0.7071	$1.2929I_0$	$0.7735/I_0$	$-0.5469a/I_0$	$-0.0051a$	$-0.7071a$	$0.0000a^2/I_0$	$0.3867a^2/I_0$
4	-27	0.8910	$1.1090I_0$	$0.9017/I_0$	$-0.8034a/I_0$	$-0.1890a$	$-0.4540a$	$0.0322a^2/I_0$	$0.1859a^2/I_0$
5	-9	0.9877	$1.0123I_0$	$0.9878/I_0$	$-0.9757a/I_0$	$-0.2857a$	$-0.1564a$	$0.0806a^2/I_0$	$0.0242a^2/I_0$
6	$+9$	0.9877	$1.0123I_0$	$0.9878/I_0$	$-0.9757a/I_0$	$-0.2857a$	$+0.1564a$	$0.0806a^2/I_0$	$0.0242a^2/I_0$
7	$+27$	0.8910	$1.1090I_0$	$0.9017/I_0$	$-0.8034a/I_0$	$-0.1890a$	$+0.4540a$	$0.0322a^2/I_0$	$0.1859a^2/I_0$
8	$+45$	0.7071	$1.2929I_0$	$0.7735/I_0$	$-0.5469a/I_0$	$-0.0051a$	$+0.7071a$	$0.0000a^2/I_0$	$0.3867a^2/I_0$
9	$+63$	0.4540	$1.5460I_0$	$0.6468/I_0$	$-0.2936a/I_0$	$+0.2480a$	$+0.8910a$	$0.0398a^2/I_0$	$0.5135a^2/I_0$
10	$+81$	0.1564	$1.8436I_0$	$0.5424/I_0$	$-0.0848a/I_0$	$+0.5456a$	$+0.9877a$	$0.1615a^2/I_0$	$0.5292a^2/I_0$
				$\Sigma = 7.7044/I_0$	$\Sigma = -5.4088a/I_0$			$\Sigma = 0.6282a^2/I_0$	$\Sigma = 3.2790a^2/I_0$

$$A = \sum \frac{\Delta s}{EI} = \frac{\Delta s}{E} \sum \frac{1}{I} = \frac{0.1\pi a}{E}\left(\frac{7.7044}{I_0}\right) = \frac{2.4210a}{EI_0}, \qquad \bar{y}' = -0.7020a, \qquad m_x = \sum \frac{y'\,\Delta s}{EI} = \frac{\Delta s}{E} \sum \frac{y'}{I} = \frac{-1.6997a^2}{EI_0}$$

$$I_x = \sum \frac{y^2\,\Delta s}{EI} = \frac{0.1\pi a}{E} \sum \frac{y^2}{I} = \frac{0.1974a^3}{EI_0}, \qquad I_{xy} = 0, \qquad I_y = \frac{0.1\pi a}{E} \sum \frac{x^2}{I} = \frac{1.0304a^3}{EI_0}$$

TABLE 6.3

Station	M_s	M_s/I	$M_s x/I$	$M_s y/I$
1	0	0	0	0
2	0	0	0	0
3	0	0	0	0
4	0	0	0	0
5	0	0	0	0
6	$0.0123Pa$	$0.0122Pa/I_0$	$0.0019Pa^2/I_0$	$-0.0035Pa^2/I_0$
7	$0.1090Pa$	$0.0983Pa/I_0$	$0.0446Pa^2/I_0$	$-0.0186Pa^2/I_0$
8	$0.2929Pa$	$0.2266Pa/I_0$	$0.1602Pa^2/I_0$	$-0.0012Pa^2/I_0$
9	$0.5460Pa$	$0.3532Pa/I_0$	$0.3147Pa^2/I_0$	$+0.0876Pa^2/I_0$
10	$0.8436Pa$	$0.4576Pa/I_0$	$0.4520Pa^2/I_0$	$+0.2497Pa^2/I_0$
		$1.1479Pa/I_0$	$0.9734Pa^2/I_0$	$+0.3140Pa^2/I_0$

The acting couples are

$$M_x = \sum \frac{M_s y' \, \Delta s}{EI} = \frac{Pa \, \Delta s}{E} \sum \frac{y'(1 - \cos \theta)}{I} \tag{57}$$

$$M_y = \sum \frac{M_s x' \, \Delta s}{EI} = \frac{Pa \, \Delta s}{E} \sum \frac{x'(1 - \cos \theta)}{I} \tag{58}$$

They are found from Table 6.3 to be

$$N = +0.3607Pa^2/EI_0 \tag{59}$$

$$M_y = +0.3058Pa^3/EI_0 \tag{60}$$

$$M_x = +0.0987Pa^3/EI_0 \tag{61}$$

Using these values we substitute into 6.6.38 to find the indeterminate moment M_i in the arch. Thus

$$M_i = \frac{N}{A} + \frac{M_x}{I_x} y + \frac{M_y}{I_y} x \tag{62}$$

$$M_i = \frac{0.3607}{2.4210} Pa + \frac{0.0987}{0.1974} Py + \frac{0.3058}{0.2968} Px \tag{63}$$

$$M_i = 0.1490Pa + 0.5000Py + 0.2968Px \tag{64}$$

At the crown ($x = 0$, $y = -0.4232a$)

$$M_i = 0.1490Pa + 0.5(-0.4232)Pa$$

$$M_i = -0.0626Pa \tag{65}$$

Thus

$$M = M_s - M_i = 0 - (-0.0626Pa) = +0.0626Pa \tag{66}$$

6.7 Column Analogy—Hinged Members

For the fixed members treated in the previous section there were three redundants present, corresponding to the fact that the members were statically indeterminate to the third degree. This meant that all three of the equations of Bresse were required in obtaining a solution. The equations used were those neglecting rib shortening, shear, and curvature effects as given by 6.6.1, 6.6.2, and 6.6.3. For the fixed arch these reduced to 6.6.4, 6.6.5, and 6.6.6.

When a *single hinge* is present the number of redundants reduces to two. We choose these as a set of mutually perpendicular forces X and Y acting at the single hinge. They may be the axial force and shear force present but need not necessarily be. It will be convenient to choose the origin of coordinates at the hinge with the x and y directions and the directions of the redundant forces positive as shown in Figure 6.29a. The bending moment at any location will then be given by

$$M = M_s + Xy + Yx \tag{1}$$

where M_s is the bending moment in the statically determinate structure in the absence of X and Y. Equations 6.6.1, 6.6.2, and 6.6.3 can best be rewritten for our present purpose in the combined form

$$u_1 = u_0 + y_0\theta_0 - y_1\theta_1 + \int_0^1 \frac{My\,ds}{EI} \tag{2}$$

$$w_1 = w_0 - x_0\theta_0 + x_1\theta_1 + \int_0^1 \frac{Mx\,ds}{EI} \tag{3}$$

A typical example of a single hinge member is shown in Figure 6.29b. Here we have $u_0 = w_0 = u_1 = w_1 = \theta_1 = 0$. Also using the axes shown, we have $y_0 = x_0 = 0$. Equations 6.7.2 and 6.7.3 now become

$$\int_0^1 \frac{My\,ds}{EI} = 0 \tag{4}$$

$$\int_0^1 \frac{Mx\,ds}{EI} = 0 \tag{5}$$

Substituting 6.7.1 in the foregoing equations and using symbols from the previous section, we find

$$M_x + XI_x + YI_{xy} = 0 \tag{6}$$

$$M_y + XI_{xy} + YI_y = 0 \tag{7}$$

We can interpret these in the language of the column analogy by noting that at the hinge the stiffness (EI) is zero since hinges can offer no resistance to relative rotation. This gives a value of $ds/EI = \infty$ at the location

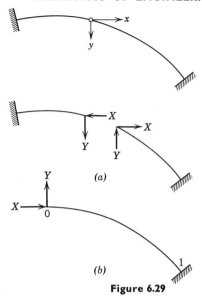

Figure 6.29

of the hinge in the analogous column. Consequently A must be ∞. With the origin of coordinates chosen at the hinge, the first moments of the total elastic area about the two axes must be zero and hence $m_x = m_y = 0$. Equations 6.6.26, 6.6.27, and 6.6.28 are thus seen to reduce to 6.7.6 and 6.7.7. Equation 6.6.38 then reduces to

$$M_i = \frac{M_x I_y - M_y I_{xy}}{I_x I_y - I_{xy}{}^2} y + \frac{M_y I_x - M_x I_{xy}}{I_x I_y - I_{xy}{}^2} x \tag{8}$$

where as before

$$M = M_s - M_i \tag{9}$$

When *two hinges* are present, there will be but a single redundant. For convenience we choose the x-axis passing through both hinges as shown for the typical structure in Figure 6.30. Here we have chosen as a redundant the Y force acting at the left hinge and thus can write

$$M = M_s + Yx \tag{10}$$

Equation 6.7.2 becomes

$$\int_0^1 \frac{Mx \, ds}{EI} = 0 \tag{11}$$

Substituting 6.7.10 into 6.7.11 and using the symbols from the previous section we find

$$M_y + YI_y = 0 \tag{12}$$

This compares with 6.6.27 when we set $m_x = 0$ and $I_{xy} = 0$. In the language

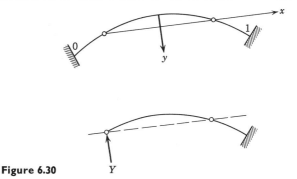

Figure 6.30

of the column analogy, we observe that the total elastic area is again infinitely large and that the axis passing through the two hinges is a principal
axis (the axis about which the moment of inertia is a minimum). The
value of I_y, however, must be finite. Equation 6.6.38 becomes

$$M_i = \frac{M_y}{I_y} x \qquad (13)$$

Example 6.7.1   Find the fixed end moments of the beam in Figure 6.31a. EI
is constant except at the hinge where it is zero, giving rise to the infinite strip
shown in Figure 6.31b. The analogous column will have $A = \infty$ and the centroid
at the hinge location. Axes will be used as shown. We find $I_y = \frac{1}{3}(1/EI)a^3 +$
$\frac{1}{3}(1/EI)(2a)^3 = 3a^3/EI$, $I_x = \infty$, $I_{xy} = 0$. Letting the shear at the hinge be the

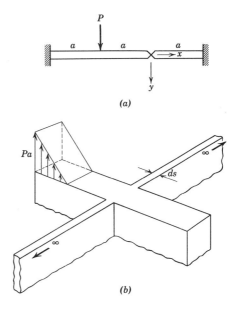

(a)

Figure 6.31   (b)

Figure 6.32

redundant, we load the column as shown in Figure 6.31b, remembering that a negative moment corresponds to a negative pressure. We find $N = Pa^2/2EI$, $M_x = 0$, and $M_y = +5Pa^3/6EI$. Thus

$$M_i = \frac{M_y}{I_y}x = \tfrac{5}{18}Px \tag{14}$$

and

$$M = M_s - \tfrac{5}{18}Px \tag{15}$$

At the left support $M_s = -Pa$, thus $M = -Pa + \tfrac{5}{9}Pa = -\tfrac{4}{9}Pa$. At the right end $M_s = 0$, thus $M = -\tfrac{5}{18}Pa$.

Example 6.7.2 To demonstrate that the statically determinate structure may be taken in any fashion without changing the result, repeat the foregoing problem, letting the moment at the right support be the redundant. The statical moment diagram, M_s, will be the same as before as shown in Figure 6.32. The column section will also be the same; hence, the final results will be the same.

Example 6.7.3 Write the bending moment equation for any point on the frame in Figure 6.33. We select our axis so as to have both hinges on one axis. These axes will then be principal axes in the analogous column. We put the left support on rollers to make the structure statically determinate. The analogous column loaded with the statical moment diagram is shown in Figure 6.34. Note the thin infinite area passing between the hinges. We find $N = -3Pa^2/2EI$, $M_x = +(Pa^2/2)(0.707)(5a/3EI + 8a/3EI) = +1.532(Pa^3/EI)$. The moment of inertia of a thin rectangular area about skewed centroidal axes is as shown in Figure 6.35. Using the parallel axis theorem, we find

$$I_x = 2\left[\tfrac{1}{12}(2a)\left(\frac{1}{EI}\right)(1.414a)^2 + \left(\frac{2a}{EI}\right)(0.707a)^2\right] = \frac{8a^3}{3EI} \tag{16}$$

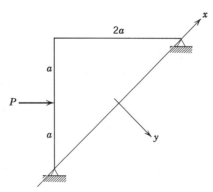

Figure 6.33

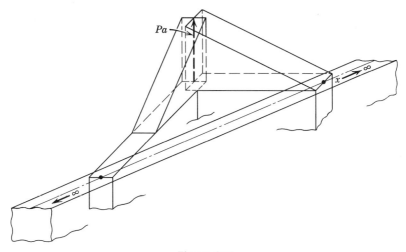

Figure 6.34

$$I_x = \frac{Aa^2}{12},$$

$$I_y = \frac{Ab^2}{12},$$

$$\text{and } I_{xy} = \frac{-Aab}{12}.$$

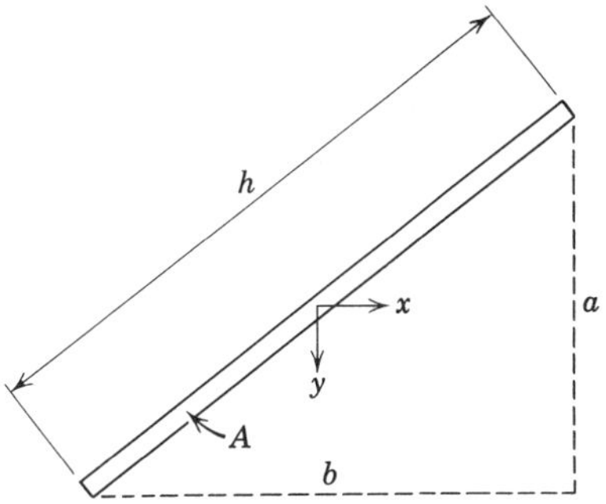

Figure 6.35

We now find

$$M_i = \frac{M_x}{I_x} y = +0.575Py \tag{17}$$

and

$$M = M_s - 0.575Py \tag{18}$$

At the rigid joint, for example, $M_s = -Pa$, $y = -1.414a$, and

$$M = -Pa + 0.575P(1.414a) = -0.187Pa \tag{19}$$

6.8 Column Analogy—General Summary

The column analogy is seen to be a natural consequence of the three equations of Bresse when axial force, shear force, and curvature are considered to be negligibly small. In using this special technique, we begin by making the structure statically determinate (and stable) and finding the associated moment diagram. The analogous column is now drawn with a width equal to the value of $1/EI$ for the member at every location. The centerline of the column section corresponds to the axis of the given member. The geometric properties of the cross section are then found: A, m_x, m_y, I_x, I_y, and I_{xy}. A hinge is considered to correspond to an infinite area and the geometric properties reflect this. Whenever a hinge is present, $A = \infty$. $I_{xy} = 0$ if an axis passes through two hinges.

The statical moment diagram, M_s, becomes the load diagram for the column. When M_s is negative the associated pressure is negative (acts upward). For the column, we then find N, M_x, and M_y.

Having the load and geometric properties, we then find the equation for the indeterminate moment, M_i, at any location. The coordinates (x, y) substituted into this expression yield the value of M_i at that point. The true value is then given by $M_s - M_i$.

The method is valid for elastic members when the indeterminacy does not exceed the third degree.

6.9 Curved Structures in Space

The approach to curved structures in space is not unlike that used for plane structures. For plane structures there could be as many as three redundants, and hence three equations of condition or deformation were needed to supplement the three equations of statics. These equations were supplied through the equations of Bresse. A member in space may be indeterminate to as much as the sixth degree and thus require six equations of condition, to obtain a complete solution to a given problem. The presence of symmetry or other special conditions may reduce the indeterminacy.

To fix ideas, we consider a member that lies in a plane and is fixed against all rotation and translation at its ends. When the applied forces lie in the plane of the member as shown in Figure 6.36, we have the problem treated

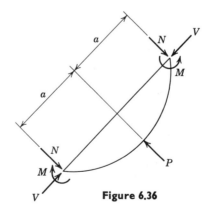

Figure 6.36

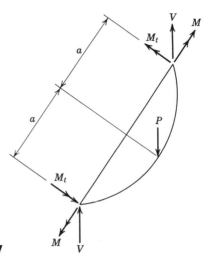

Figure 6.37

in §6.1. The stress resultants present consist of two components of force at any section lying in the plane of the member and a couple represented by a vector normal to the plane of the member. Since no other stress resultants come into play, the number of redundants is, at most, three. If the member is symmetrical as regards geometry, material, and loading, we note that the forces N will be equal to one-half the applied load, that the forces V and couples M will be equal but of unknown magnitude. Symmetry has thus reduced the indeterminacy to the second degree.

When the same member is subjected to a force normal to its plane and symmetrically placed as shown in Figure 6.37, the stress resultants will consist of shear forces normal to the plane of the member and bending and twisting couples represented by vectors in the plane of the member. The shear forces will each be equal to $P/2$ due to symmetry. Furthermore, it should be noted that no twisting moment occurs on the cross section cut by the symmetry plane. This gives us a special condition and reduces the indeterminacy to the first degree. If we can find the bending moment at the load point, all other stress resultants can be found from statics.

The equations of Bresse for each of the plane problems were found using the method of virtual work with the structure loaded as shown in Figure 6.38 as the system II. Energy associated with axial force, shear force, and bending moment was considered although the first two of these were seen to be negligibly small in some instances.

For the new problem we choose as system II the structures loaded as in Figure 6.39. Energy due to shear force, bending moment, and twisting moment will be stored in this structure. We shall neglect the contribution of shear.

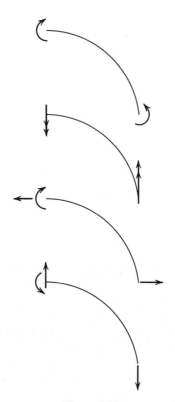

Figure 6.38

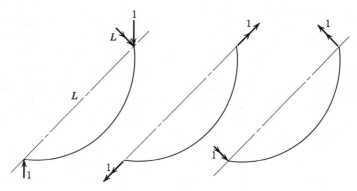

Figure 6.39

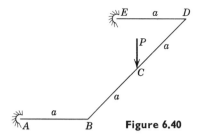

Figure 6.40

Example 6.9.1   Find the stress resultants in the balcony frame of Figure 6.40. A free body of the structure is shown in Figure 6.41. Since there is no twisting moment on the section cut by the plane of symmetry, we are able to express all stress resultants in terms of a single unknown M_0. Let us consider each of the Figures 6.39 in turn and see which is best suited for the problem. Beginning with the first we have Figure 6.42, and find the following:

$$AB: \quad m = x \qquad M = -\frac{P}{2}(a - x)$$

$$t = 0 \qquad T = M_0 \tag{1}$$

$$BC: \quad m = y \qquad M = M_0 + \frac{P}{2}y$$

$$t = -a \qquad T = 0 \tag{2}$$

$$CD: \quad m = y \qquad M = M_0 + Pa - \frac{Py}{2}$$

$$t = -a \qquad T = 0 \tag{3}$$

$$ED: \quad m = -x \qquad M = -\frac{P}{2}(a - x)$$

$$t = -2a \qquad T = -\dot{M}_0 \tag{4}$$

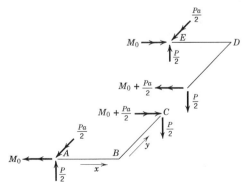

Figure 6.41

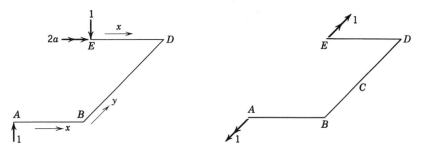

Figure 6.42   **Figure 6.43**

Now using the method of virtual work, we find

$$\frac{1}{EI}\int_0^a (x)\left(-\frac{P}{2}\right)(a-x)\,dx + \frac{1}{EI}\int_0^a y\left(M_0 + \frac{P}{2}y\right)dy$$

$$+ \frac{1}{EI}\int_a^{2a} (y)\left(M_0 + Pa - \frac{Py}{2}\right)dy$$

$$+ \frac{1}{EI}\int_0^a (-x)\left(-\frac{P}{2}\right)(a-x)\,dx + \frac{1}{GC}\int_0^a (-M_0)(-2a)\,dx = 0 \qquad (5)$$

This yields

$$M_0 = -\frac{Pa}{4\left[1 + \dfrac{EI}{GC}\right]} \qquad (6)$$

If instead of the first of Figures 6.39 we use the second, we have Figure 6.43. The method of virtual work now requires

$$
\begin{array}{llll}
AB: & m = -1 & CD: & m = 0 \\
 & t = 0 & & t = 1 \qquad\qquad (7)
\end{array}
$$

$$
\begin{array}{llll}
BC: & m = 0 & ED: & m = 1 \\
 & t = 1 & & t = 0 \qquad\qquad (8)
\end{array}
$$

This gives $0 = 0$ and hence no useful information.

Now using the third of Figures 6.39 as shown in Figure 6.44 we get the same result given by 6.9.6.

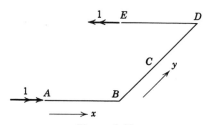

Figure 6.44

Problems

6.1.1 Show that an equation equivalent to 6.1.12 would have been obtained if, instead of Figure 6.4 being used as system II, we use the following figure.

Problem 6.1.1

6.1.2 Show that consideration of the following as system II will yield the same equation as 6.1.17.

Problem 6.1.2

6.1.3 Derive an appropriate equation using the following as system II and show that this is not independent of the three equations 6.1.12, 6.1.17, and 6.1.21. That is, it can be derived from these three.

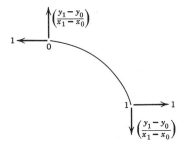

Problem 6.1.3

6.2.1 Support A of the following structure is displaced to the right 1 in. and downward 1 in. and is rotated clockwise through a 0.5° angle. What are the displacement and rotation components of B? $a = 50$ in.

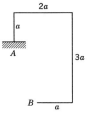

Problem 6.2.1

6.2.2   Find the horizontal displacement of joint C if bar AB is caused to rotate clockwise through an angle of $1°$.

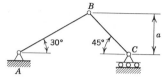

Problem 6.2.2

6.3.1   Use the second moment-area theorem to find the deflection at the free end of a cantilever beam loaded with a force P at mid-span. Neglect shear.

6.3.2   Use the first moment-area theorem to find the end slopes and the second moment-area theorem to find the mid-span deflection of the following beam.

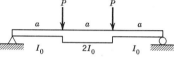

Problem 6.3.2

6.3.3   Use the equations of Bresse to find the free end displacements of the following structure.

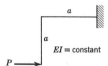

Problem 6.3.3

6.4.1   For the structure of Example 6.4.4, let the moment of inertia at the crown be I_c and let the moment of inertia at any other location be given by $I = I_c/\cos \alpha$. Find u_1 for this case. Consider effects due only to bending moment.

6.4.2   Find the horizontal displacement of the two hinged circular arch shown. Consider only bending and axial force effects. Neglect curvature.

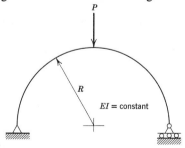

Problem 6.4.2

6.4.3   Find the amount of rotation at the free end of the following structure. Neglect nothing. $J = 1.05I$ $I = 10^{-5}a^4$, $A = 10^{-2}a^2$.

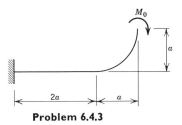

Problem 6.4.3

6.5.1 Find the reactions at support BB of the following structures. $EI =$ constant. Neglect shear.

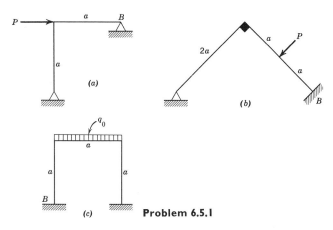

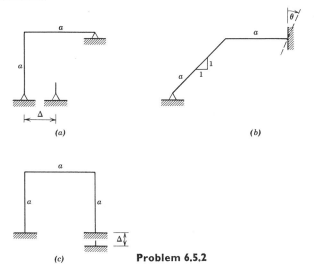

(c)   **Problem 6.5.1**

6.5.2 Find the reactions associated with the impressed displacements shown. EI = constant.

(a)   (b)

(c)   **Problem 6.5.2**

6.5.3 Find the stress resultants for a right circular pipe subjected to an internal fluid pressure of p_0.

6.5.4 Find the amount of change in the pipe diameter of Problem 6.5.3.

6.6.1 Sketch the elastic areas for the following members and find their geometric properties (area, centroid, moments of inertia, and products of inertia). Use initial reference axes as shown.

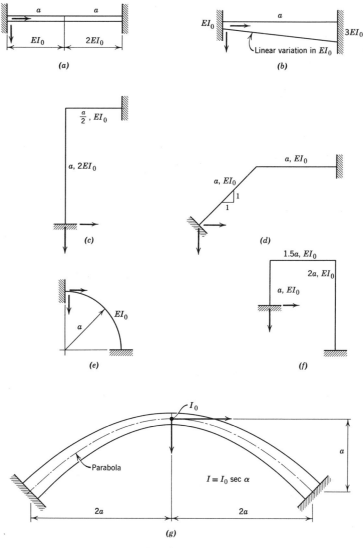

Problem 6.6.1

6.6.2   Find the fixed end moments for the following beams. EI is constant throughout. Let the left end be free in the statically determinate structures.

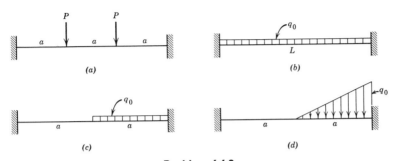

(a)   *(b)*

(c)   *(d)*

Problem 6.6.2

6.6.3   Repeat Problem 6.6.2(*b*) but let the right end be free in the primary structure. Compare results.

6.6.4   Repeat Problem 6.6.2(*b*) but let the statically determinate structure be a simply supported beam. Do the results still agree?

6.6.5   Find the stress resultants at the top of the right column in Problem 6.6.1(*f*) due to a uniformly distributed load q_0 acting to the right all along the length of the left column.

6.6.6   Find the reactions of Problem 6.6.1(*g*) due to a concentrated vertical load P acting at the right quarter point.

6.6.7   Follow through equations 6.6.1, 6.6.2, and 6.6.3 and determine the nature of the load on the analogous column due only to a displacement θ_0 of the support O.

6.6.8   Repeat foregoing problem for a displacement w_0 at the support O.

6.7.1   Find the moments due to a concentrated load P at mid-span at the ends of a uniform beam having the left end hinged and the right end fixed.

6.7.2   A beam is fixed at both ends. Its length is L and a hinge is located a distance nL from the left support where n is a pure number. A rotation θ_0 of the left support occurs due to some unspecified disturbance. Find the moment induced at the left support due to this rotation. Plot a curve of moment at left support versus n.

6.7.3   Find the reactions of the structure shown below.

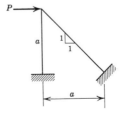

Problem 6.7.3

6.7.4 Find the points of inflection in the columns of the structure shown below. How will they shift if the right support is hinged rather than the left?

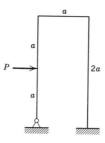

Problem 6.7.4

6.7.5 Find the reactions of the two-hinged arch shown below. Take advantage of symmetry in finding the answer. *EI* is constant throughout. Divide arch into 12 segments of 5° each in finding the solution.

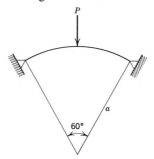

Problem 6.7.5

6.9.1 Find the reactions of the circular arch balcony beam shown below.

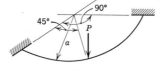

Problem 6.9.1

6.9.2 Find the reactions of the beam of Problem 6.9.1 due to a uniformly distributed load of q_0 along the beam.

6.9.3 Find the reactions of the gable frame shown below.

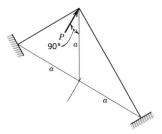

Problem 6.9.3

6.9.4 Repeat the Example 6.9.1 with the load at the third point of the main member.

6.9.5 Prove that the twisting moment is indeed zero on a section of a balcony beam cut by a plane of symmetry.

7 SLOPE-DEFLECTION EQUATIONS AND THE METHOD OF MOMENT DISTRIBUTION

7.1 Introduction

The general method of redundant reactions becomes long and tedious for highly indeterminate structures. For example, in Figure 7.1 we see that there are twelve possible reaction components resulting in the need for twelve equations. Three of these equations are given by the laws of statics and the other nine must be derived from deformation or energy considerations. Although the solution of nine simultaneous equations is certainly not impossible, other methods of solution are usually used that are more convenient for normal use.

The classical slope-deflection equations and the method of moment distribution derived from them are discussed in this chapter. The first leads to a set of simultaneous algebraic equations expressed in terms of a few key

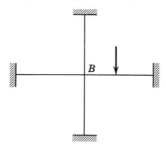

Figure 7.1

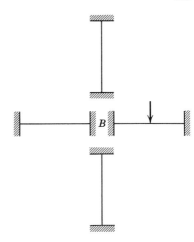

Figure 7.2

unknowns. The second is in reality a mechanical method of successive convergence for solving these equations that leads to a considerable economy in thought and time.

7.2 Slope-Deflection Equations

Let us redraw Figure 7.1 as Figure 7.2. Here we have broken the structure into four fixed end beams. The fixed end moments of these beams can be readily derived or found from published tables. Let us examine the consequences of changing the structure from that of Figure 7.1 to Figure 7.2. In Figure 7.2, no rotation of joint B is possible; hence the slopes of members framing into B remain unchanged under load. In Figure 7.1, on the other hand, some rotation is possible, which gives rise to changes in slope as indicated in Figure 7.3.

These changes in slope lead to changes in bending moments at the ends

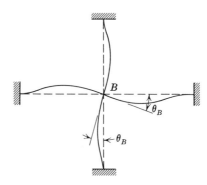

Figure 7.3

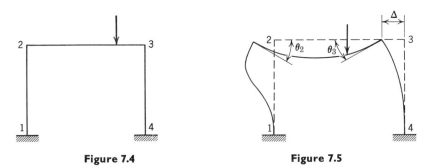

Figure 7.4   **Figure 7.5**

of the members at joint B as well as at other joints in the structure. Actual values of the bending moments are given by the algebraic summation of the fixed end moments and the changes in end moments due to rotation through the angle θ_B. We will evaluate these changes in end moments after discussing another related problem.

Let us consider the rigid frame shown in Figure 7.4. The elastic curve for this frame is shown greatly exaggerated in Figure 7.5. Again, let us break this structure into three fixed end beams as shown in Figure 7.6. The fixed end moments are known quantities. In order to evaluate the difference between the structure of Figure 7.4 and 7.6 we examine each member separately. The end 2 of member 1–2 rotates through an angle θ_2 and translates an amount Δ. This rotation and translation causes the bending moment to change from that associated with Figure 7.6. This change at end 2 of member 1–2 also gives rise to a change in bending moment at end 1 of member 1–2. Note further that end 2 of member 2–3 is caused to rotate through an angle θ_2. This rotation modifies the bending moment at end 2 and also the bending moment at end 3. Also we see that end 3 of member 2–3 rotates through an angle θ_3 thus modifying the bending moments at ends 2 and 3. Finally, the rotation and translation of joint 3 causes changes in the bending moments at ends 3 and 4.

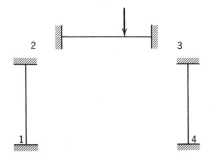

Figure 7.6

We conclude from these two illustrations that the bending moment at any end of a member in Figure 7.4 is equal to the bending moment that would be required to fix that end against rotation and translation (as indicated in Figure 7.6) added algebraically to the bending moments resulting solely from rotation and translation of the ends of the member.

We can express the bending moment M_i at the end i of a typical member i–j through the principle of superposition as

$$M_i = M_i{}^F + [M_i]_{\theta_i} + [M_i]_{\theta_j} + [M_i]_{\Delta_i} + [M_i]_{\Delta_j} \qquad (1)$$

where the contributions to the right hand side of equation 7.1 are defined as follows:

$M_i{}^F$ = Bending moment due to applied loads when end slopes and deflections are zero.

$[M_i]_{\theta_i}$ = Bending moment due to rotation θ_i at end i when applied loads, end deflections, and the rotation of end j are zero.

$[M_i]_{\theta_j}$ = Bending moment due to rotation θ_j at end i when applied loads, end deflections, and the rotation of end i are zero.

$[M_i]_{\Delta_i}$ = Bending moment due to deflection Δ_i at end i when applied loads, end rotations and Δ_j are zero.

$[M_i]_{\Delta_j}$ = Bending moment due to deflection Δ_j at end i when applied loads, end rotations and Δ_i are zero.

These contributions may be evaluated by the conjugate beam method as discussed in Chapter 3.

Problems of complex structures are appreciably simplified if the couples acting at the ends of the members can be described purely in terms of the rotations of the end sections. We shall therefore associate a positive couple with a clockwise rotation of the end sections as shown in Figure 7.7. Note that all couples are shown acting clockwise on the member (and counterclockwise on the joints) and are taken as positive. We shall define these couples as *end moments* and give them the symbol M_{ij}, denoting the clockwise couple acting at the end i of the member i–j. M_{32}, for example, represents the clockwise couple acting at the end 3 of member 3–2. Note further that the bending moment at any section is always described with a single subscript. The preparation of bending moment diagrams need give us no difficulty if we remember to draw them always on the compression side of the member. For example, the bending moment diagram for member 1–2 will be as shown in Figure 7.7b. End moment M_{12} clearly causes compression on the top fibers whereas end moment M_{21} causes compression on the bottom fibers. The bending moment diagram drawn for these two end moments will thus be as shown.

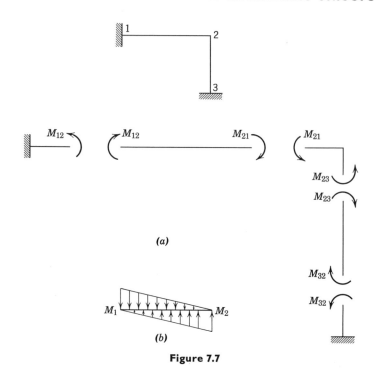

(a)

(b)

Figure 7.7

An expression such as 7.2.1 is also valid for end moments and may be written as follows:

$$M_{ij} = M_{ij}{}^F + [M_{ij}]_{\theta_{ij}} + [M_{ij}]_{\theta_{ji}} + [M_{ij}]_{\Delta_{ij}} + [M_{ij}]_{\Delta_{ji}} \tag{2}$$

Note the double subscripts indicating end moments to be at the end i of the member $i\text{--}j$. The end moment corresponding to the symbol $M_{ij}{}^F$ is defined as the *fixed end moment* at end i of member $i\text{--}j$, since it represents complete fixity of the ends corresponding to zero translation and zero rotation at the ends of the member.

In the general case of applied end moments, applied loads, and applied shears we have the free body as shown in Figure 7.8a. The associated conjugate for the member is shown in Figure 7.8b. For $[M_{ij}]_{\theta_{ij}}$, no lateral load is applied and $\Delta_{ij} = \Delta_{ji} = \theta_{ji} = 0$. Its conjugate beam will appear as shown in Figure 7.9a and an equilibrium analysis of the conjugate yields

$$\theta_{ij} = \frac{M_{ij}L_{ij}}{2EI_{ij}} - \frac{M_{ji}L_{ij}}{2EI_{ij}} \tag{3}$$

$$M_{ij} = 2M_{ji} \tag{4}$$

Substituting 7.2.4 into 7.2.3 and rearranging, we find

$$M_{ij} = \frac{4EI_{ij}\theta_{ij}}{L_{ij}} \tag{5}$$

$$M_{ji} = \frac{2EI_{ij}\theta_{ij}}{L_{ij}} \tag{6}$$

For $[M_{ji}]_{\theta_{ji}}$, no lateral load is applied and $\Delta_{ij} = \Delta_{ji} = \theta_{ij} = 0$. Its conjugate will appear as shown in Figure 7.9b and an equilibrium analysis of the conjugate yields

$$\theta_{ji} = \frac{-M_{ij}L_{ij}}{2EI_{ij}} + \frac{M_{ji}L_{ij}}{2EI_{ij}} \tag{7}$$

$$M_{ji} = 2M_{ij} \tag{8}$$

Substituting 7.2.8 into 7.2.7 and rearranging, we find

$$M_{ij} = \frac{2EI_{ij}\theta_{ji}}{L_{ij}} \tag{9}$$

$$M_{ji} = \frac{4EI_{ij}\theta_{ji}}{L_{ij}} \tag{10}$$

For $[M_{ij}]_{\Delta_{ij}}$, no lateral load is applied and $\Delta_{ji} = \theta_{ij} = \theta_{ji} = 0$. Its conjugate will appear as shown in Figure 7.9c, and an equilibrium analysis of the conjugate yields

$$M_{ij} = M_{ji} \tag{11}$$

$$\Delta_{ij} = \frac{+M_{ij}L_{ij}^2}{3EI_{ij}} - \frac{M_{ji}L_{ij}^2}{6EI_{ij}} \tag{12}$$

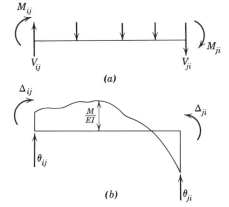

Figure 7.8

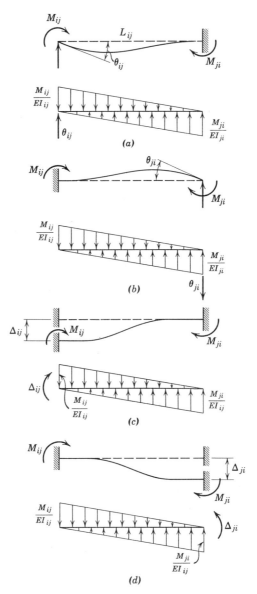

Figure 7.9

Substituting 7.2.11 into 7.2.12 and rearranging, we find

$$M_{ij} = \frac{6EI_{ij}\Delta_{ij}}{L_{ij}^2} \qquad (13)$$

$$M_{ji} = \frac{6EI_{ij}\Delta_{ij}}{L_{ij}^2} \qquad (14)$$

For $[M_{ij}]_{\Delta_{ji}}$, no lateral load is applied and $\Delta_{ij} = \theta_{ij} = \theta_{ji} = 0$. Its conjugate will appear as shown in Figure 7.9d and an equilibrium analysis of the conjugate yields

$$M_{ij} = M_{ji} \qquad (15)$$

$$\Delta_{ji} = \frac{M_{ij}L_{ij}^2}{6EI_{ij}} - \frac{M_{ji}L_{ij}^2}{3EI_{ij}} \qquad (16)$$

Substituting 7.2.15 into 7.2.16 and rearranging, we find

$$M_{ij} = -\frac{6EI_{ij}\Delta_{ji}}{L_{ij}^2} \qquad (17)$$

$$M_{ji} = -\frac{6EI_{ij}\Delta_{ji}}{L_{ij}^2} \qquad (18)$$

This completes the computation of all terms in equation 7.2.2. Substituting, we find the complete form of the *slope-deflection equations.*[*]

$$M_{ij} = M_{ij}{}^F + \frac{4EI_{ij}\theta_{ij}}{L_{ij}} + \frac{2EI_{ij}\theta_{ji}}{L_{ij}} + \frac{6EI_{ij}\Delta_{ij}}{L_{ij}^2} - \frac{6EI_{ij}\Delta_{ji}}{L_{ij}^2} \qquad (19)$$

$$M_{ji} = M_{ji}{}^F + \frac{2EI_{ij}\theta_{ij}}{L_{ij}} + \frac{4EI_{ij}\theta_{ji}}{L_{ij}} + \frac{6EI_{ij}\Delta_{ij}}{L_{ij}^2} - \frac{6EI_{ij}\Delta_{ji}}{L_{ij}^2} \qquad (20)$$

The quantity EI/L occurs so frequently in structural analysis that we give it the special symbol K, called the *stiffness factor*. Introducing this into equations 7.2.19 and 7.2.20 and combining terms we find

$$M_{ij} = 2K_{ij}(2\theta_{ij} + \theta_{ji}) - \frac{6K_{ij}}{L_{ij}}(\Delta_{ji} - \Delta_{ij}) + M_{ij}{}^F \qquad (21)$$

$$M_{ji} = 2K_{ji}(\theta_{ij} + 2\theta_{ji}) - \frac{6K_{ji}}{L_{ij}}(\Delta_{ji} - \Delta_{ij}) + M_{ji}{}^F \qquad (22)$$

The relative displacement $(\Delta_{ji} - \Delta_{ij})$ is frequently given the symbol Δ. The slope θ_{ij} is equal to the rotation of joint i which is denoted by θ_i.

---

[*] The slope-deflection equations were developed by A. Bendixen in Germany in 1914 and independently by G. A. Maney in the United States in 1915.

This rotation has been established as positive when clockwise. Similarly $\theta_{ji} = \theta_j$. Introducing the relative displacement and end rotations, equations 7.2.21 and 7.2.22 become

$$M_{ij} = 2K_{ij}\left(2\theta_i + \theta_j - 3\frac{\Delta}{L_{ij}}\right) + M_{ij}{}^F \qquad (23)$$

$$M_{ji} = 2K_{ji}\left(\theta_i + 2\theta_j - 3\frac{\Delta}{L_{ij}}\right) + M_{ji}{}^F \qquad (24)$$

It should be emphasized that the fixed end moments are considered positive when they act clockwise on the ends of the member.

We now have equations expressing the end moments on each end of every member of a structure. These end moments are in terms of θ_i, θ_j, and Δ/L_{ij}. To solve for these key unknowns, we need apply only the laws of statics, which will be shown in illustrations that follow.

7.3 Slope-Deflection Equations—Continuous Beams

In this section continuous beams are considered with and without joint translations. All of the illustrative problems in §7.3 through §7.6 are restricted to members having constant EI values over their lengths. The moments of inertia and stiffnesses are expressed in relative terms.

Example 7.3.1 Prepare a complete analysis of the two-span beam shown in Figure 7.10a. For the left span we apply the slope-deflection equation with $i = 1$ and $j = 2$. Similarly for the right span $i = 2$ and $j = 3$. Applying the slope-deflection equations, we find

$$M_{12} = (2)(6)(\theta_2) - \frac{(3)(40)^2}{12} = 12\theta_2 - 400 \qquad (1)$$

$$M_{21} = (2)(6)(2\theta_2) + \frac{(3)(40)^2}{12} = 24\theta_2 + 400 \qquad (2)$$

$$M_{23} = (2)(8)(2\theta_2) - \frac{(40)(30)}{8} = 32\theta_2 - 150 \qquad (3)$$

$$M_{32} = (2)(8)(\theta_2) + \frac{(40)(30)}{8} = 16\theta_2 + 150 \qquad (4)$$

For each unknown θ appearing in the slope-deflection equations we need one special equation of condition. In the present analysis this is provided by the condition that the sum of moments around joint 2 equals zero. Thus

$$M_{21} + M_{23} = 0 \qquad (5)$$

Substituting 7.3.2 and 7.3.3 into 7.3.5 we find

$$24\theta_2 + 400 + 32\theta_2 - 150 = 0 \qquad (6)$$

yielding

$$\theta_2 = -4.464 \qquad (7)$$

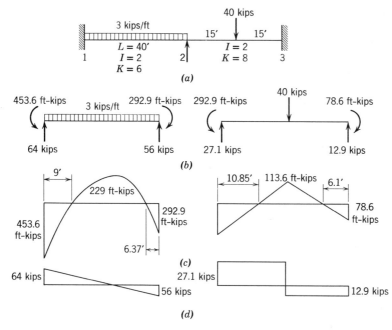

Figure 7.10

The negative sign corresponds to a counter-clockwise rotation of joint 2. Substituting this value of θ_2 in 7.3.1, 7.3.2, 7.3.3 and 7.3.4 we get

$$M_{12} = (12)(-4.464) - 400 = -453.6 \text{ ft-kips}$$
$$M_{21} = (24)(-4.464) + 400 = +292.9 \text{ ft-kips}$$
$$M_{23} = (32)(-4.464) - 150 = -292.9 \text{ ft-kips} \tag{8}$$
$$M_{32} = (16)(-4.464) + 150 = +78.6 \;\; \text{ft-kips}$$

With the end moments determined, the free body diagrams for all members may be drawn as shown in Figure 7.10b. The corresponding bending moment diagrams and shear force diagrams are shown in Figure 7.10c and 7.10d. Note that bending moment diagrams are drawn on the compression side of the beam. The directions of the end moments used in constructing the free body diagrams depend on the signs for these moments obtained from the slope-deflection equations. The positive end moment, it will be recalled, is a clockwise end moment. The negative end moment is a counter-clockwise end moment.

Example 7.3.2 Analyze the beam shown in Figure 7.11a. The slope-deflection equations are

$$M_{12} = (2)(6)(2\theta_1 + \theta_2) - 400 = 24\theta_1 + 12\theta_2 - 400 \tag{9}$$
$$M_{21} = (2)(6)(2\theta_2 + \theta_1) + 400 = 12\theta_1 + 24\theta_2 + 400 \tag{10}$$
$$M_{23} = (2)(8)(2\theta_2 + \theta_3) - 150 = 32\theta_2 + 16\theta_3 - 150 \tag{11}$$
$$M_{32} = (2)(8)(2\theta_3 + \theta_2) + 150 = 16\theta_2 + 32\theta_3 + 150 \tag{12}$$

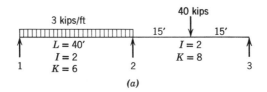

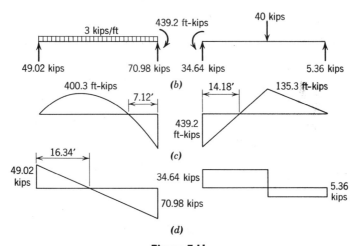

Figure 7.11

Inspection of the foregoing equations shows that we have three unknowns, therefore we need three equations of condition. These three equations are given by the conditions that the end moments are zero at the exterior supports and the sum of the end moments at the interior support is zero. Thus

$$M_{12} = 0 = M_{32}, \qquad M_{21} + M_{23} = 0 \qquad (13)$$

Making use of these conditional equations we obtain

$$\theta_1 = 21.13, \qquad \theta_2 = -8.93, \qquad \theta_3 = -0.222 \qquad (14)$$

These values indicate that θ_1 is a clockwise rotation and that θ_2 and θ_3 are counter-clockwise rotations. Substituting these values of θ into 7.3.10 and 7.3.11 gives

$$M_{21} = (12)(21.13) + (24)(-8.93) + 400 = +439.2 \text{ ft-kips}$$
$$M_{23} = (32)(-8.93) + (16)(-0.222) - 150 = -439.2 \text{ ft-kips} \qquad (15)$$

The free body, shear, and moment diagrams are shown in Figure 7.11. Note the great difference in the moment diagram brought about by changing the end condition of this beam from that of Figure 7.10. Note also slight change in shear diagram.

Example 7.3.3 The structure shown in Figure 7.12 suffers a downward vertical settlement of its right support of 0.3 inches and a counter-clockwise rotation of its left support of 0.1 radian. Find the induced end moments in the structure.

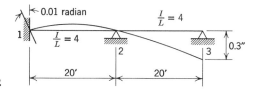

Figure 7.12

The rotation of joint one is counter-clockwise, therefore minus. The sign of Δ/L for span 23 is positive as Δ/L is a clockwise angle. Writing the slope-deflection equations, we find

$$M_{12} = (2)(4E)[(2)(-0.1) + \theta_2] = E(-1.6 + 8\theta_2) \tag{16}$$

$$M_{21} = (2)(4E)[2\theta_2 + (1)(-0.1)] = E(-0.8 + 16\theta_2) \tag{17}$$

$$M_{23} = (2)(4E)\left[2\theta_2 + \theta_3 - (3)\left(\frac{0.3}{240}\right)\right] = E(16\theta_2 + 8\theta_3 - 0.030) \tag{18}$$

$$M_{32} = (2)(4E)\left[2\theta_3 + \theta_2 - (3)\left(\frac{0.3}{240}\right)\right] = E(16\theta_3 + 8\theta_2 - 0.030) \tag{19}$$

The two necessary equations of condition are that $M_{21} + M_{23}$ equals zero and that M_{32} equals zero. Making use of these two conditions and solving for θ_2 and θ_3, we find

$$\theta_2 = +0.0291$$

$$\theta_3 = -0.01268 \tag{20}$$

Substituting 7.3.20 into 7.3.16–19 and using $E = 30,000$ ksi yields

$$M_{12} = 30,000[-1.6 + (8)(0.0291)] = -41,016 \text{ in.-kips}$$

$$M_{21} = 30,000[-0.8 + (16)(0.0291)] = -10,032 \text{ in.-kips} \tag{21}$$

$$M_{23} = 30,000[(16)(0.0291) + (8)(-0.01268) - 0.03] = +10,032 \text{ in.-kips}$$

$$M_{32} = 0$$

7.4 Slope-Deflection Equations—Simple Bents

For purposes of this section we shall consider a simple bent as one having a single story and a single bay. Several illustrative examples demonstrate the use of the slope-deflection equations in analyzing such structures.

Example 7.4.1 Prepare a complete analysis of the frame in Figure 7.13*a*.

Since the frame and loading are symmetric there will be no joint translation in the horizontal direction. Furthermore, we neglect deformations due to axial stresses, which implies no joint translation in the vertical direction. The slope-deflection equations are

$$M_{12} = (2)(4)(\theta_2) = 8\theta_2 \tag{1}$$

$$M_{21} = (2)(4)(2\theta_2) = 16\theta_2 \tag{2}$$

$$M_{23} = (2)(9)(2\theta_2 + \theta_3) - 400 = 36\theta_2 + 18\theta_3 - 400 \tag{3}$$

$$M_{32} = (2)(9)(2\theta_3 + \theta_2) + 400 = 18\theta_2 + 36\theta_3 + 400 \tag{4}$$

$$M_{34} = (2)(4)(2\theta_3) = 16\theta_3 \tag{5}$$

$$M_{43} = (2)(4)(\theta_3) = 8\theta_3 \tag{6}$$

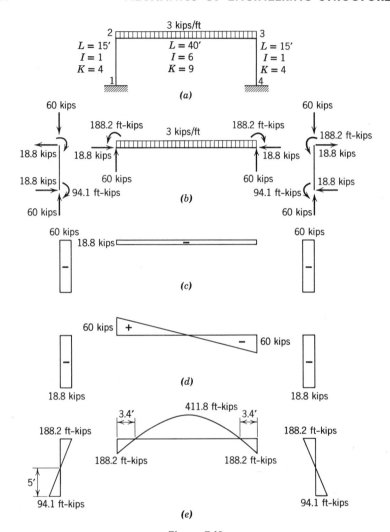

Figure 7.13

The two conditional equations are

$$\sum M_2 = 0 \qquad \sum M_3 = 0 \tag{7}$$

or

$$M_{21} + M_{23} = 0 \tag{8}$$

and

$$M_{32} + M_{34} = 0 \tag{9}$$

Combining the preceding, we obtain

$$52\theta_2 + 18\theta_3 - 400 = 0$$
$$18\theta_2 + 52\theta_3 + 400 = 0 \tag{10}$$

The solution of 7.4.10 gives

$$\theta_2 = 11.76, \qquad \theta_3 = -11.76 \tag{11}$$

The equal and opposite values of the joint rotations will be seen to be consistent with the symmetry of the structure. The symmetry of this structure leads to certain computational simplifications that are discussed in detail in §7.5.

The substitution of 7.4.11 into 7.4.1–6 yields

$$
\begin{aligned}
M_{12} &= 94.1 \text{ ft-kips} & M_{32} &= 188.2 \text{ ft-kips} \\
M_{21} &= 188.2 \text{ ft-kips} & M_{34} &= -188.2 \text{ ft-kips} \\
M_{23} &= -188.2 \text{ ft-kips} & M_{43} &= -94.1 \text{ ft-kips}
\end{aligned} \tag{12}
$$

The free body diagram for each member is shown in Figure 7.13b, the axial force diagrams shown in Figure 7.13c, the shear force diagrams in Figure 7.13d, and the moment diagrams plotted on the compression sides in Figure 7.13e.

Example 7.4.2 Find the end moments of the bent in Figure 7.14. Again the bent and load are symmetric, thus no joint translation occurs. The slope-deflection equations are

$$M_{12} = (2)(4)(2\theta_1 + \theta_2) = 16\theta_1 + 8\theta_2 \tag{13}$$

$$M_{21} = (2)(4)(2\theta_2 + \theta_1) = 8\theta_1 + 16\theta_2 \tag{14}$$

$$M_{23} = (2)(9)(2\theta_2 + \theta_3) - 400 = 36\theta_2 + 18\theta_3 - 400 \tag{15}$$

$$M_{32} = (2)(9)(2\theta_3 + \theta_2) + 400 = 18\theta_2 + 36\theta_3 + 400 \tag{16}$$

$$M_{34} = (2)(4)(2\theta_3 + \theta_4) = 16\theta_3 + 8\theta_4 \tag{17}$$

$$M_{43} = (2)(4)(2\theta_4 + \theta_3) = 8\theta_3 + 16\theta_4 \tag{18}$$

The four conditional equations are

$$\sum M_2 = 0, \qquad \sum M_3 = 0, \qquad M_{12} = 0, \qquad M_{43} = 0 \tag{19}$$

Solving equations 7.4.13–18 yields

$$\theta_1 = -6.67, \qquad \theta_2 = 13.33, \qquad \theta_3 = -13.33, \qquad \theta_4 = 6.67 \tag{20}$$

and substituting these values in 7.4.13–18 gives

$$
\begin{aligned}
M_{12} &= 0 & M_{21} &= 160 \text{ ft-kips} & M_{23} &= -160 \text{ ft-kips} \\
M_{32} &= 160 \text{ ft-kips} & M_{34} &= -160 \text{ ft-kips} & M_{43} &= 0
\end{aligned} \tag{21}
$$

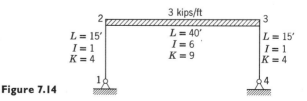

Figure 7.14

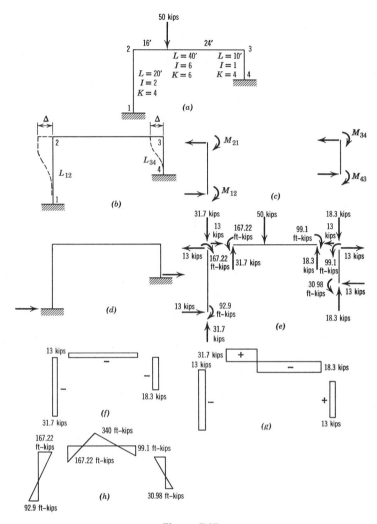

Figure 7.15

Example 7.4.3 Find the end moments for the bent of Figure 7.15. Neither the bent nor its loading is symmetric. Either of these dissymmetries produces a horizontal joint translation. This joint translation in plane frames is often referred to as *side sway* or *side lurch*. The slope-deflection equations are

$$M_{12} = (2)(4)\left(\theta_2 - 3\frac{\Delta}{L_{12}}\right) = 8\theta_2 - 24\frac{\Delta}{L_{12}} \tag{22}$$

$$M_{21} = (2)(4)\left(2\theta_2 - 3\frac{\Delta}{L_{12}}\right) = 16\theta_2 - 24\frac{\Delta}{L_{12}} \tag{23}$$

$$M_{23} = (2)(6)(2\theta_2 + \theta_3) - 288 = 24\theta_2 + 12\theta_3 - 288 \qquad (24)$$

$$M_{32} = (2)(6)(2\theta_3 + \theta_2) + 192 = 12\theta_2 + 24\theta_3 + 192 \qquad (25)$$

$$M_{34} = (2)(4)\left(2\theta_3 - 3\frac{\Delta}{L_{34}}\right) = \left(16\theta_3 - 24\frac{\Delta}{L_{34}}\right) \qquad (26)$$

$$M_{43} = (2)(4)\left(\theta_3 - 3\frac{\Delta}{L_{34}}\right) = 8\theta_3 - 24\frac{\Delta}{L_{34}} \qquad (27)$$

We see that there are four unknowns: θ_2, θ_3, Δ/L_{12}, and Δ/L_{34}, therefore, we require the following four conditional equations

$$\sum M_2 = 0, \qquad \sum M_3 = 0, \qquad \sum H = 0, \qquad \frac{\Delta}{L_{12}} = \tfrac{1}{2}\frac{\Delta}{L_{34}} \qquad (28)$$

Inspection of Figure 7.15b will show the fourth conditional equation to be true. Using the fourth conditional equation, we may write equations 7.4.26 and 7.4.27 as

$$M_{34} = 16\theta_3 - 48\frac{\Delta}{L_{12}}$$

$$ \qquad (29)$$

$$M_{43} = 8\theta_3 - 48\frac{\Delta}{L_{12}}$$

The first two conditional equations are used as in previous problems, but the third equation, $\sum H = 0$, requires special consideration. Before this equation is useful it must be related to the slope-deflection equations. Consider the Figure 7.15c. Here the end moments are shown applied to the ends of both columns. To put these moments in equilibrium requires a balancing couple as indicated by the horizontal forces shown. Each of the horizontal forces on the left column would be equal to $(M_{12} + M_{21})/L_{12}$ and each of the horizontal forces on the right column would be equal to $(M_{34} + M_{43})/L_{34}$. These horizontal forces are usually called shears due to continuity, and considering Figure 7.15d we note that these shears due to continuity are equal to the horizontal reactions. Since there are no horizontal forces applied to this structure, it follows that the sum of these reactions is given by

$$\frac{M_{12} + M_{21}}{L_{12}} + \frac{M_{34} + M_{43}}{L_{34}} = 0 \qquad (30)$$

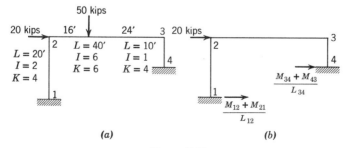

(a)   (b)

Figure 7.16

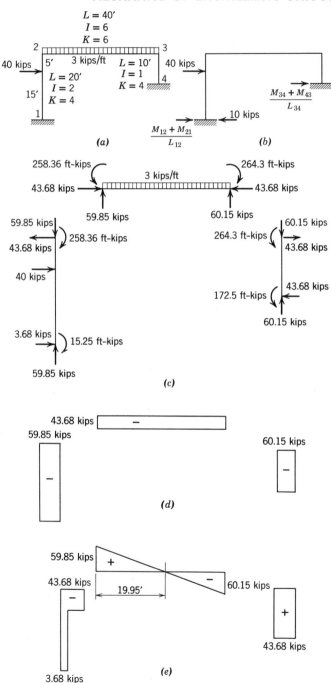

$$L = 40'$$
$$I = 6$$
$$K = 6$$

2 | 3 kips/ft | 3
40 kips | 5' | $L = 10'$ | 40 kips
$L = 20'$ | $I = 1$ | 4
15' | $I = 2$ | $K = 4$
$K = 4$ | 10 kips
1

$$\frac{M_{12} + M_{21}}{L_{12}}$$

$$\frac{M_{34} + M_{43}}{L_{34}}$$

(a)

(b)

258.36 ft-kips   3 kips/ft   264.3 ft-kips
43.68 kips   43.68 kips

59.85 kips   59.85 kips   60.15 kips

59.85 kips   60.15 kips
258.36 ft-kips   264.3 ft-kips   43.68 kips
43.68 kips

40 kips   43.68 kips
                        172.5 ft-kips
3.68 kips   60.15 kips
15.25 ft-kips

59.85 kips

(c)

43.68 kips [−   ]
59.85 kips   60.15 kips

−   −

(d)

59.85 kips [+]
43.68 kips   60.15 kips
−   19.95'   +

3.68 kips   43.68 kips

(e)

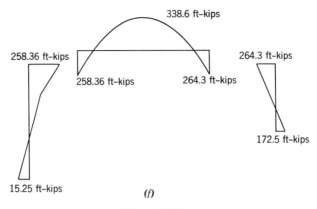

Figure 7.17

The solution of the given sets of equations yields

$$\theta_2 = 9.2907, \qquad \theta_3 = -8.517, \qquad \frac{\Delta}{L_{12}} = -0.774 \qquad (31)$$

We then find

$M_{12} = 92.9$ ft-kips $M_{21} = 167.22$ ft-kips $M_{23} = -167.22$ ft-kips
$M_{32} = 99.1$ ft-kips $M_{34} = -99.1$ ft-kips $M_{43} = -30.98$ ft-kips

The free body diagram is shown in Figure 7.15e, the axial force diagram in 7.15f, the shear force diagram in 7.15g and the moment diagram in 7.15h.

Example 7.4.4 What would be the effect of adding a 20-kip horizontal load to the structure in Figure 7.15a as shown in Figure 7.16a? The addition of the 20-kip horizontal load will not change any of the slope-deflection equations as written in 7.4.22 through 7.4.27. The conditional equations will also be the same. The only change will lie in the interpretation of the conditional equation $\Sigma H = 0$. Figure 7.16b shows all the horizontal forces acting on this structure. Static equilibrium requires that

$$\frac{M_{12} + M_{21}}{L_{12}} + \frac{M_{34} + M_{43}}{L_{34}} + 20 = 0 \qquad (33)$$

Example 7.4.5 Prepare a complete analysis of the bent in Figure 7.17a. The slope-deflection equations are

$$M_{12} = (2)(4)\left(\theta_2 - 3\frac{\Delta}{L_{12}}\right) - 37.5 = 8\theta_2 - 24\frac{\Delta}{L_{12}} - 37.5 \qquad (34)$$

$$M_{21} = (2)(4)\left(2\theta_2 - 3\frac{\Delta}{L_{12}}\right) + 112.5 = 16\theta_2 - 24\frac{\Delta}{L_{12}} + 112.5 \qquad (35)$$

$$M_{23} = (2)(6)(2\theta_2 + \theta_3) - 400 = 24\theta_2 + 12\theta_3 - 400 \qquad (36)$$

$$M_{32} = (2)(6)(2\theta_3 + \theta_2) + 400 = 12\theta_2 + 24\theta_3 + 400 \qquad (37)$$

$$M_{34} = (2)(4)\left(2\theta_3 - 3\frac{\Delta}{L_{34}}\right) = 16\theta_3 - 24\frac{\Delta}{L_{34}} \qquad (38)$$

$$M_{43} = (2)(4)\left(\theta_3 - 3\frac{\Delta}{L_{34}}\right) = 8\theta_3 - 24\frac{\Delta}{L_{34}} \qquad (39)$$

Making use of the relationship $\Delta/L_{12} = \frac{1}{2}(\Delta/L_{34})$ and rewriting 7.4.39 and 7.4.38 we get

$$M_{34} = (2)(4)\left(2\theta_3 - 6\frac{\Delta}{L_{12}}\right) = 16\theta_3 - 48\frac{\Delta}{L_{12}} \tag{40}$$

$$M_{43} = (2)(4)\left(\theta_3 - 6\frac{\Delta}{L_{12}}\right) = 8\theta_3 - 48\frac{\Delta}{L_{12}} \tag{41}$$

Three unknowns require three conditional equations. They are

$$\sum M_2 = 0, \qquad \sum M_3 = 0, \qquad \sum H = 0 \tag{42}$$

To interpret $\sum H = 0$, consider Figure 7.17b, which shows the horizontal forces acting on the frame. These horizontal forces are expressed as

$$\frac{M_{12} + M_{21}}{L_{12}} + \frac{M_{34} + M_{43}}{L_{34}} + 40 - 10 = 0 \tag{43}$$

where the 10-kip force represents shear due to simple beam action. Thus

$$\frac{8\theta_2 - 24\frac{\Delta}{L_{12}} - 37.5 + 16\theta_2 - 24\frac{\Delta}{L_{12}} + 112.5}{20}$$

$$+ \frac{16\theta_3 - 48\frac{\Delta}{L_{12}} + 8\theta_3 - 48\frac{\Delta}{L_{12}}}{10} + 30 = 0 \tag{44}$$

which reduces to

$$24\theta_2 + 48\theta_3 - 240\frac{\Delta}{L_{12}} + 675 = 0 \tag{45}$$

The final values of slopes and deflections will be

$$\theta_2 = +11.6286 \qquad \theta_3 = -11.4736 \qquad \frac{\Delta}{L_{12}} = +1.6816 \tag{46}$$

Finally, we obtain end moments of

$$\begin{aligned} M_{12} &= +15.25 \text{ ft-kips} & M_{21} &= +258.36 \text{ ft-kips} & M_{23} &= -258.36 \text{ ft-kips} \\ M_{32} &= +264.3 \text{ ft-kips} & M_{34} &= -264.3 \text{ ft-kips} & M_{43} &= -172.5 \text{ ft-kips} \end{aligned} \tag{47}$$

Free body, axial force, shear, and moment diagrams are shown in Figure 7.17(c–f).

All of the preceding problems of this chapter have dealt with beams or frames where all of the members were mutually perpendicular. In these problems the joint translations were readily related to one another. Figure 7.18a illustrates a frame for which this condition is not met. The general slope deflection equations are not changed for this problem, however. Two

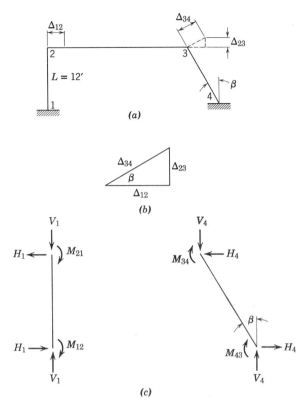

Figure 7.18

points that require special consideration are: (1) the relationship between the joint translations must be established and (2) the conditional equation $\Sigma H = 0$ involving the vertical reactions of the inclined members as well as the end moments and horizontal reactions must be explained.

The joint displacements are indicated in Figure 7.18a. Since the length of each member is constant and all deflections are assumed to be small, we may say that the relative displacement of the end of a given member is normal to the original axis of that member. This leads to Figure 7.18b, which shows the relationship between Δ_{12}, Δ_{23}, and Δ_{34}. Any side of the triangle may be taken as a reference and the others related to it. Here we choose Δ_{12} as a reference; other magnitudes are given by

$$\Delta_{23} = \tan \beta \, \Delta_{12}$$

$$\Delta_{34} = \frac{\Delta_{12}}{\cos \beta} \tag{48}$$

Now consider the signs. Figure 7.18a shows that angles Δ_{12}/L_{12} and Δ_{34}/L_{34} are clockwise and are therefore positive. Angle Δ_{23}/L_{23} is a counter-clockwise angle and is therefore negative. Corrected equation 7.4.48 reads

$$\Delta_{23} = -\tan \beta \; \Delta_{12}$$

$$\Delta_{34} = \frac{\Delta_{12}}{\cos \beta} \tag{49}$$

From equation 7.4.49 we see that

$$\frac{\Delta_{23}}{L_{23}} = -\tan \beta \frac{\Delta_{12}}{L_{23}} \tag{50}$$

and

$$\frac{\Delta_{34}}{L_{34}} = \frac{\Delta_{12}}{L_{12}} \tag{51}$$

To make the conditional equation $\Sigma H = 0$ useful, refer to Figure 7.18c. Here

$$H_1 = \frac{M_{21} + M_{12}}{L_{12}} \tag{52}$$

and

$$H_4 = \frac{M_{34} + M_{43} - (V_4)(L_{34})(\sin \beta)}{L_{34} \cos \beta} \tag{53}$$

or

$$\frac{M_{21} + M_{12}}{L_{12}} + \frac{M_{34} + M_{43} - (V_4)(L_{34})(\sin \beta)}{L_{34} \cos \beta} = 0 \tag{54}$$

Example 7.4.6   Find the end moments for the bent in Figure 7.19. The slope deflection equations are

$$M_{12} = (2)(1)\left(\theta_2 - 3\frac{\Delta_{12}}{L_{12}}\right) = 2\theta_2 - 6\frac{\Delta_{12}}{L_{12}} \tag{55}$$

$$M_{21} = (2)(1)\left(2\theta_2 - 3\frac{\Delta_{12}}{L_{12}}\right) = 4\theta_2 - 6\frac{\Delta_{12}}{L_{12}} \tag{56}$$

$$M_{23} = (2)(1)\left(2\theta_2 + \theta_3 - 3\frac{\Delta_{23}}{L_{23}}\right) - 400 = 4\theta_2 + 2\theta_3 - 6\frac{\Delta_{23}}{L_{23}} - 400 \tag{57}$$

$$M_{32} = (2)(1)\left(2\theta_3 + \theta_2 - 3\frac{\Delta_{23}}{L_{23}}\right) + 400 = 4\theta_3 + 2\theta_2 - 6\frac{\Delta_{23}}{L_{23}} + 400 \tag{58}$$

$$M_{34} = (2)(1)\left(2\theta_3 - 3\frac{\Delta_{34}}{L_{34}}\right) = 4\theta_3 - 6\frac{\Delta_{34}}{L_{34}} \tag{59}$$

$$M_{43} = (2)(1)\left(\theta_3 - 3\frac{\Delta_{34}}{L_{34}}\right) = 2\theta_3 - 6\frac{\Delta_{34}}{L_{34}} \tag{60}$$

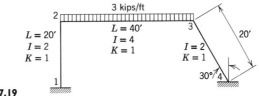

Figure 7.19

From 7.4.49 with β as 30°, these equations are written as

$$M_{12} = 2\theta_2 - 6\frac{\Delta_{12}}{L_{12}} \tag{61}$$

$$M_{21} = 4\theta_2 - 6\frac{\Delta_{12}}{L_{12}} \tag{62}$$

$$M_{23} = 4\theta_2 + 2\theta_3 - 6\left(\frac{-0.577\Delta_{12}}{2L_{12}}\right) - 400 = 4\theta_2 + 2\theta_3 + \frac{1.731\Delta_{12}}{L_{12}} - 400 \tag{63}$$

$$M_{32} = 4\theta_3 + 2\theta_2 + 1.731\frac{\Delta_{12}}{L_{12}} + 400 \tag{64}$$

$$M_{34} = 4\theta_3 - 6\left(\frac{\Delta_{12}}{L_{12}}\right) = 4\theta_3 - 6\frac{\Delta_{12}}{L_{12}} \tag{65}$$

$$M_{43} = 2\theta_3 - 6\frac{\Delta_{12}}{L_{12}} \tag{66}$$

The conditional equations are

$$M_{21} + M_{23} = 0, \qquad M_{32} + M_{34} = 0, \qquad \Sigma H = 0 \tag{67}$$

Combination of the first two conditions gives

$$8\theta_2 + 2\theta_3 - 4.269\frac{\Delta_{12}}{L_{12}} - 400 = 0 \tag{68}$$

$$2\theta_2 + 8\theta_3 - 4.269\frac{\Delta_{12}}{L_{12}} + 400 = 0 \tag{69}$$

Conditional equation $\Sigma H = 0$ is expressed in 7.4.54 as

$$\frac{M_{21} + M_{12}}{L_{12}} + \frac{M_{34} + M_{43} - (V_4)(L_{34})(\sin \beta)}{L_{34} \cos \beta} = 0$$

Expressing $V_4 = \dfrac{M_{32} + M_{23}}{40} + 60$ and substituting, we find

$$\frac{4\theta_2 - 6\dfrac{\Delta_{12}}{L_{12}} + 2\theta_2 - 6\dfrac{\Delta_{12}}{L_{12}}}{L_{12}}$$

$$+ \frac{4\theta_3 - 6\dfrac{\Delta_{12}}{L_{12}} + 2\theta_3 - 6\dfrac{\Delta_{12}}{L_{12}} - \left(\dfrac{6\theta_2 + 6\theta_3 + 3.462\dfrac{\Delta_{12}}{L_{12}}}{40} + 60\right)10}{0.866 L_{34}} = 0 \tag{70}$$

Equation 7.4.70 reduces to

$$0.2134\theta_2 + 0.2598\theta_3 - 1.3428\frac{\Delta_{12}}{L_{12}} - 34.642 = 0 \tag{71}$$

The solution of equations 7.4.68, 7.4.69 and 7.4.71 gives

$$\theta_2 = 52.5462, \qquad \theta_3 = -80.7876, \qquad \frac{\Delta_{12}}{L_{12}} = -33.0769 \tag{72}$$

Substituting these values into 7.4.61–66, we find

$$
\begin{array}{ll}
M_{12} = 303.6 \text{ ft-kips} & M_{32} = 124.7 \text{ ft-kips} \\
M_{21} = 408.6 \text{ ft-kips} & M_{34} = -124.7 \text{ ft-kips} \\
M_{23} = -408.6 \text{ ft-kips} & M_{43} = 36.9 \text{ ft-kips}
\end{array} \tag{73}
$$

Example 7.4.7 Find the slopes of the ends of all members of Figure 7.20 if the center column settles 0.25 inch. For any settlement Δ of the center column, the slope-deflection equations are

$$M_{12} = (2)(1)\left(\theta_2 - 3\frac{\Delta}{L_{12}}\right) \tag{74}$$

$$M_{21} = (2)(1)\left(2\theta_2 - 3\frac{\Delta}{L_{12}}\right) \tag{75}$$

$$M_{23} = (2)(\tfrac{3}{4})\left(2\theta_2 - 3\frac{\Delta}{L_{23}}\right) \tag{76}$$

$$M_{24} = (2)(1)(2\theta_2) \tag{77}$$

$$M_{32} = (2)(\tfrac{3}{4})\left(\theta_2 - 3\frac{\Delta}{L_{23}}\right) \tag{78}$$

$$M_{42} = (2)(1)(\theta_2) \tag{79}$$

Since $\Delta/L_{23} = -\tfrac{3}{4}\,\Delta/L_{12}$, these may be written as

$$M_{12} = (2)(1)\left(\theta_2 - 3\frac{\Delta}{L_{12}}\right) = 2\theta_2 - 6\frac{\Delta}{L_{12}} \tag{80}$$

$$M_{21} = (2)(1)\left(2\theta_2 - 3\frac{\Delta}{L_{12}}\right) = 4\theta_2 - 6\frac{\Delta}{L_{12}} \tag{81}$$

$$M_{23} = (2)(\tfrac{3}{4})\left(2\theta_2 + \frac{9}{4}\frac{\Delta}{L_{12}}\right) = 3\theta_2 + 3.375\frac{\Delta}{L_{12}} \tag{82}$$

$$M_{24} = (2)(1)(2\theta_2) \tag{83}$$

$$M_{32} = (2)(\tfrac{3}{4})\left(\theta_2 + \frac{9}{4}\frac{\Delta}{L_{12}}\right) = 1.5\theta_2 + 3.375\frac{\Delta}{L_{12}} \tag{84}$$

$$M_{42} = (2)(1)(\theta_2) \tag{85}$$

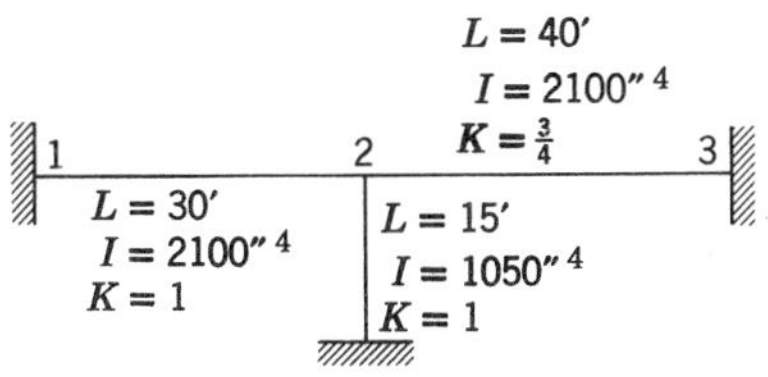

$$L = 40'$$
$$I = 2100''^4$$
$$K = \tfrac{3}{4}$$

1		2		3

$$L = 30'$$
$$I = 2100''^4$$
$$K = 1$$

$$L = 15'$$
$$I = 1050''^4$$
$$K = 1$$

Figure 7.20

Applying the condition of equilibrium that $M_{21} + M_{24} + M_{23} = 0$, we find

$$11\theta_2 - 2.625 \frac{\Delta}{L_{12}} = 0 \tag{86}$$

or

$$\theta_2 = 0.2386 \frac{\Delta}{L_{12}} \tag{87}$$

Since in this problem $\Delta/L_{12} = 0.25/360$, 7.4.87 becomes

$$\theta_2 = 0.0001657 \text{ radians} \tag{88}$$

7.5 Slope-Deflection Equations—Special Techniques

The treatment of the preceding problems in this chapter has been general with no mention being made of special techniques for reducing the labor required. Such techniques exist when there is complete symmetry and/or when hinged supports are present.

Consider the structure in Figure 7.21 having the slope-deflection relations

$$M_{12} = 2EK\left(2\theta_1 + \theta_2 - 3\frac{\Delta_{12}}{L_{12}}\right) + M_{12}{}^F \tag{1}$$

$$M_{21} = 2EK\left(\theta_1 + 2\theta_2 - 3\frac{\Delta_{12}}{L_{12}}\right) + M_{21}{}^F \tag{2}$$

Since the end moment is zero at a hinge support, M_{12} is equal to zero and we may solve 7.5.1 to get

$$\theta_1 = \frac{M_{12}{}^F}{4EK} - \frac{\theta_2}{2} + \frac{3\Delta_{12}}{2L_{12}} \tag{3}$$

Substituting 7.5.3 into 7.5.2, we find

$$M_{21} = 3EK\left(\theta_2 - \frac{\Delta_{12}}{L_{12}}\right) + M_{21}{}^F - \frac{M_{12}{}^F}{2} \tag{4}$$

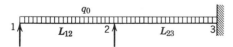

$$q_0$$

1	L_{12}	2	L_{23}	3

Figure 7.21

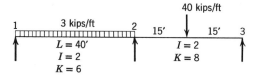

Figure 7.22

Note that $M_{12}{}^F$ contributes positively to end moment M_{12} as seen in equation 7.5.1, but contributes negatively to the end moment M_{21} as seen in 7.5.4. The contribution to M_{21} is only one-half that to M_{12}. Equation 7.5.4 may always be used in place of 7.5.2 if one end of the member is hinged.

Example 7.5.1 Find the end moments for the structure of Figure 7.22a. The slope-deflection equations, using 7.5.4, are

$$M_{21} = (3)(6)(\theta_2) + 400 + 200 = 18\theta_2 + 600 \tag{5}$$

$$M_{23} = (3)(8)(\theta_2) - 150 - 75 = 24\theta_2 - 225 \tag{6}$$

Only one conditional equation is necessary:

$$\sum M_2 = 0 \quad \text{or} \quad M_{21} + M_{23} = 0 \tag{7}$$

Therefore $18\theta_2 + 600 + 24\theta_2 - 225 = 0$ or

$$\theta_2 = -8.93 \tag{8}$$

The end moments equal

$$M_{21} = (18)(-8.93) + 600 = +439.3 \text{ ft-kips}$$

$$M_{23} = (24)(-8.93) - 225 = -439.3 \text{ ft-kips} \tag{9}$$

This modification for hinged ends is valid for columns as well as beams.

Example 7.5.2 Find the end moments for the frame of Figure 7.13a. Inspection of this figure shows that because of symmetry of loading and symmetry of construction, $\theta_2 = -\theta_3$. Writing the slope-deflection equations, we find

$$M_{12} = (2)(4)(\theta_2) = 8\theta_2 \tag{10}$$

$$M_{21} = (2)(4)(2\theta_2) = 16\theta_2 \tag{11}$$

$$M_{23} = (2)(9)(2\theta_2 - \theta_2) -400 = 18\theta_2 - 400 \tag{12}$$

$$M_{32} = (2)(9)(+\theta_2 - 2\theta_2) +400 = -18\theta_2 + 400 \tag{13}$$

$$M_{34} = (2)(4)(-2\theta_2) = -16\theta_2 \tag{14}$$

$$M_{43} = (2)(4)(-\theta_2) = -8\theta_2 \tag{15}$$

Again only one conditional equation is necessary, that is,

$$\sum M_2 = 0 \tag{16}$$

or

$$16\theta_2 + 18\theta_2 - 400 = 0 \tag{17}$$

therefore

$$\theta_2 = +11.76 \tag{18}$$

and

$$M_{12} = +94.1 \text{ ft-kips} \quad M_{21} = +188.2 \text{ ft-kips} \quad M_{23} = -188.2 \text{ ft-kips}$$

$$M_{32} = +188.2 \text{ ft-kips} \quad M_{34} = -188.2 \text{ ft-kips} \quad M_{43} = -94.1 \text{ ft-kips} \tag{19}$$

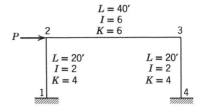

Figure 7.23

Example 7.5.3 Set up the slope-deflection equations for the structure in Figure 7.23. In this structure we note that because of the symmetry of construction and the peculiar nature of the loading, the joint rotations θ_2 and θ_3 are equal and have the same sign. The equations of condition are

$$M_{21} + M_{23} = 0 \quad \text{or} \quad M_{32} + M_{34} = 0 \quad \text{and} \quad \sum H = 0 \tag{20}$$

The final set of slope-deflection equations are

$$M_{12} = (2)(4)(\theta_2 - 3R) = 8\theta_2 - 24R \tag{21}$$

$$M_{21} = (2)(4)(2\theta_2 - 3R) = 16\theta_2 - 24R \tag{22}$$

$$M_{23} = (2)(6)(2\theta_2 + \theta_2) = 36\theta_2 \tag{23}$$

$$M_{32} = (2)(6)(2\theta_2 + \theta_2) = 36\theta_2 \tag{24}$$

$$M_{34} = (2)(4)(2\theta_2 - 3R) = 16\theta_2 - 24R \tag{25}$$

$$M_{43} = (2)(4)(\theta_2 - 3R) = 8\theta_2 - 24R \tag{26}$$

where $R = \Delta/L_{12} = \Delta/L_{34}$.

7.6 Slope-Deflection Equations—Complex Frames

For the purposes of this chapter, a complex frame will be defined as a frame having more than one story or more than one bay. Two illustrations have been chosen to illustrate the use of the slope-deflection equations.

Example 7.6.1 Find the joint displacements for the structure shown in Figure 7.24. For this structure we see that

$$\frac{\Delta}{L_{34}} = \frac{2\Delta}{L_{12}} = \frac{2\Delta}{L_{56}} \tag{1}$$

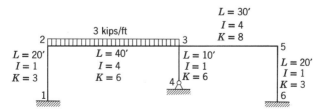

Figure 7.24

Also we may make use of the special equation for a hinged member in treating member 34 to obtain the following set of slope-deflection equations.

$$M_{12} = (2)(3)\left(\theta_2 - 3\frac{\Delta}{L_{12}}\right) = 6\theta_2 - 18\frac{\Delta}{L_{12}} \tag{2}$$

$$M_{21} = (2)(3)\left(2\theta_2 - 3\frac{\Delta}{L_{12}}\right) = 12\theta_2 - 18\frac{\Delta}{L_{12}} \tag{3}$$

$$M_{23} = (2)(6)(2\theta_2 + \theta_3) - 400 = 24\theta_2 + 12\theta_3 - 400 \tag{4}$$

$$M_{32} = (2)(6)(2\theta_3 + \theta_2) + 400 = 12\theta_2 + 24\theta_3 + 400 \tag{5}$$

$$M_{34} = (3)(6)\left(\theta_3 - 2\frac{\Delta}{L_{12}}\right) = 18\theta_3 - 36\frac{\Delta}{L_{12}} \tag{6}$$

$$M_{35} = (2)(8)(2\theta_3 + \theta_5) = 32\theta_3 + 16\theta_5 \tag{7}$$

$$M_{53} = (2)(8)(2\theta_5 + \theta_3) = 16\theta_3 + 32\theta_5 \tag{8}$$

$$M_{56} = (2)(3)\left(2\theta_5 - 3\frac{\Delta}{L_{12}}\right) = 12\theta_5 - 18\frac{\Delta}{L_{12}} \tag{9}$$

$$M_{65} = (2)(3)\left(\theta_5 - 3\frac{\Delta}{L_{12}}\right) = 6\theta_5 - 18\frac{\Delta}{L_{12}} \tag{10}$$

The four conditional equations are

$$M_{21} + M_{23} = 0 \qquad M_{32} + M_{34} + M_{35} = 0 \qquad M_{53} + M_{56} = 0$$

$$\frac{M_{21} + M_{12}}{20} + \frac{M_{34}}{10} + \frac{M_{56} + M_{65}}{20} = 0 \tag{11}$$

These conditional equations and their solution yields

$$\theta_2 = 13.89686 \qquad \frac{\Delta}{L_{12}} = 0.04184$$

$$\theta_3 = -8.2945 \qquad \theta_5 = 3.0333 \tag{12}$$

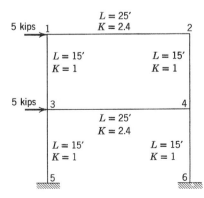

Figure 7.25

Example 7.6.2 Determine the end moments of the structure shown in Figure 7.25a. The slope-deflection equations are

$$M_{12} = (2)(2.4)(2\theta_1 + \theta_2) = 9.6\theta_1 + 4.8\theta_2 \tag{13}$$

$$M_{13} = (2)(1)\left(2\theta_1 + \theta_3 - 3\frac{\Delta_{13}}{L_{13}}\right) = 4\theta_1 + 2\theta_3 - 6\frac{\Delta_{13}}{L_{13}} \tag{14}$$

$$M_{31} = (2)(1)\left(2\theta_3 + \theta_1 - 3\frac{\Delta_{13}}{L_{31}}\right) = 2\theta_1 + 4\theta_3 - 6\frac{\Delta_{13}}{L_{13}} \tag{15}$$

$$M_{34} = (2)(2.4)(2\theta_3 + \theta_4) = 9.6\theta_3 + 4.8\theta_4 \tag{16}$$

$$M_{35} = (2)(1)\left(2\theta_3 + \theta_5 - 3\frac{\Delta_{35}}{L_{35}}\right) = 4\theta_3 + 2\theta_5 - 6\frac{\Delta_{35}}{L_{35}} \tag{17}$$

$$M_{21} = (2)(2.4)(2\theta_2 + \theta_1) = 9.6\theta_2 + 4.8\theta_1 \tag{18}$$

$$M_{24} = (2)(1)\left(2\theta_2 + \theta_4 - 3\frac{\Delta_{13}}{L_{13}}\right) = 4\theta_2 + 2\theta_4 - 6\frac{\Delta_{13}}{L_{13}} \tag{19}$$

$$M_{42} = (2)(1)\left(2\theta_4 + \theta_2 - 3\frac{\Delta_{13}}{L_{13}}\right) = 2\theta_2 + 4\theta_4 - 6\frac{\Delta_{13}}{L_{13}} \tag{20}$$

$$M_{43} = (2)(2.4)(2\theta_4 + \theta_3) = 9.6\theta_4 + 4.8\theta_3 \tag{21}$$

$$M_{46} = (2)(1)\left(2\theta_4 - 3\frac{\Delta_{35}}{L_{35}}\right) = 4\theta_4 - 6\frac{\Delta_{35}}{L_{35}} \tag{22}$$

$$M_{64} = (2)(1)\left(\theta_4 - 3\frac{\Delta_{35}}{L_{35}}\right) = 2\theta_4 - 6\frac{\Delta_{35}}{L_{35}} \tag{23}$$

$$M_{53} = (2)(1)\left(\theta_3 - 3\frac{\Delta_{35}}{L_{35}}\right) = 2\theta_3 - 6\frac{\Delta_{35}}{L_{35}} \tag{24}$$

The six unknowns require six conditional equations:

$$M_{12} + M_{13} = 0 \qquad\qquad M_{42} + M_{43} + M_{46} = 0$$

$$M_{21} + M_{24} = 0 \qquad\qquad M_{31} + M_{34} + M_{35} = 0$$

$$\frac{M_{13} + M_{31}}{15} + \frac{M_{24} + M_{42}}{15} + 5 = 0 \qquad \frac{M_{35} + M_{53}}{15} + \frac{M_{46} + M_{64}}{15} + 10 = 0 \tag{25}$$

Symmetry of the structure may also be used. Symmetry requires

$$\theta_1 = \theta_2 \qquad\qquad \theta_3 = \theta_4 \tag{26}$$

Solving yields

$$\theta_1 = \theta_2 = 1.45 \qquad \frac{\Delta_{13}}{L_{13}} = 5.6$$

$$\theta_3 = \theta_4 = 3.5 \qquad \frac{\Delta_{35}}{L_{35}} = 8 \tag{27}$$

Substitution of these values in 7.6.13–24 yields

$$M_{12} = M_{21} = 20.8 \text{ ft-kips} \qquad M_{13} = M_{24} = -20.8 \text{ ft-kips}$$

$$M_{31} = M_{42} = -16.7 \text{ ft-kips} \qquad M_{34} = M_{43} = 50.5 \text{ ft-kips} \qquad (28)$$

$$M_{35} = M_{46} = -34 \text{ ft-kips} \qquad M_{53} = M_{64} = -41 \text{ ft-kips}$$

7.7 Slope-Deflection Equations—Summary

In reviewing the derivation and applications of the slope-deflection equations as presented in previous sections, we note that certain special conditions must apply to a given problem before these equations can be used.

First, the structure to be analyzed must consist of straight, elastic members of uniform section throughout. Although the value of EI may vary from member to member, it must have a constant value along any particular member. Members with variable moment of inertia are the best treated by other methods. The method of moment distribution used in conjunction with the method of column analogy is especially popular and is discussed in more advanced textbooks on structural theory.

Second, the structure must lie in a single plane and be loaded by forces and couples in that plane. This is necessary since out-of-plane loadings and space structures experience bending as well as twisting of members. The slope-deflection equations do not take account of such twisting.

The slope-deflection equations experienced wide use after their first publication but were almost totally replaced in the early thirties by the method of moment distribution. Today they have regained much of their earlier popularity because of their special suitability when solving complicated problems using electronic computers.

7.8 The Method of Moment Distribution

The moment distribution method is a special means of interpreting the slope-deflection equations of §7.2. Assume a structure, such as that shown in Figure 7.26. Assume further that joint 1 is not permitted to rotate under load. The fixed end moments shown in Figure 7.27a may all be calculated at the ends of the members and joint 1 will not necessarily be in equilibrium under the action of these fixed end moments alone. We conclude that there would have to be applied to joint 1 an external *locking moment* equal and opposite to the algebraic sum of the fixed end moments present at the joint. This locking moment is shown in Figure 7.27b. All of the joints are now locked against rotation and translation. We now

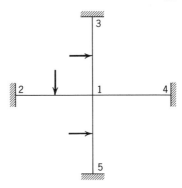

Figure 7.26

unlock joint 1, keeping the opposite ends of all members fixed against displacement, and permit it to rotate through some angle θ_1 until a state of equilibrium is reached. The deflected structure will be as shown in Figure 7.28. The moment necessary to rotate joint 1 through θ_1 is called the *unlocking* or *balancing moment* and it is equal in magnitude but opposite in direction to the *locking moment*.

Setting $EI/L = K$ and writing the slope-deflection equations for the end moments of the members framing into joint 1 in Figure 7.26, we have

$$M_{12} = 2K_{12}(2\theta_1) + M_{12}{}^F \qquad M_{13} = 2K_{13}(2\theta_1) + M_{13}{}^F$$
$$M_{14} = 2K_{14}(2\theta_1) + M_{14}{}^F \qquad M_{15} = 2K_{15}(2\theta_1) + M_{15}{}^F \tag{1}$$

Equilibrium of joint 1 supplies the necessary equation of condition that

$$M_{12} + M_{13} + M_{14} + M_{15} = 0 \tag{2}$$

or

$$4\theta_1(K_{12} + K_{13} + K_{14} + K_{15}) = -M_{12}{}^F - M_{14}{}^F - M_{13}{}^F - M_{15}{}^F$$

and

$$\theta_1 = \frac{-\sum M^F}{4(K_{12} + K_{13} + K_{14} + K_{15})} = \frac{-\sum M^F}{4\sum K} \tag{3}$$

Substituting 7.8.3 into 7.8.1, we find

$$M_{12} = \frac{K_{12}}{\sum K}\left[-\sum M^F\right] + M_{12}{}^F$$

$$M_{13} = \frac{K_{13}}{\sum K}\left[-\sum M^F\right] - M_{13}{}^F$$

$$M_{14} = \frac{K_{14}}{\sum K}\left[-\sum M^F\right] - M_{14}{}^F \tag{4}$$

$$M_{15} = \frac{K_{15}}{\sum K}\left[-\sum M^F\right] + M_{15}{}^F$$

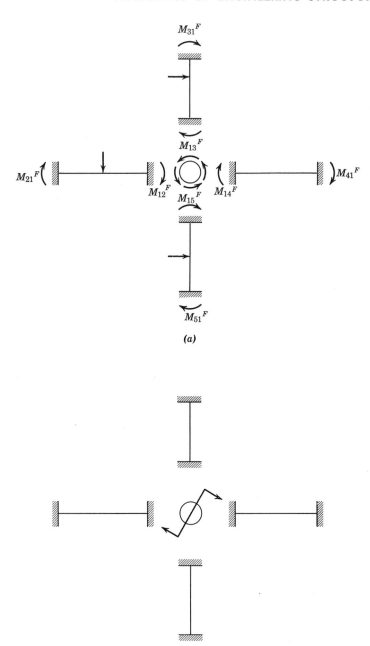

(a)

(b)

Figure 7.27

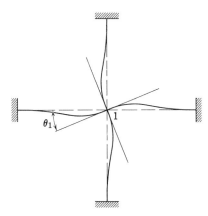

Figure 7.28

Since the unlocking or balancing moment is equal and opposite to the locking moment, we may write 7.8.4 as

$$M_{12} = \frac{K_{12}}{\sum K} \text{(balancing moment)} + M_{12}{}^F$$

$$M_{13} = \frac{K_{13}}{\sum K} \text{(balancing moment)} - M_{13}{}^F$$

$$M_{14} = \frac{K_{14}}{\sum K} \text{(balancing moment)} - M_{14}{}^F \tag{5}$$

$$M_{15} = \frac{K_{15}}{\sum K} \text{(balancing moment)} + M_{15}{}^F$$

Inspection of equations 7.8.5 shows that any end moment at joint 1 is equal to some factor $K/\sum K$ multiplied by the balancing moment and added to any fixed end moment acting on that end of the member in Figure 7.26. This factor $K/\sum K$ is called a *distribution factor* (DF) where K, called the *stiffness factor*, is equal to the value of EI/L for the member whose end moment is desired, and $\sum K$ is the summation of all stiffness factors present at the joint at which the end moment is desired. $K/\sum K$ is actually a proportional part of the $\sum K$, thus we can say that any unbalanced moment present at a joint is balanced by a balancing moment that is distributed to the ends of all members framing into that joint in proportion to their relative stiffnesses.

The beam stiffness is defined as the moment necessary to rotate the freely supported end of a member through an angle of unity when the opposite end is fixed against all displacements. Considering the beam with no applied loads in Figure 7.29, we may write the slope-deflection equation for M_{12} as

$$M_{12} = 2K(2\theta_1) = 4K\theta_1 \tag{6}$$

Figure 7.29   Figure 7.30

But if θ_1 is equal to unity, 7.8.6 becomes

$$M_{12} = 4K \qquad (7)$$

If the opposite end of the beam is hinged, as shown in Figure 7.30, we may write equation 7.5.4 as

$$M_{12} = 3K(\theta_1) \qquad (8)$$

or, since θ_1 is equal to unity, 7.8.8 becomes

$$M_{12} = 3K \qquad (9)$$

Comparing 7.8.7 to 7.8.9, we note that a member with one end hinged is three-fourths as stiff as the same member with that end fixed.

Thus far we have considered only the effects on joint 1 when the balancing moment is applied at joint 1. Consider again the beam in Figure 7.29 with M_{12} being some balancing moment applied at end 1. The slope-deflection equation for M_{21} is

$$M_{21} = 2K(\theta_1) = 2K\theta_1 \qquad (10)$$

Comparing equations 7.8.10 and 7.8.6, we see that M_{21} is exactly one-half of M_{12}. This ratio one-half is called the *carry-over factor* and signifies that when a balancing moment is applied to one end of a straight prismatic section, there will be carried over to the opposite end of that member a moment equal to one-half the value of the balancing moment.

We may thus summarize our discussion this far. First, all joints of a given structure are considered locked against displacement by some locking moment equal and opposite to the sum of the fixed end moments. Second, one joint is unlocked by applying an unlocking moment equal and opposite to the locking moment. This unlocking or balancing moment is distributed to all members present at that joint in accordance with their stiffness factors. Third, one-half of any balancing moment applied to one end of a member is carried over to the opposite end of that member.

Note that we have restricted our discussion to the special structure with but a single joint capable of rotating. This would not be the case for the bent shown in Figure 7.31. We can adapt our procedure to solve such problems by adding a fourth step, which is to relock a joint after it has been put in equilibrium and repeat the process for all other joints capable of rotating. We usually consider one cycle of distribution complete when all

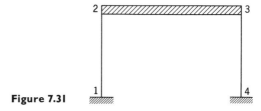

Figure 7.31

joints capable of rotating have been balanced one time. The degree of accuracy desired determines the number of cycles required but usually two or three cycles are sufficient. The following examples will illustrate the use of the moment distribution method of solving for end moments.*

7.9 Moment Distribution—Illustrative Problems

Example 7.9.1 Find the end moments for the beam shown in Figure 7.32a. One arrangement for the solution is shown beneath the figure. Relative values of EI are shown as 2 for both spans, therefore relative values of K are 3 for the left span and 4 for the right span. The distribution factor for end 2 of the member 12 is equal to $K_{12}/\Sigma K = \frac{3}{7} = 0.429$. The distribution factor for end 2 of the

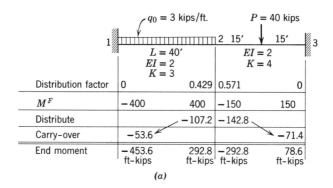

Distribution factor	0	0.429	0.571	0
M^F	−400	400	−150	150
Distribute		−107.2	−142.8	
Carry-over	−53.6			−71.4
End moment	−453.6 ft−kips	292.8 ft−kips	−292.8 ft−kips	78.6 ft−kips

(a)

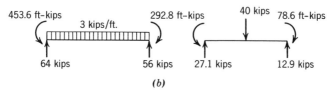

(b)

Figure 7.32

* The method of moment distribution was published in 1930 by Professor Hardy Cross. In spirit it is closely akin to the method of relaxation proposed in 1935 by Sir Richard Southwell in Great Britain. A method of balancing angle changes was published in 1936 by Professor Linton E. Grinter.

member 23 is equal to $K_{23}/\Sigma K = \frac{4}{7} = 0.571$. The distribution factors at the fixed ends are equal to zero since fixed joints are automatically in equilibrium. This relationship can be realized if we consider the stiffness of the support necessary to insure fixity. Such a condition of no rotation would require the stiffness of the support to be infinitely large compared to the stiffness of the member. Thus the distribution factor for end 1 of member 12 is equal to $K_{12}/\Sigma K$ $= 3/\infty = 0$.

Following the outlined procedure, we first lock all joints and determine the fixed end moments. The unbalanced fixed end moments at any joint are equal to the locking moment; thus at joint 2 the locking moment is $+250$ ft-kips. Second, we unlock one joint that is capable of rotating and permit it to rotate until equilibrium exists. Inspection of the figure indicates that this must be joint 2 since joints 1 and 3 are fixed and are therefore incapable of rotation. The balancing moment at joint 2 is -250 ft-kips and is distributed according to the distribution factors as shown. Thus a balancing moment of $(0.429)(-250) =$ -107.2 ft-kips is applied to end 2 of member 12 and a balancing moment of

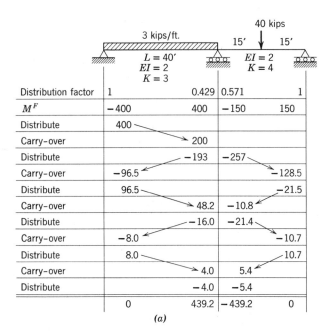

Distribution factor	1		0.429	0.571		1
M^F	-400		400	-150	150	
Distribute	400					
Carry-over			200			
Distribute			-193	-257		
Carry-over	-96.5					-128.5
Distribute	96.5				-21.5	
Carry-over			48.2	-10.8		
Distribute			-16.0	-21.4		
Carry-over	-8.0					-10.7
Distribute	8.0				10.7	
Carry-over			4.0	5.4		
Distribute			-4.0	-5.4		
	0		439.2	-439.2		0

(a)

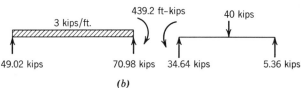

(b)

Figure 7.33

$(0.571)(-250) = -142.8$ ft-kips is applied to end 2 of member 23. Joint 2 is now in equilibrium. In applying a balancing moment of -107.2 ft-kips at 21 we also induce or carry over a moment of -53.6 ft-kips at 12 (see equation 7.8.10) and in applying a balancing moment of -142.8 ft-kips at 23, we also develop a moment of -71.4 ft-kips at 32. These are the carry-over moments shown on the figure. Since only one joint in this problem can rotate, only one cycle of distribution is necessary. The end moment at any joint is the summation of all moments which are acting at that joint. Thus

$$M_{12} = -453.6 \text{ ft-kips} \qquad M_{23} = -292.8 \text{ ft-kips}$$
$$M_{21} = 292.8 \text{ ft-kips} \qquad M_{32} = 78.6 \text{ ft-kips} \tag{12}$$

The free body diagrams are shown in Figure 7.32b.

Example 7.9.2 Find the end moments of the beam shown in Figure 7.33. Again we begin by locking all joints against rotation and determining the fixed end moments. The distribution factors are computed. Note that DF_{12} is equal to one because $DF_{12} = K_{12}/\Sigma K = \frac{6}{6} = 1$. One joint at a time is unlocked and balanced, moments carried over and then this joint relocked. This procedure is applied to all the joints which may rotate. The number of cycles is usually dependent on the degree of accuracy required. The final free body diagrams are shown in Figure 7.32b.

Example 7.9.3 Determine the end moments for all the members of the rigid frame shown in Figure 7.34a. The solution to the problem is shown in Figure 7.34b. The free body diagrams are shown in Figure 7.34d. From observation we see that M_{23} should be equal in magnitude but opposite in sign to M_{32}. The slight difference would have disappeared with one or two more cycles. The accuracy shown is satisfactory for design purposes.

Example 7.9.4 Determine the end moments for all of the members of the rigid frame shown in Figure 7.35a. Thus far none of the structures considered have experienced joint translation. Because of dissymmetry of the loading and of the frame, the structure shown in Figure 7.35a will experience joint translation or side sway. Our procedure must be modified to consider the effect of this side sway. First, analyze the structure, neglecting side sway. This solution is shown in Figure 7.35b. The free body diagrams of the columns for this solution are shown in Figure 7.35c. The horizontal reactions at the bases of the columns are the only horizontal forces acting on this structure and therefore should be equal and opposite. Figure 7.35d shows that they are not equal but are unbalanced by 6.98 kips to the left. We conclude that this unbalanced horizontal force must therefore be balanced by the horizontal forces resulting from side sway. To determine these horizontal forces, consider the structure shown in Figure 7.35e. Here we see the frame moved through some deflection Δ, keeping the joints locked against rotation. From equations 7.2.13 and 7.2.14 we see that this translation produces moments at the ends of member 12 and member 34 of

$$M_{12} = M_{21} = \frac{6EI_{12}\Delta}{L_{12}{}^2} \tag{13}$$

and

$$M_{43} = M_{34} = \frac{6EI_{34}\Delta}{L_{34}{}^2} \tag{14}$$

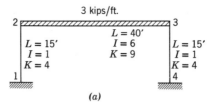

(a)

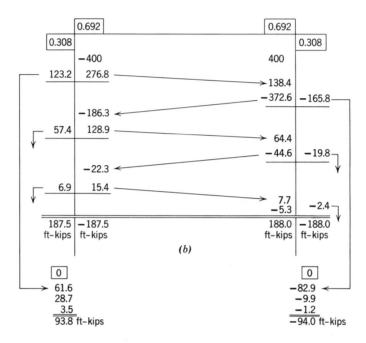

(b)

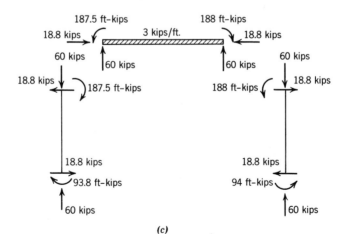

(c)

Figure 7.34

330

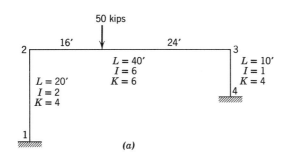

50 kips

2   16'   24'   3
L = 40'   L = 10'
I = 6   I = 1
L = 20'   K = 6   K = 4
I = 2   4
K = 4

1

(a)

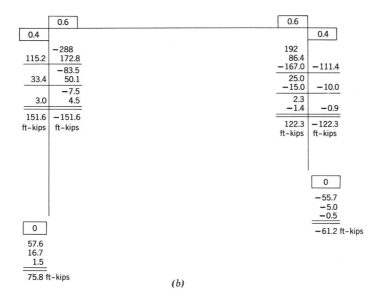

0.6				0.6	
0.4					0.4
	−288			192	
115.2	172.8			86.4	
	−83.5			−167.0	−111.4
33.4	50.1			25.0	
	−7.5			−15.0	−10.0
3.0	4.5			2.3	
				−1.4	−0.9
151.6	−151.6			122.3	−122.3
ft−kips	ft−kips			ft−kips	ft−kips

0
−55.7
−5.0
−0.5
−61.2 ft−kips

0

57.6
16.7
1.5
75.8 ft−kips

(b)

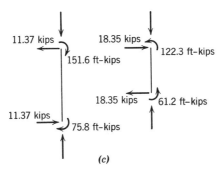

11.37 kips   18.35 kips   122.3 ft−kips
151.6 ft−kips

18.35 kips   61.2 ft−kips

11.37 kips   75.8 ft−kips

(c)

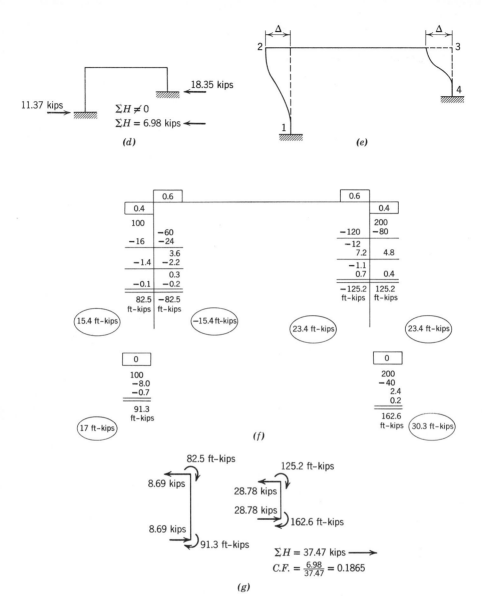

(d)

(e)

(f)

(g)

$\Sigma H = 37.47$ kips ⟶

$C.F. = \dfrac{6.98}{37.47} = 0.1865$

(h)

Figure 7.35

332

Since $I_{12}/I_{12} = K_{12}$ and $I_{34}/I_{34} = K_{34}$, 7.8.13 and 7.8.14 may be written as

$$M_{12} = M_{21} = \frac{6EK_{12}\Delta}{L_{12}} \tag{15}$$

$$M_{43} = M_{34} = \frac{6EK_{34}\Delta}{L_{34}} \tag{16}$$

Since Δ is unknown, the magnitude of these end moments cannot be determined, but equations 7.8.13 and 7.8.14 show the magnitudes to be related by the K/L values. From Figure 7.35a

$$\frac{K_{12}}{L_{12}} = \frac{4}{20} \qquad \frac{K_{34}}{L_{34}} = \frac{4}{10} \tag{17}$$

Therefore

$$M_{12} = M_{21} = \frac{M_{43}}{2} = \frac{M_{34}}{2} \tag{18}$$

Assume values for these end moments as shown in Figure 7.35f and perform the distribution. Figure 7.35g shows the column end moments resulting from the distribution of these assumed moments. The resulting shears amount to 37.47 kips to the right. We conclude that the assumed moments are too large since the system was unbalanced by only 6.98 kips to the left as shown in Figure 7.35d. Thus a correction factor must be applied to these end moments due to side sway. This correction factor will be

$$\text{C.F.} = \frac{\text{Horizontal force needed for equilibrium}}{\text{Horizontal force resulting from assumed end moments}}$$

or

$$\text{C.F.} = \frac{6.98}{37.47} = 0.1865 \tag{19}$$

The corrected end moments due to side sway are shown circled in Figure 7.35f. The end moments due to sway are added to the end moments neglecting sway as shown in Figure 7.35h.

Example 7.9.5 Determine the end moments for all of the members of the rigid frame shown in Figure 7.36a. As outlined in Example 7.9.4, the structure will first be analyzed, neglecting side sway. This analysis is shown in Figure 7.36b. The column end moments and horizontal forces are shown in Figure 7.36c, and indicate that side sway must produce horizontal forces amounting to 15.11 kips to the left. Figure 7.36d shows the distribution of the column end moments assumed due to side sway. The horizontal forces shown in Figure 7.36e total 18.7 kips to the right; thus the correction factor equals

$$\text{C.F.} = \frac{-15.11}{18.7} = -0.81 \tag{20}$$

The minus sign indicates that the directions of the assumed moments are incorrect. The final end moments are shown in Figure 7.36f.

7.10 Moment Distribution—Special Techniques

Special techniques for reducing the labor required will exist when there is complete symmetry and/or when hinged supports are present.

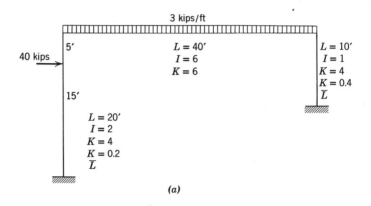

(a)

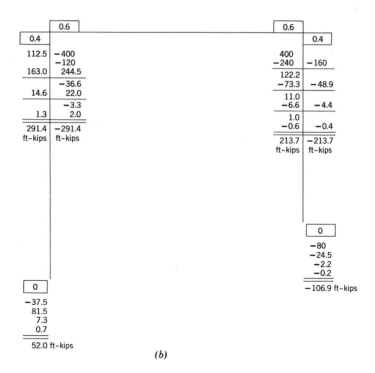

(b)

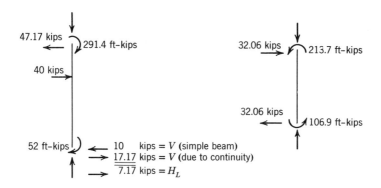

47.17 kips   291.4 ft-kips

40 kips

52 ft-kips   10   kips = V (simple beam)
              17.17 kips = V (due to continuity)
              7.17 kips = H_L

32.06 kips   213.7 ft-kips

32.06 kips   106.9 ft-kips

$\Sigma H = 15.11$ kips →

Need 15.11 kips ←

(c)

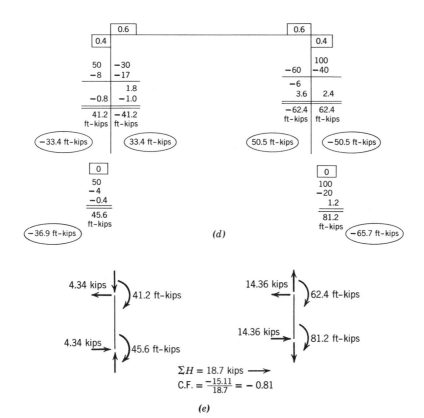

	0.6		0.6	
0.4				0.4
50	−30	−60	100 −40	
−8	−17			
	1.8	−6		
−0.8	−1.0	3.6	2.4	
41.2	−41.2	−62.4	62.4	
ft-kips	ft-kips	ft-kips	ft-kips	

(−33.4 ft-kips)   (33.4 ft-kips)   (50.5 ft-kips)   (−50.5 ft-kips)

0		0
50		100
−4		−20
−0.4		1.2
45.6		81.2
ft-kips		ft-kips

(−36.9 ft-kips)   (d)   (−65.7 ft-kips)

4.34 kips   41.2 ft-kips

4.34 kips   45.6 ft-kips

14.36 kips   62.4 ft-kips

14.36 kips   81.2 ft-kips

$\Sigma H = 18.7$ kips →

C.F. $= \dfrac{-15.11}{18.7} = -0.81$

(e)

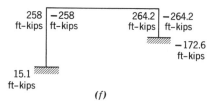

(f)

Figure 7.36

Consider the beams shown in Figure 7.37. If we write the slope-deflection equation for M_{21} for the beam of Figure 7.37a we find

$$M_{21} = 2EK_{12}(2\theta_2) + M_{21}{}^F \qquad (1)$$

and for the beam of Figure 7.37b, using 7.5.4, we find

$$M_{21} = 3EK_{12}(\theta_2) + M_{21}{}^F - \frac{M_{12}{}^F}{2} \qquad (2)$$

From a comparison of these two equations we draw the following conclusions.

(1) The span 12 of the beam of Figure 7.37b is three-fourths as stiff as the span 12 of the beam of Figure 7.37a.

(2) The fixed end moment at 2 when end 1 is hinged is decreased by half of the fixed end moment at 1.

The application of these conclusions is shown in the following example.

Example 7.10.1 Determine the end moments for the beam shown in Figure 7.38a. Applying the foregoing first conclusion, we find that the stiffness factor K for span 12 is modified from 1 to $\frac{3}{4}$. Applying the second conclusion, we have

$$M_{21}{}^F - \frac{M_{12}{}^F}{2} = 300 + 150 = 450 \text{ ft-kips} \qquad (3)$$

The solution is shown in Figure 7.38b.

Example 7.10.2 Determine the end moments of the members of the rigid frame shown in Figure 7.39a. From symmetry

$$\theta_2 = -\theta_3 \qquad (4)$$

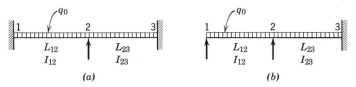

(a)   (b)

Figure 7.37

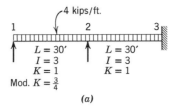

(a)

	1	2		3
Distribution factor		0.429	0.571	0
M^F		450	−300	300
Distribution		−64.4	−85.6	
Carry-over				−42.8
End moments		385.6 ft–kips	−385.6 ft–kips	257.2 ft–kips

(b)

Figure 7.38

therefore the slope-deflection equation for M_{23} is

$$M_{23} = 2EK_{23}(2\theta_2 - \theta_2) + M_{23}{}^F \qquad (5)$$

or

$$M_{23} = 2EK_{23}\theta_2 + M_{23}{}^F \qquad (6)$$

If end 3 had been fixed against rotation, the slope-deflection equation for M_{23} would have been

$$M_{23} = 2EK(2\theta_2) + M_{23}{}^F = 4EK\theta_2 + M_{23}{}^F \qquad (7)$$

From comparison of 7.10.6 and 7.10.7 we conclude that the beam 23 is half as stiff as it would have been if end 3 were fixed; therefore the stiffness factor K

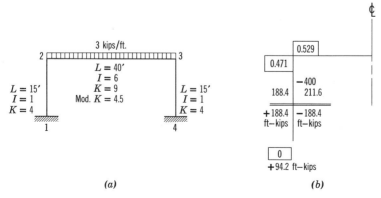

(a)   (b)

Figure 7.39

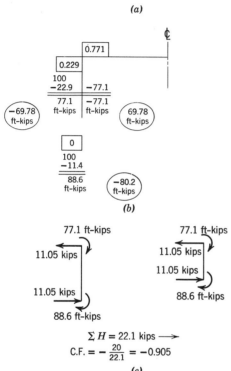

$L = 40'$
$I = 6$
$K = 9$
Mod. $K = \frac{3}{2}(9) = 13.5$

20 kips 2   3

$L = 15'$ $L = 15'$
$I = 1$ $I = 1$
1 $K = 4$ $K = 4$

4

(a)

0.771

0.229

100
−22.9   −77.1

77.1   −77.1
-69.78 ft–kips   ft–kips   69.78
ft–kips   ft–kips

0

100
−11.4

88.6   −80.2
ft–kips ft–kips

(b)

77.1 ft–kips   77.1 ft–kips

11.05 kips   11.05 kips

                             11.05 kips

11.05 kips

                             88.6 ft–kips

88.6 ft–kips

$\Sigma\, H = 22.1$ kips $\longrightarrow$

C.F. $= -\dfrac{20}{22.1} = -0.905$

(c)   **Figure 7.40**

may be modified as shown in Figure 7.39a. Because of this symmetry and modification, no carry-over is made to the right half of the structure. The solution is shown in Figure 7.39b.

Example 7.10.3 Determine the end moments for the members of the rigid frame shown in Figure 7.40a. Here θ_2 equals θ_3 and the slope-deflection equation for M_{23} is

$$M_{23} = 2EK(2\theta_2 + \theta_3) = 6EK\theta_2 \tag{8}$$

If end 3 had been fixed against rotation, the slope-deflection equation for M_{23} would have been

$$M_{23} = 2EK(2\theta_2) = 4EK\theta_2 \tag{9}$$

The stiffness factor for the beam 23 may be modified as shown in Figure 7.40a. No carry-over is made to the right half of the structure because of this modification. The loading shown in Figure 7.40a does not produce any fixed end moments; therefore fixed end moments at the ends of the columns have to be assumed. The distribution of these moments is shown in Figure 7.40b. The shears produced by the resulting end moments are shown in Figure 7.40c. For equilibrium to exist, these shears would have to equal 20 kips to the left; therefore a correction factor

$$\text{C.F.} = -\frac{20}{22.1} = -0.905 \tag{10}$$

needs to be applied to all end moments. These corrected end moments are shown circled in Figure 7.40b.

7.11   Moment Distribution—Complex Frames

Example 7.11.1   Determine the end moments of all members of the structure shown in Figure 7.41a. The dissymmetry of the structure and of the loading causes side sway. Following our procedure, we analyze the structure, neglecting side sway as shown in Figure 7.41b. Figure 7.41c shows the horizontal forces to be unbalanced by an amount of 0.26 kips to the right. Before we apply the assumed moments due to sway, we must give consideration to the condition of two of these columns being fixed at the base and the other column being hinged at the base. Consider the column shown in Figure 7.42a being moved through some deflection Δ. The conjugate beam is shown in Figure 7.42b, and solving for Δ we get

$$\frac{M_{21}L}{EI_0}(\tfrac{1}{2})(\tfrac{2}{3})(L) - \frac{M_{21}L}{EI_0}\left(\frac{L}{3}\right)(\tfrac{1}{2}) - \Delta = 0 \tag{1}$$

or

$$M_{21} = \frac{6EI_0\Delta}{L^2} \tag{2}$$

The same column is shown in Figure 7.42c but with the base hinged. The conjugate beam is shown in Figure 7.42d, and solving for Δ we get

$$\frac{M_{21}L}{EI_0}\left(\frac{L}{2}\right) - \frac{M_{21}}{EI_0}\left(\frac{L}{2}\right)\left(\frac{L}{3}\right) - \Delta = 0 \tag{3}$$

or

$$M_{21} = \frac{3EI_0\Delta}{L^2} \tag{4}$$

Thus we conclude that the fixed end moments at the top and bottom of the fixed end column are twice the fixed end moment at the top of the hinged column. Applying this conclusion to problem 7.41, we assume fixed end moments at the ends of the exterior column to be 30 ft-kips and the fixed end moment at the top of the center column to be 60 ft-kips. The distribution of these moments is shown in Figure 7.41d. The resulting end moments develop horizontal forces equal to 9.93 kips to the right as shown in Figure 7.41e; therefore these end moments must be corrected by a correction factor equal to

$$\text{C.F.} = -\frac{0.26}{9.93} = -0.02618 \tag{5}$$

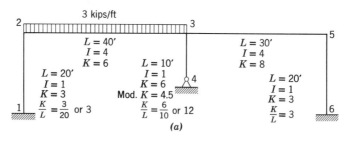

3 kips/ft

| 2 | | 3 | | 5 |

$L = 40'$
$I = 4$
$K = 6$

$L = 30'$
$I = 4$
$K = 8$

$L = 20'$
$I = 1$
$K = 3$
$\frac{K}{L} = \frac{3}{20}$ or 3

$L = 10'$
$I = 1$
$K = 6$
Mod. $K = 4.5$
$\frac{K}{L} = \frac{6}{10}$ or 12

4

$L = 20'$
$I = 1$
$K = 3$
$\frac{K}{L} = 3$

1

6

(a)

ft–kips 367.3 | −217.9 ft–kips

−0.4	−0.5
0.5	0.7
−3.0	−4.1
3.8	5.6
−22.9	−30.7
28.8	42.0
−172.8	−230.9
133.3	
400.0	

| 0.667 | | 0.324 | 0.433 | | 0.727 | |
| 0.333 | | | 0.243 | | | 0.273 |

0.333
133.3

−400.0
266.7

−129.6
−17.2
−2.3
−0.3

−149.4
ft–kips

−115.5
84.0
−15.4
11.2
−2.0
1.5
−0.3
0.2

−36.3
ft–kips

31.5
4.2
0.5
0.1

36.3
ft–kips

28.8 | 57.6
−86.4

3.8 | 7.7
−11.5

0.5 | 1.0
−1.5

166.4
ft–kips

−166.4
ft–kips

| 0 | | | 0 |

66.6
14.4
1.9
0.2
83.1 ft–kips

15.8
2.1
0.3
18.2
ft–kips

(b)

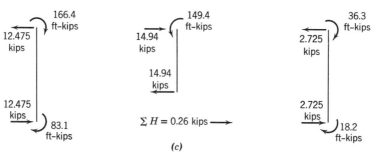

166.4
ft–kips

12.475
kips

12.475
kips

83.1
ft–kips

149.4
ft–kips

14.94
kips

14.94
kips

$\Sigma H = 0.26$ kips →

36.3
ft–kips

2.725
kips

2.725
kips

18.2
ft–kips

(c)

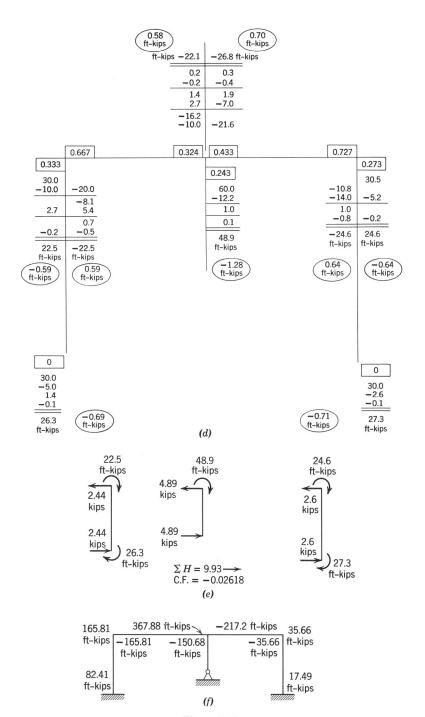

Figure 7.41

341

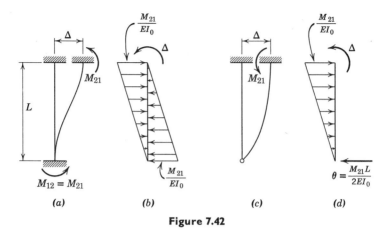

Figure 7.42

The corrected moments due to sway are shown circled in Figure 7.41d and the final end moments are

$$M_{12} = +82.4 \text{ ft-kips} \qquad M_{32} = +367.9 \text{ ft-kips}$$
$$M_{21} = +165.8 \text{ ft-kips} \qquad M_{34} = -150.7 \text{ ft-kips}$$
$$M_{23} = -165.8 \text{ ft-kips} \qquad M_{35} = -217.2 \text{ ft-kips} \tag{6}$$
$$M_{56} = +35.7 \text{ ft-kips} \qquad M_{65} = +17.5 \text{ ft-kips}$$

Example 7.11.2   Determine the end moments of the members of the structure shown in Figure 7.43a. Since $\theta_2 = \theta_5$ and $\theta_3 = \theta_4$, the stiffness factors for the two girders may be modified and only half of the frame considered. An assumed fixed end moment of 50 ft-kips is applied to the top and bottom of the top story columns. These moments are distributed as shown in Figure 7.43b and the resulting shears are shown in Figure 7.43c. A fixed end moment of 50 ft-kips is also applied to the ends of the bottom story columns. The distribution of these moments is shown in Figure 7.43d and the resulting shears are shown in Figure 7.43e. In the application of the fixed end moments to the top story columns, we assumed the structure to act as shown in Figure 7.43i and in the application of the fixed end moments to the bottom story columns we assumed the structure to act as shown in Figure 7.43j.

We may correct these assumed moments by making use of the conditional equation $\Sigma H = 0$. Passing the plane 1–1 through the structure just above the bottom story and isolating the top part as a free body, we may write an equation which states that the sum of all horizontal forces above plane 1–1 equals zero. This equation is

$$S_{TT}F_1 + S_{TB}F_2 + 5 = 0 \tag{7}$$

where S_{TT} is the shear in the top-story columns due to the application of the fixed end moments to the top story; F_1 is a correction factor to correct these assumed fixed end moments applied to the top story; S_{TB} is the shear in the top-story columns due to the application of the fixed end moments to the bottom story; and F_2 is a correction factor to correct these assumed fixed end moments applied to the bottom story.

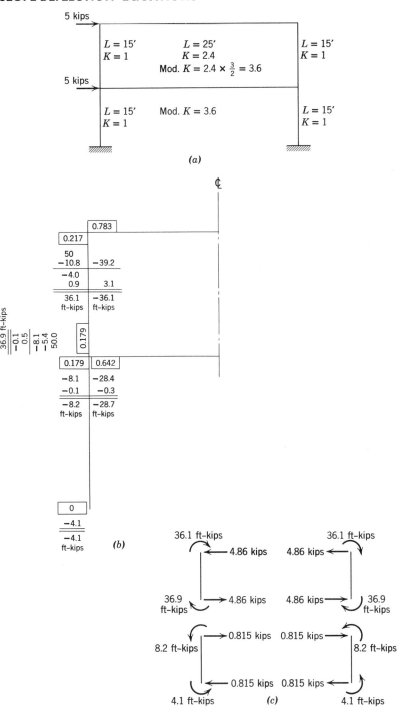

5 kips

$L = 15'$ $L = 25'$ $L = 15'$
$K = 1$ $K = 2.4$ $K = 1$
              Mod. $K = 2.4 \times \frac{3}{2} = 3.6$

5 kips

$L = 15'$ Mod. $K = 3.6$ $L = 15'$
$K = 1$ $K = 1$

(a)

¢

0.783

0.217

50
−10.8   −39.2
−4.0
0.9   3.1

36.1   −36.1
ft-kips ft-kips

36.9 ft-kips
−0.1
0.5
−8.1
−5.4
50.0

0.179

0.179   0.642

−8.1   −28.4
−0.1   −0.3

−8.2   −28.7
ft-kips ft-kips

0

−4.1

−4.1
ft-kips   (b)

36.1 ft-kips   36.1 ft-kips

←—— 4.86 kips   4.86 kips ←——

36.9   ——→ 4.86 kips   4.86 kips ——→   36.9
ft-kips   ft-kips

——→ 0.815 kips   0.815 kips ——→
8.2 ft-kips   8.2 ft-kips

←—— 0.815 kips   0.815 kips ←——
4.1 ft-kips   (c)   4.1 ft-kips

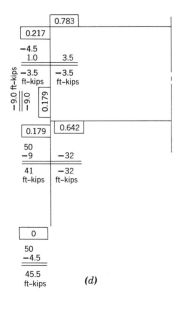

-9.0 ft-kips

(d)

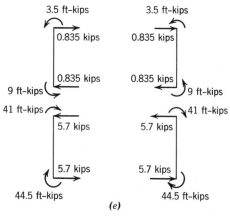

3.5 ft-kips   3.5 ft-kips

0.835 kips   0.835 kips

0.835 kips   0.835 kips

9 ft-kips   9 ft-kips

41 ft-kips   41 ft-kips

5.7 kips   5.7 kips

5.7 kips   5.7 kips

44.5 ft-kips   44.5 ft-kips

(e)

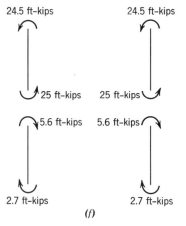

24.5 ft-kips   24.5 ft-kips

25 ft-kips   25 ft-kips

5.6 ft-kips   5.6 ft-kips

2.7 ft-kips   2.7 ft-kips

(f)

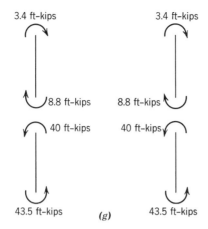

3.4 ft-kips   3.4 ft-kips

8.8 ft-kips   8.8 ft-kips

40 ft-kips   40 ft-kips

43.5 ft-kips   43.5 ft-kips
(g)

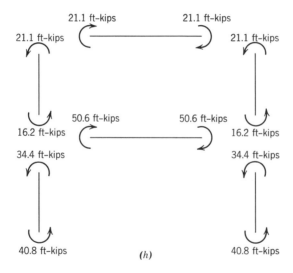

21.1 ft-kips   21.1 ft-kips
21.1 ft-kips   21.1 ft-kips

50.6 ft-kips   50.6 ft-kips
16.2 ft-kips   16.2 ft-kips

34.4 ft-kips   34.4 ft-kips

40.8 ft-kips   40.8 ft-kips
(h)

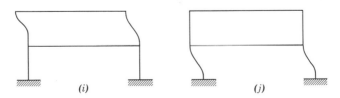

(i)   (j)

Figure 7.43

Passing the plane 2–2 just above the base of the structure and isolating everything above this plane as a free body, we write an equation which states that the sum of all horizontal forces above plane 2–2 equals zero. This equation is

$$S_{BT}F_1 + S_{BB}F_2 + 10 = 0 \qquad (8)$$

where S_{BT} is the shear in the bottom-story columns due to the application of the fixed end moments to the top story, and S_{BB} is the shear in the bottom-story columns due to the application of the fixed end moments to the bottom story.

Solving 7.11.7 and 7.11.8, we find

$$F_2 = -0.975 \qquad F_1 = -0.68 \qquad (9)$$

Applying the correction factor F_1 to the end moments of the columns in Figure 7.43c, we obtain the end moments shown in Figure 7.43f. Applying the correction factor F_2 to the end moments of the columns in Figure 7.43e, we obtain the end moments shown in Figure 7.43g. The final end moments are the sum of the end moments as shown in Figure 7.43h.

This procedure may be applied to a structure having more than two stories, but a conditional equation such as 7.11.7 and 7.11.8 is necessary for each story.

Problems

7.1 There are no problems for this section.

7.2 There are no problems for this section.

7.3.1 Using the slope-deflection equations, prepare a complete analysis of the beams shown. This analysis should include shear and moment diagrams.

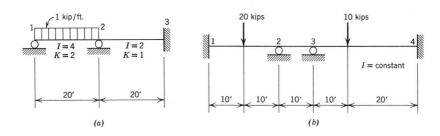

(a)

(b)

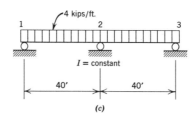

(c)

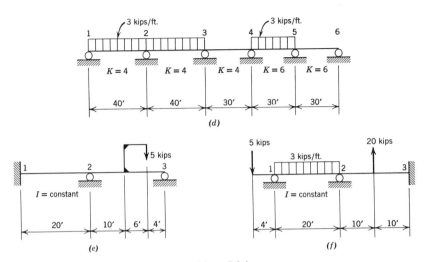

(d)

(e)

(f)

Problem 7.3.1

7.3.2 Determine the slope at points 1 and 2 of the beams shown in Problem 7.3.1(*a, f*).

7.4.1 Using the slope-deflection equations, prepare a complete analysis of the rigid frames shown.

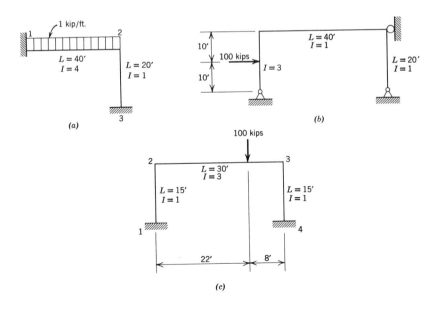

(a)

(b)

(c)

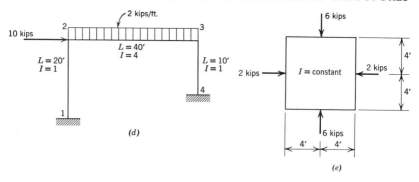

(d)

(e)

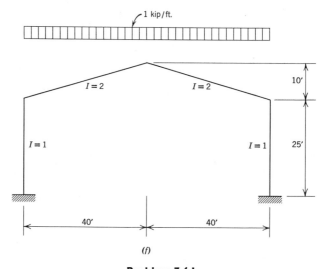

(f)

Problem 7.4.1

7.5.1   Solve Problem 7.3.1(a, c, d, e, f) by the special techniques of §7.5.

7.6.1   Using the slope-deflection equations, prepare a complete analysis of the rigid frames shown.

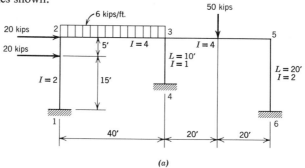

(a)

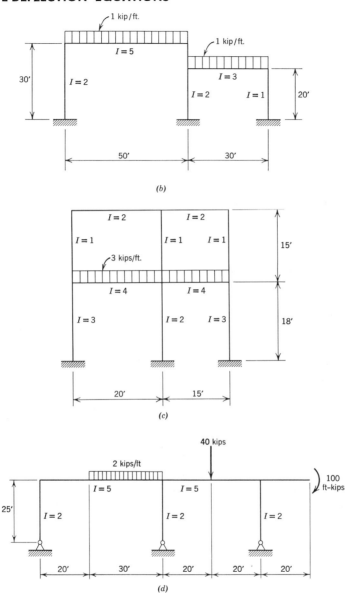

(b)

(c)

(d)

Problem 7.6.1

7.7 There are no problems for this section.

7.8.1 Rework Problem 7.3.1 using the method of moment distribution.

7.9.1 Rework Problem 7.4.1 using the method of moment distribution.

7.10.1 Rework Problem 7.5.1 using the method of moment distribution.

7.11.1 Rework Problem 7.6.1 using the method of moment distribution.

8 MATRIX METHODS IN STRUCTURAL ANALYSIS

8.1 Matrices and Linear Algebraic Equations

Many of the problems encountered in structural mechanics can be expressed mathematically by a set of linear algebraic equations. The analysis of bar forces in trusses and end moments in frames are but two examples previously encountered in this book.

This method of approaching structures has been by-passed during this century because of the great labor involved in solving sets of simultaneous equations manually. Methods based more on physical than on mathematical techniques, such as the method of joints and the method of moment distribution, have enjoyed wide use. But as the engineer attempts to analyze more and more complicated and sophisticated structures, even these methods, when applicable, become excessively tedious to use, especially when three-dimensional framed structures are treated.

Exact analysis of many structures was impractical until the advent of the large scale electronic computers. Today, however, with the wide availability of such machines we have reevaluated our techniques for solving structures, and we find that the classical solutions involving sets of simultaneous equations are once again preferred. They exhibit the special, desirable characteristic of being relatively simple to "program." The fact that much tedious work is required in solving the equations is of little significance since the nature of the work consists of the kind of routine computation in which computers excel, both in speed and accuracy.

In this section we discuss some of the basic notions of *matrix algebra*, a tool that lends itself beautifully to the handling of large sets of equations. It might be said that matrix analysis is the natural language of the engineer who treats complicated framed structures.

A set of linear algebraic equations of the form

$$
\begin{aligned}
a_{11}x_1 + a_{12}x_2 + a_{13}x_3 + a_{14}x_4 + \cdots + a_{1n}x_n &= c_1 \\
a_{21}x_1 + a_{22}x_2 + a_{23}x_3 + a_{24}x_4 + \cdots + a_{2n}x_n &= c_2 \\
a_{31}x_1 + a_{32}x_2 + a_{33}x_3 + a_{34}x_4 + \cdots + a_{3n}x_n &= c_3 \\
a_{41}x_1 + a_{42}x_2 + a_{43}x_3 + a_{44}x_4 + \cdots + a_{4n}x_n &= c_4 \\
\cdots \quad \cdots \quad \cdots \quad \cdots \quad \cdots \quad \cdots \quad \cdots & \\
a_{m1}x_1 + a_{m2}x_2 + a_{m3}x_3 + a_{m4}x_4 + \cdots + a_{mn}x_n &= c_m
\end{aligned}
\tag{1}
$$

may be interpreted as a linear transformation of the set of x values into the set of c values. The exact nature of the transformation is specified by the coefficients a_{ij}. The rectangular array of these coefficients is called a *matrix*. It has m rows and n columns. The typical element a_{ij} is located in the ith row and the jth column. It is conventional to represent the set of x values and the set of c values as $\{x_i\}$ and $\{c_i\}$, or $\mathbf{x}$ and $\mathbf{c}$, where the braces indicate a single column matrix but the bold-face type suggests a matrix of any shape. Thus,

$$
\mathbf{x} = \{x_i\} =
\begin{Bmatrix}
x_1 \\
x_2 \\
x_3 \\
x_4 \\
\cdots \\
\cdots \\
x_n
\end{Bmatrix}
\qquad
\mathbf{c} = \{c_i\} =
\begin{Bmatrix}
c_1 \\
c_2 \\
c_3 \\
c_4 \\
\cdots \\
\cdots \\
c_n
\end{Bmatrix}
\tag{2}
$$

The rectangular array of elements is conventionally represented in the form

$$
\mathbf{a} = [a_{ij}] =
\begin{bmatrix}
a_{11} & a_{12} & a_{13} & a_{14} & \cdots & a_{1n} \\
a_{21} & a_{22} & a_{23} & a_{24} & \cdots & a_{2n} \\
a_{31} & a_{32} & a_{33} & a_{34} & \cdots & a_{3n} \\
a_{41} & a_{42} & a_{43} & a_{44} & \cdots & a_{4n} \\
\cdots & \cdots & \cdots & \cdots & \cdots & \cdots \\
a_{m1} & a_{m2} & a_{m3} & a_{m4} & \cdots & a_{mn}
\end{bmatrix}
\tag{3}
$$

Using these forms, we may rewrite 8.1.1 in either of the following ways

$$
[a_{ij}]\{x_i\} = \{c_i\} \qquad \text{or} \qquad \mathbf{ax} = \mathbf{c}
\tag{4}
$$

Any equation of 8.1.1 may also be written in the form

$$
\sum_{k=1}^{n} a_{ik}x_k = c_i, \qquad \text{where } i = 1, 2, 3, \cdots
\tag{5}
$$

and where the summation is taken only over the k's. Using this we may rewrite 8.1.4 as

$$[a_{ij}]\,\{x_i\} = \{c_i\} = \left\{\sum_{k=1}^{n} a_{ik}x_k\right\} \tag{6}$$

From 8.1.6 we get our definition of matrix multiplication.

Expression 8.1.5 is a special case of the more general expansion

$$\sum_k a_{ik}b_{kj} = a_{i1}b_{1j} + a_{i2}b_{2j} + a_{i3}b_{3j} + \cdots + a_{in}b_{nj} \tag{7}$$

which is defined as the *inner product* or *scalar product* of the ith row of the matrix $[a_{ij}]$ with the jth column of the matrix $[b_{ij}]$, and reads: "The sum of products of the elements of the ith row of matrix **a** with the corresponding elements of the jth column of matrix **b**."

We use this expression to write a more general expression for 8.1.6 which is valid for matrices having several columns:

$$[a_{ij}]\,[b_{ij}] = (\mathbf{ab}) = \left[\sum_k a_{ik}b_{kj}\right] = [c_{ij}] \tag{8}$$

where the form with square brackets or with parentheses may equally well be used. This states that the element of the ith row and the jth column of the product matrix **c** is equal to the scalar product of the ith row of **a** and the jth column of **b**. When **b** is a single column matrix such as **x**, it is evident that the product $(\mathbf{ab})$ will also be a single column matrix.

The product $(\mathbf{ab})$ is defined only if the number of columns in **a** equals the number of rows in **b**. It is easily verified that the product $(\mathbf{ab})$ is not necessarily the same as the product $(\mathbf{ba})$. Confusion can be avoided if we speak of the first as the matrix **b** *premultiplied* by the matrix **a** and the second as the matrix **b** *postmultiplied* by the matrix **a**.

Example 8.1.1 Evaluate the following matrix products.

$$\begin{bmatrix} 1 & 0 \\ 2 & 4 \\ 3 & 5 \end{bmatrix}\begin{bmatrix} 5 & 1 & 2 \\ 0 & 3 & 4 \end{bmatrix} = \begin{bmatrix} (1\times5+0\times0)(1\times1+0\times3)(1\times2+0\times4) \\ (2\times5+4\times0)(2\times1+4\times3)(2\times2+4\times4) \\ (3\times5+5\times0)(3\times1+5\times3)(3\times2+5\times4) \end{bmatrix}$$

$$= \begin{bmatrix} 5 & 1 & 2 \\ 10 & 14 & 20 \\ 15 & 18 & 26 \end{bmatrix} \tag{9}$$

$$\begin{bmatrix} 5 & 1 & 2 \\ 0 & 3 & 4 \end{bmatrix}\begin{bmatrix} 1 & 0 \\ 2 & 4 \\ 3 & 5 \end{bmatrix} = \begin{bmatrix} (5\times1+1\times2+2\times3)(5\times0+1\times4+2\times5) \\ (0\times1+3\times2+4\times3)(0\times0+3\times4+4\times5) \end{bmatrix}$$

$$= \begin{bmatrix} 13 & 14 \\ 18 & 32 \end{bmatrix} \tag{10}$$

The sum of two matrices is given by

$$[a_{ij}] + [b_{ij}] = [a_{ij} + b_{ij}] = [c_{ij}] \tag{11}$$

which reads: "The element of the summation matrix **c** which lies in the ith row and the jth column is equal to the sum of the elements in the ith rows and the jth columns of the two matrices **a** and **b**."

The product of a constant λ and a matrix a is given by

$$\lambda\mathbf{a} = \lambda[a_{ij}] = [\lambda a_{ij}] \tag{12}$$

Each element of the **a** matrix is multiplied by λ in order to give the new product matrix.

Furthermore, it should be noted that the addition of matrices is commutative:

$$\mathbf{a} + \mathbf{b} = \mathbf{b} + \mathbf{a} \tag{13}$$

and associative:

$$\mathbf{a} + (\mathbf{b} + \mathbf{c}) = (\mathbf{a} + \mathbf{b}) + \mathbf{c} \tag{14}$$

Also, the multiplication of matrices is associative:

$$\mathbf{a}(\mathbf{bc}) = (\mathbf{ab})\mathbf{c} \tag{15}$$

and distributive:

$$\mathbf{a}(\mathbf{b} + \mathbf{c}) = \mathbf{ab} + \mathbf{ac} \tag{16}$$

Associated with any square matrix **a**, we have the *determinant*

$$|\mathbf{a}| = \begin{vmatrix} a_{11} & a_{12} & \cdots & a_{1n} \\ a_{21} & a_{22} & \cdots & a_{2n} \\ \cdots & \cdots & \cdots & \cdots \\ a_{n1} & a_{n2} & \cdots & a_{nn} \end{vmatrix} \tag{17}$$

The *minor* $\mathscr{M}_{ij}$ of any element a_{ij} is the determinant resulting from the determinant $|\mathbf{a}|$ when all the elements of the ith row and the jth column have been deleted. The *cofactor* A_{ij} of any element a_{ij} is defined by the relation

$$A_{ij} = (-1)^{i+j}\mathscr{M}_{ij} \tag{18}$$

The numerical value of a determinant is equal to the sum of the products of the elements of any single row or column by their cofactors as given by the *Laplace expansion formula*.

$$|\mathbf{a}| = \sum_k a_{ik}A_{ik} \tag{19}$$

The following numerical example will illustrate these formulas.

Example 8.1.2   For the square matrix given below, find the minors and cofactors of every element of the third row and the value of the determinant.

$$\mathbf{a} = [a_{ij}] = \begin{bmatrix} 1 & 2 & 3 \\ 4 & 5 & 6 \\ 5 & 4 & 3 \end{bmatrix} \tag{20}$$

The calculations involve the evaluation of a determinant for a 2×2 matrix.

It has the value $a_{11}a_{22} - a_{12}a_{21}$. Using this, we find that the minors of the elements a_{3j} are

$$\mathscr{M}_{31} = 2 \times 6 - 5 \times 3 = -3$$
$$\mathscr{M}_{32} = 1 \times 6 - 4 \times 3 = -6 \tag{21}$$
$$\mathscr{M}_{33} = 1 \times 5 - 4 \times 2 = -3$$

The cofactors A_{3j} are given by

$$A_{31} = (-1)^{3+1}(-3) = -3$$
$$A_{32} = (-1)^{3+2}(-6) = +6 \tag{22}$$
$$A_{33} = (-1)^{3+3}(-3) = -3$$

The determinant of the 3×3 matrix is now found, from 8.1.19, to be

$$|\mathbf{a}| = \sum_{k=1}^{3} a_{3k}A_{3k} = (5)(-3) + (4)(+6) + (3)(-3) = 0 \tag{23}$$

The value of the determinant could have been found equally well by using the elements of any other row or the elements of any of the columns.

Returning now to a set of linear algebraic equations, 8.1.1, we state *Cramer's rule** for finding the value of any of the unknowns, say x_s:

$$x_s = \frac{|\mathbf{a}_s|}{|\mathbf{a}|} \tag{24}$$

where the symbol $|\mathbf{a}_s|$ is used to denote the determinant of the coefficients of $\mathbf{x}$ (the $\mathbf{a}$ matrix) with the elements of the s column replaced by the elements of the $\mathbf{c}$ matrix. When all the elements of the $\mathbf{c}$ matrix are zero, the set of algebraic equations is said to be *homogeneous* and x_s, by 8.1.19, will have the value of zero unless the determinant $|\mathbf{a}|$ is zero itself, when the values are not defined. We may say, in general, that for a set of linear, algebraic, homogeneous equations to have nontrivial ($x_s \neq 0$) solutions, it is necessary that the determinant of the coefficient matrix be equal to zero.

Example 8.1.3   Find the value of x_2 in the set of equations given below using Cramer's rule.

$$x_1 + 2x_2 + 3x_3 = 4$$
$$x_2 + 4x_3 = 2 \tag{25}$$
$$x_1 + x_2 + x_3 = 0$$

This may be written in the matrix form

$$\begin{bmatrix} 1 & 2 & 3 \\ 0 & 1 & 4 \\ 1 & 1 & 1 \end{bmatrix} \begin{Bmatrix} x_1 \\ x_2 \\ x_3 \end{Bmatrix} = \begin{Bmatrix} 4 \\ 2 \\ 0 \end{Bmatrix} \tag{26}$$

* For a discussion of Cramer's rule and matrix analysis in general, the reader is referred to F. B. Hildebrand, *Methods of Applied Mathematics*, Prentice-Hall, Englewood Cliffs, N. J., 1952.

and the value of x_2 is found to be

$$x_2 = \frac{\begin{vmatrix} 1 & 4 & 3 \\ 0 & 2 & 4 \\ 1 & 0 & 1 \end{vmatrix}}{\begin{vmatrix} 1 & 2 & 3 \\ 0 & 1 & 4 \\ 1 & 1 & 1 \end{vmatrix}} = \frac{12}{2} = 6 \tag{27}$$

Several other matrix forms will now be defined.

(a) *Transpose* of **a**, designated by $\mathbf{a}^T$, and defined as

$$\mathbf{a}^T = [a_{ji}] = \begin{bmatrix} a_{11} & a_{21} & \cdots & a_{m1} \\ a_{12} & a_{22} & \cdots & a_{m2} \\ \cdots & \cdots & \cdots & \cdots \\ a_{1n} & a_{2n} & \cdots & a_{mn} \end{bmatrix} \tag{28}$$

It is easily verified that

$$(\mathbf{ab})^T = \mathbf{b}^T \mathbf{a}^T \tag{29}$$

(b) *Adjoint* of **a**, designated by Adj **a**, and defined by

$$\text{Adj } \mathbf{a} = [A_{ji}] = \begin{bmatrix} A_{11} & A_{21} & \cdots & A_{n1} \\ A_{12} & A_{22} & \cdots & A_{n2} \\ \cdots & \cdots & \cdots & \cdots \\ A_{1n} & A_{2n} & \cdots & A_{nm} \end{bmatrix} \tag{30}$$

where A_{ij} is the cofactor of a_{ij} and where the matrix is square. From this it can be shown that

$$\text{Adj } (\mathbf{ab}) = (\text{Adj } \mathbf{b} \cdot \text{Adj } \mathbf{a}) \tag{31}$$

(c) *Unit matrix*, designated by I, a square matrix defined by

$$\mathbf{I} = \begin{bmatrix} 1 & 0 & 0 & \cdots & 0 \\ 0 & 1 & 0 & \cdots & 0 \\ \cdot & \cdot & \cdot & \cdots & \cdot \\ 0 & 0 & 0 & \cdots & 1 \end{bmatrix} \tag{32}$$

where the line of ones is called the *principal diagonal*.

(d) *Null matrix*, in which all elements are zero.

(e) *Diagonal matrix*, in which we have a square array of numbers with all equal to zero except those on the principal diagonal. This matrix is defined by

$$\mathbf{d} = [d_i \, \delta_{ij}] = [d_j \, \delta_{ij}] \tag{33}$$

where *Kronecker delta*, δ_{ij}, has the meaning

$$\delta_{pq} = \begin{cases} 0, \text{ when } p \neq q \\ 1, \text{ when } p = q \end{cases} \tag{34}$$

(*f*) *Scalar matrix*, a diagonal matrix with all elements of the diagonal equal to each other.

(*g*) *Singular matrix*, a square matrix whose determinant vanishes.

(*h*) *Symmetric matrix*, in which $a_{ij} = a_{ji}$.

(*i*) *Skew-symmetric matrix*, in which $a_{ij} = -a_{ji}$ and $a_{ii} = 0$.

(*j*) *Inverse matrix* (or reciprocal matrix) of **a**, designated by $\mathbf{a}^{-1}$ and defined so as to give

$$\mathbf{aa}^{-1} = \mathbf{a}^{-1}\mathbf{a} = \mathbf{I} \tag{35}$$

Elements of the inverse matrix are given by

$$a_{ij}^{-1} = \frac{A_{ji}}{|\mathbf{a}|} \tag{36}$$

A matrix can have only one inverse when an inverse exists. Note that

$$(\mathbf{ab})^{-1} = \mathbf{b}^{-1}\mathbf{a}^{-1} \tag{37}$$

This states that the inverse of a product is the product of the inverses in reverse order.

Example 8.1.4   Find the transpose, adjoint and inverse matrix of

$$\mathbf{a} = \begin{bmatrix} 19{,}000 & -9{,}000 & 0 \\ -9{,}000 & 17{,}000 & -8{,}000 \\ 0 & -8{,}000 & 8{,}000 \end{bmatrix} \tag{38}$$

The transpose is given by

$$\mathbf{a}^T = \begin{bmatrix} 19{,}000 & -9{,}000 & 0 \\ -9{,}000 & 17{,}000 & -8{,}000 \\ 0 & -8{,}000 & 8{,}000 \end{bmatrix} \tag{39}$$

which is identical to **a** since **a** is symmetric. The adjoint is given by

$$\text{Adj } \mathbf{a} = 10^6 \begin{bmatrix} 72 & 72 & 72 \\ 72 & 152 & 152 \\ 72 & 152 & 242 \end{bmatrix} \tag{40}$$

The determinant is found to be

$$|\mathbf{a}| = 10^9[19(136 - 64) - (-9)(-72)] = 72 \times 10^{10} \tag{41}$$

Finally, the inverse matrix is

$$\mathbf{a}^{-1} = 10^{-3} \begin{bmatrix} 0.1000 & 0.1000 & 0.1000 \\ 0.1000 & 0.2111 & 0.2111 \\ 0.1000 & 0.2111 & 0.3361 \end{bmatrix} \tag{42}$$

The modern electronic computer is capable of solving for the inverse of very large matrices, but the person without benefit of such a computer will find the required calculations to be prohibitive if there are more than three rows and three columns. We shall confine our attention to problems involving the inverting of such small matrices.

Example 8.1.5 Solve for the unknown values of $\mathbf{x}$ in the following set of equations using the inverse matrix.

$$
\begin{aligned}
19{,}000x_1 - 9{,}000x_2 &= 1000 \\
-9{,}000x_1 + 17{,}000x_2 - 8{,}000x_3 &= 2000 \\
-8{,}000x_2 + 8{,}000x_3 &= 500
\end{aligned}
\tag{43}
$$

We begin by writing this in the matrix form

$$
\mathbf{ax} = \mathbf{b} \tag{44}
$$

where $\mathbf{a}$ is the matrix of coefficients of $\mathbf{x}$ and is identical with 8.1.38 in the previous example. We have

$$
\mathbf{x} = \begin{Bmatrix} x_1 \\ x_2 \\ x_3 \end{Bmatrix} \qquad \mathbf{b} = \begin{Bmatrix} 1000 \\ 2000 \\ 500 \end{Bmatrix} \tag{45}
$$

We premultiply both sides of 8.1.44 by the inverse of $\mathbf{a}$ to find

$$
\mathbf{a}^{-1}\mathbf{ax} = \mathbf{a}^{-1}\mathbf{b} \tag{46}
$$

Equation 8.1.35 gives

$$
\mathbf{x} = \mathbf{a}^{-1}\mathbf{b} \tag{47}
$$

Equation 8.1.42 gives $\mathbf{a}^{-1}$ for this particular problem and we thus proceed to write

$$
\mathbf{x} = \begin{Bmatrix} 0.3500 \\ 0.6278 \\ 0.6903 \end{Bmatrix} \tag{48}
$$

A single-column matrix $\mathbf{x}$ or its transpose, the single-row matrix $\mathbf{x}^T$, is sometimes spoken of as a *vector*. The elements of the vector, $x_1, x_2, \cdots x_n$, may be considered as being the components of $\mathbf{x}$ in the $x_1, x_2, \cdots x_n$ directions. The length L of the vector is given by

$$
L^2 = \mathbf{x}^T\mathbf{x} = x_1{}^2 + x_2{}^2 + \cdots + x_3{}^2 \tag{49}
$$

If $L = 1$, the vector is said to be a unit vector. We denote it by $\mathbf{u}$.

The scalar product of two vectors $\mathbf{a}$ and $\mathbf{b}$ is equal to $\mathbf{a}^T\mathbf{b}$ or $\mathbf{b}^T\mathbf{a}$. When the scalar product of two vectors $\mathbf{a}$ and $\mathbf{b}$ is zero; that is,

$$
(\mathbf{ab}) = \mathbf{a}^T\mathbf{b} = \mathbf{b}^T\mathbf{a} = 0 \tag{50}
$$

the vectors are said to be *orthogonal*.

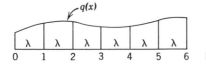

0   1   2   3   4   5   6   **Figure 8.1**

8.2 Equivalent Matrices

In many practical problems we deal with distributed quantities which may vary over a given distance. For example, the distributed load on a beam written as $q(x)$ suggests a variation with x. The deflection $y(x)$ and slope $\theta(x)$ likewise are distributed quantities. It is necessary to replace such "distributed parameters" with "discrete parameters" when matrix methods are employed, since we deal with a finite number of segments of a structure rather than with the structure as given. Thus, a distributed load, for example, is replaced by a set of concentrated loads.

One such problem is the distributed load $q(x)$ acting over a length of member as indicated in Figure 8.1. We begin by dividing the member into a number of segments of equal length λ and calling the end points of the segments *stations* and numbering them consecutively. We next approximate the distributed load by a series of concentrated forces acting only at the chosen stations. This is accomplished by imagining that cross beams lie normal to the given member and that the distributed load comes to the given member through "floor beams" that are simply supported on the cross beams, as seen in Figure 8.2. The concentrated force at any station is the sum of the two reactions of the floor beams at that station. Denoting the intensity of load at any station by q_i and the equivalent concentrated load at that station by R_i, we express all concentrated loads through the matrix relation

$$\mathbf{R} = \mathbf{N}\mathbf{q} \tag{1}$$

A first approximation to any distributed load is given by the simple expedient of setting each value of R equal to the given value of q multiplied by the station spacing λ. This gives

$$\mathbf{N} = \lambda \mathbf{I} \tag{2}$$

in 8.2.1 where $\mathbf{I}$ is the unit matrix and λ is a scalar.

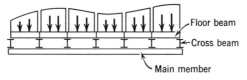

Floor beam
Cross beam
Main member

Figure 8.2

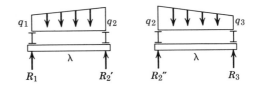

Figure 8.3

When the loading is uniformly distributed throughout of intensity q_0, each element of $\mathbf{q}$ in 8.2.1 is equal to q_0, and every R is equal to λq_0.

When the loading is linearly varying between stations, we find, for example, (see Figure 8.3),

$$R_2'\lambda = \frac{q_1\lambda^2}{2} + \frac{(q_2 - q_1)\lambda}{2}\left(\frac{2\lambda}{3}\right) = \frac{\lambda^2}{6}(q_1 + 2q_2) \tag{3}$$

$$R_2''\lambda = \frac{q_3\lambda^2}{2} + \frac{(q_2 - q_3)\lambda}{2}\left(\frac{2\lambda}{3}\right) = \frac{\lambda^2}{6}(2q_2 + q_3) \tag{4}$$

or

$$R_2 = \frac{\lambda}{6}(q_1 + 4q_2 + q_3) \tag{5}$$

In general, for stations $i - 1$, i, and $i + 1$ we have

$$R_i = \frac{\lambda}{6}(q_{i-1} + 4q_i + q_{i+1}) \tag{6}$$

At the first station at the left, station 0 in Figure 8.1, we have

$$R_0 = \frac{\lambda}{6}(2q_0 + q_1) \tag{7}$$

Similarly, at the right end, station n, we find

$$R_n = \frac{\lambda}{6}(q_{n-1} + 2q_n) \tag{8}$$

We thus have

$$R_0 = \frac{\lambda}{6}(2q_0 + q_1)$$

$$R_1 = \frac{\lambda}{6}(q_0 + 4q_1 + q_2)$$

$$R_2 = \frac{\lambda}{6}(q_1 + 4q_2 + q_3)$$

$$\cdots\cdots\cdots\cdots$$

$$R_{n-1} = \frac{\lambda}{6}(q_{n-2} + 4q_{n-1} + q_n)$$

$$R_n = \frac{\lambda}{6}(q_{n-1} + 2q_n)$$

$$\tag{9}$$

In compact matrix form, we find the **N** matrix of 8.2.1 to be

$$\mathbf{N} = \frac{\lambda}{6}\begin{bmatrix} 2 & 1 & 0 & 0 & \cdots & 0 & 0 & 0 \\ 1 & 4 & 1 & 0 & \cdots & 0 & 0 & 0 \\ 0 & 1 & 4 & 1 & \cdots & 0 & 0 & 0 \\ \cdot & \cdot & \cdot & \cdot & \cdots & \cdot & \cdot & \cdot \\ 0 & 0 & 0 & 0 & \cdots & 1 & 4 & 1 \\ 0 & 0 & 0 & 0 & \cdots & 0 & 1 & 2 \end{bmatrix} \tag{10}$$

When the distributed load does not vary linearly between stations, the foregoing formulation does not yield exact results, and we use a matrix formulation of the formulas proposed by Newmark* for obtaining the equivalent concentrated loads. These are

$$R_i = \frac{\lambda}{12}(q_{i-1} + 10q_i + q_{i+1}) \tag{11}$$

except at the ends 0 and n where

$$R_0 = \frac{\lambda}{12}(3.5q_0 + 3q_1 - 0.5q_2) \tag{12}$$

$$R_n = \frac{\lambda}{12}(1.5q_{n-1} + 5q_n - 0.5q_{n+1}) \tag{13}$$

Note that if n is the end station at the right, then by definition, station $n + 1$ does not exist. Note station 7 in Figure 8.1 as an example. The value of q_{n+1} is intended in such cases to be an estimate of the ordinate to the loading diagram if the diagram were extrapolated to that point. When we use this formulation we find the **N** matrix of 8.2.1 becoming

$$\mathbf{N} = \frac{\lambda}{12}\begin{bmatrix} 3.5 & 3 & -0.5 & \cdots & 0 & 0 & 0 \\ 1 & 10 & 1 & \cdots & 0 & 0 & 0 \\ 0 & 1 & 10 & \cdots & 0 & 0 & 0 \\ \cdots & \cdots & \cdots & \cdots & \cdots & \cdots & \cdots \\ 0 & 0 & 0 & & 10 & 1 & 0 \\ 0 & 0 & 0 & & 1.5 & 5 & -0.5 \end{bmatrix} \tag{14}$$

There will also be an extra value of q_{n+1} in the **q** matrix.

In §1.8 we found that the bending moment distribution on a beam could be expressed approximately in the finite difference form

$$M_{i-1} - 2M_i + M_{i+1} = -R_i\lambda \tag{15}$$

* See N. M. Newmark, "Numerical Procedure for Computing Deflections, Moments, and Buckling Loads," *Transactions*, ASCE, v. 108, 1943, pp. 1161–1234.

when R_i is the equivalent concentrated load at station i and where λ is the distance between stations. Since the R values may be given in terms of the $\mathbf{N}$ matrix of 8.2.2, 8.2.10, or 8.2.14, we write

$$\mathbf{aM} = -\lambda\mathbf{Nq} \qquad (16)$$

where $\mathbf{M}$ is a single column of M values and where $\mathbf{a}$ is the coefficient matrix generated by the left hand side of 8.2.15. Thus

$$\mathbf{M} = -\lambda\mathbf{a}^{-1}\mathbf{Nq} \qquad (17)$$

Similarly, in §3.4 it was seen that in employing the conjugate beam method we use 8.2.17 where the $\mathbf{M}$ in the conjugate beam corresponds to the deflection $\mathbf{y}$ in the given beam, and the load ordinates $\mathbf{q}$ in the conjugate beam represent the ordinates of the M/EI diagram in the given beam. By giving the $\mathbf{M}/\mathbf{EI}$ matrix the symbol $\mathbf{M}^*$, we thus find the deflection matrix for the given beam by writing

$$\mathbf{y} = -\lambda\mathbf{a}^{-1}\mathbf{NM}^* \qquad (18)$$

Example 8.2.1 Divide a simply supported beam into four equal segments, and using the matrix method described previously, find the bending moments at the three interior stations due to a distributed load that varies linearly from zero at the left support to a maximum value of $4\bar{q}$ at the right support.

We begin by reducing the distributed load to a series of equivalent concentrated loads acting at the various stations. We designate the five stations as 0, 1, 2, 3, 4. Using 8.2.10 and 8.2.1, we find

$$\mathbf{R} = \frac{\lambda}{6}\begin{bmatrix} 2 & 1 & 0 & 0 & 0 \\ 1 & 4 & 1 & 0 & 0 \\ 0 & 1 & 4 & 1 & 0 \\ 0 & 0 & 1 & 4 & 1 \\ 0 & 0 & 0 & 1 & 2 \end{bmatrix}\begin{Bmatrix} q_0 \\ q_1 \\ q_2 \\ q_3 \\ q_4 \end{Bmatrix} = \mathbf{Nq} \qquad (19)$$

where $\lambda = L/4$, L being the overall length of the beam. Since the reactions R_0 and R_4 at the supports do not influence the results we need only the values of R_1, R_2, and R_3. We rewrite 8.2.19 as

$$\mathbf{R} = \frac{L}{24}\begin{bmatrix} 1 & 4 & 1 & 0 & 0 \\ 0 & 1 & 4 & 1 & 0 \\ 0 & 0 & 1 & 4 & 1 \end{bmatrix}\begin{Bmatrix} q_0 \\ q_1 \\ q_2 \\ q_3 \\ q_4 \end{Bmatrix} = \begin{Bmatrix} R_1 \\ R_2 \\ R_3 \end{Bmatrix} \qquad (20)$$

Equation 8.2.15 when written for each station becomes

$$\begin{bmatrix} 1 & -2 & 1 & 0 & 0 \\ 0 & 1 & -2 & 1 & 0 \\ 0 & 0 & 1 & -2 & 1 \end{bmatrix}\begin{Bmatrix} M_0 \\ M_1 \\ M_2 \\ M_3 \\ M_4 \end{Bmatrix} = -\frac{L}{24}\begin{Bmatrix} R_1 \\ R_2 \\ R_3 \end{Bmatrix} \qquad (21)$$

Since $M = 0$ at the support of a simply supported beam we may rewrite 8.2.21 in the reduced form

$$\begin{bmatrix} -2 & 1 & 0 \\ 1 & -2 & 1 \\ 0 & 1 & -2 \end{bmatrix} \begin{Bmatrix} M_1 \\ M_2 \\ M_3 \end{Bmatrix} = -\frac{L}{24} \begin{Bmatrix} R_1 \\ R_2 \\ R_3 \end{Bmatrix} \tag{22}$$

or

$$\mathbf{aM} = -\frac{L}{24} \mathbf{R} \tag{23}$$

Substituting 8.2.20 in 8.2.22, we find

$$\begin{bmatrix} -2 & 1 & 0 \\ 1 & -2 & 1 \\ 0 & 1 & -2 \end{bmatrix} \begin{Bmatrix} M_1 \\ M_2 \\ M_3 \end{Bmatrix} = -\left(\frac{L}{4}\right)\left(\frac{L}{24}\right) \begin{bmatrix} 1 & 4 & 1 & 0 & 0 \\ 0 & 1 & 4 & 1 & 0 \\ 0 & 0 & 1 & 4 & 1 \end{bmatrix} \begin{Bmatrix} q_0 \\ q_1 \\ q_2 \\ q_3 \\ q_4 \end{Bmatrix} \tag{24}$$

or

$$\mathbf{aM} = -\left(\frac{L^2}{96}\right)\mathbf{Nq} \tag{25}$$

The inverse of $\mathbf{a}$ is given by

$$\mathbf{a}^{-1} = \begin{bmatrix} -0.75 & -0.50 & -0.25 \\ -0.50 & -1.00 & -0.50 \\ -0.25 & -0.50 & -0.75 \end{bmatrix} \tag{26}$$

We now write

$$\mathbf{M} = -\left(\frac{L^2}{96}\right)\mathbf{a}^{-1}\mathbf{Nq} \tag{27}$$

or

$$\mathbf{M} = -\left(\frac{L^2}{96}\right) \begin{bmatrix} -0.75 & -0.50 & -0.25 \\ -0.50 & -1.00 & -0.50 \\ -0.25 & -0.50 & -0.75 \end{bmatrix} \begin{bmatrix} 1 & 4 & 1 & 0 & 0 \\ 0 & 1 & 4 & 1 & 0 \\ 0 & 0 & 1 & 4 & 1 \end{bmatrix} \begin{Bmatrix} 0 \\ 1 \\ 2 \\ 3 \\ 4 \end{Bmatrix} \bar{q} \tag{28}$$

where $q_0 = 0$, $q_1 = \bar{q}$, $q_2 = 2\bar{q}$, $q_3 = 3\bar{q}$, and $q_4 = 4\bar{q}$ have been substituted for q. Carrying this out, we find

$$\mathbf{M} = \begin{Bmatrix} 0.1563 \\ 0.2500 \\ 0.2188 \end{Bmatrix} \bar{q}L^2 \tag{29}$$

Here we have exact values for the M.

Example 8.2.2 Find the deflection matrix for the beam of the previous example. In finding the deflections we divide each value of M in 8.2.29 by the value of EI at the station to find the matrix $\mathbf{M}^*$ for use in 8.2.18. Let EI vary linearly from a value of 0 at the left support to a value of $4\overline{EI}$ at the right support.

Then $\mathbf{M}^*$ will be, from 8.2.29,

$$\mathbf{M}^* = \begin{pmatrix} 0.1563 \\ 0.1250 \\ 0.0729 \end{pmatrix} \frac{\bar{q}L^2}{EI} \tag{30}$$

The values of $\mathbf{N}$ and $\mathbf{a}^{-1}$ are already known, since the conjugate beam is simply supported just as was the given beam. We use 8.2.18 to write

$$\mathbf{y} = \begin{Bmatrix} y_1 \\ y_2 \\ y_3 \end{Bmatrix} = \frac{L}{4} \begin{bmatrix} 0.75 & 0.50 & 0.25 \\ 0.50 & 1.00 & 0.50 \\ 0.25 & 0.50 & 0.75 \end{bmatrix} \begin{bmatrix} 1 & 4 & 1 & 0 & 0 \\ 0 & 1 & 4 & 1 & 0 \\ 0 & 0 & 1 & 4 & 1 \end{bmatrix} \begin{Bmatrix} 0 \\ M_1{}^* \\ M_2{}^* \\ M_3{}^* \\ 0 \end{Bmatrix}$$

$$= \begin{Bmatrix} 0.2579 \\ 0.3282 \\ 0.2162 \end{Bmatrix} \frac{\bar{q}L^3}{EI} \tag{31}$$

It will be observed that although the matrix method did not yield a simpler solution than conventional methods for Example 8.2.1, the method is considerably simpler for Example 8.2.2.

8.3 Influence Coefficients

A very useful technique for finding deflections in beams is based on the use of *influence coefficients*. Briefly, if we divide the beam into a number of stations and let δ_{ij} be defined as the deflection at station i due to a unit force at station j, we may write

$$\Delta_i = \delta_{i1}R_1 + \delta_{i2}R_2 + \cdots + \delta_{in}R_n \tag{1}$$

where Δ_i is the total deflection at station i due to applied loads R at the various stations (or equivalent concentrated loads found according to the methods of the previous section when distributed loads are given). The term $\delta_{in}R_n$ represents the contribution to the deflection at station i due to the presence of a concentrated force R_n at station n. We may write an equation such as 8.3.1 for each station and get a set of simultaneous equations that can be given the matrix form

$$\Delta = \delta R \tag{2}$$

Or using 8.2.1, we find

$$\Delta = \delta N q \tag{3}$$

Example 8.3.1 Use the method of influence coefficients to find the deflections at the quarter points and midpoint of a simply supported uniform beam loaded as shown in Figure 8.4. We first find the influence coefficients δ_{11}, δ_{21}, δ_{31}, δ_{22}. From symmetry we have $\delta_{11} = \delta_{33}$ and $\delta_{21} = \delta_{32}$. From Maxwell's reciprocal theorem we also have $\delta_{12} = \delta_{21}$ and $\delta_{23} = \delta_{32}$. These are illustrated in Figure 8.5. The values are

$$\delta_{11} = \delta_{33} = \frac{3L^3}{256EI}$$

$$\delta_{21} = \delta_{12} = \delta_{32} = \delta_{23} = \frac{3.67L^3}{256EI} \qquad (4)$$

$$\delta_{13} = \delta_{31} = \frac{2.33L^3}{256EI}$$

$$\delta_{22} = \frac{5.33L^3}{256EI}$$

The influence coefficient matrix δ thus becomes

$$\delta = \frac{L^3}{256EI} \begin{bmatrix} 3.00 & 3.67 & 2.33 \\ 3.67 & 5.33 & 3.67 \\ 2.33 & 3.67 & 3.00 \end{bmatrix} \qquad (5)$$

The load matrix is given by 8.2.14 as

$$\mathbf{Nq} = \frac{L}{48} \begin{bmatrix} 3.5 & 3 & -0.5 & 0 & 0 \\ 0 & 1 & 10 & 1 & 0 \\ 0 & 0 & 1 & 10 & 1 \end{bmatrix} \begin{Bmatrix} q_0 \\ q_1 \\ q_2 \\ q_3 \\ q_4 \end{Bmatrix} \qquad (6)$$

Thus, we find

$$\begin{Bmatrix} \Delta_1 \\ \Delta_2 \\ \Delta_3 \end{Bmatrix} = q_0 \left(\frac{L^3}{256EI} \right) \left(\frac{L}{48} \right) \begin{bmatrix} 3.00 & 3.67 & 2.33 \\ 3.67 & 5.33 & 3.67 \\ 2.33 & 3.67 & 3.00 \end{bmatrix} \begin{bmatrix} 1 & 10 & 1 & 0 & 0 \\ 0 & 1 & 10 & 1 & 0 \\ 0 & 0 & 1 & 10 & 1 \end{bmatrix} \begin{Bmatrix} 10 \\ 20 \\ 20 \\ 30 \\ 34 \end{Bmatrix}$$

or

$$\begin{Bmatrix} \Delta_1 \\ \Delta_2 \\ \Delta_3 \end{Bmatrix} = \frac{q_0 L^4}{(48)(256)EI} \begin{Bmatrix} 2432 \\ 3476 \\ 2515 \end{Bmatrix} = \frac{q_0 L^4}{EI} \begin{Bmatrix} 0.198 \\ 0.283 \\ 0.205 \end{Bmatrix} \qquad (7)$$

Note that it was not necessary to interpolate for a value of q_5 since the load concentrated at the right end ($i = 4$) does not contribute to the deflections.

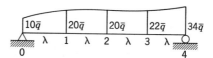

Figure 8.4

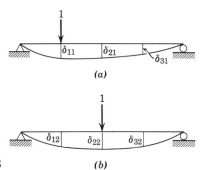

Figure 8.5 (b)

The great drawback of this method lies in finding the influence coefficients δ_{ij}, especially when we are dealing with a beam of variable section or with a frame. A convenient approach is through an approximate formulation of the law of conservation of energy for the structure.* We begin by assuming that the prescribed loading has been reduced to a series of concentrated forces acting at the various stations of the beam. The deflections at the various stations are given by the matrix product

$$\mathbf{\Delta} = \mathbf{\delta R} \tag{8}$$

The external work done by the forces $\mathbf{R}$ in undergoing the deflection $\mathbf{\Delta}$ is given by

$$W = \tfrac{1}{2}\mathbf{R}^T\,\mathbf{\delta R} \tag{9}$$

Internal strain energy is stored due to the presence of bending moments. Over a length of beam extending from station i to station j, for example, we have

$$U = -\tfrac{1}{2}\int_i^j M\,d\theta \tag{10}$$

If M were constant over the prescribed distance, we would have

$$U = \tfrac{1}{2}M(\theta_i{}^{ij} - \theta_j{}^{ij}) \tag{11}$$

If we work with end moments, as in Chapter 7, rather than bending moments, we have

$$U = \tfrac{1}{2}M(\theta_i{}^{ij} + \theta_j{}^{ij}) \tag{12}$$

since the end moment has the same sign as the bending moment at the

* A very general formulation using energy principles and matrix analysis is reviewed by W. J. Crichlow and G. W. Haggenmacher in "The Analysis of Redundant Structures by the Use of High-Speed Digital Computers," *Journal* IAS, August 1960, pp. 595–606.

left end of the segment but an opposite sign at the right end. In matrix form we write the end moments $M_i{}^{ij}$ and $M_j{}^{ij}$ as

$$\begin{Bmatrix} M_i{}^{ij} \\ M_j{}^{ij} \end{Bmatrix} = \mathbf{M}^{ij} = \begin{Bmatrix} +1 \\ -1 \end{Bmatrix} M \tag{13}$$

For the usual problem the moment is not constant over the length of the segment between stations. We then take as an approximation to the exact expression for U

$$U = \tfrac{1}{2}(M_i \theta_i{}^{ij} - M_j \theta_j{}^{ij}) \tag{14}$$

or in terms of end moments

$$U = \tfrac{1}{2}(M_i{}^{ij} \theta_j{}^{ij} + M_j{}^{ij} \theta_j{}^{ij}) \tag{15}$$

We may also write this in the form

$$U = \tfrac{1}{2}\{M_i{}^{ij}, M_j{}^{ij}\} \begin{Bmatrix} \theta_i{}^{ij} \\ \theta_j{}^{ij} \end{Bmatrix} = \tfrac{1}{2}(\mathbf{M}^{ij})^T \boldsymbol{\theta}^{ij} \tag{16}$$

The total strain energy stored in all of the segments between stations can be expressed in the general form

$$U = \tfrac{1}{2}\mathbf{M}^T \boldsymbol{\theta} \tag{17}$$

where the matrix $\mathbf{M}$ is the matrix of all end moments and $\boldsymbol{\theta}$ is the matrix of all end slopes. In the calculation of U from 8.3.10, it is apparent that the change in slope $(\theta_i{}^{ij} - \theta_j{}^{ij})$ will be the same as that calculated for a simply supported beam having the same bending moment distribution as that occurring over the segment in question (see Figure 8.6). The results will not be affected, therefore, if we calculate the end slopes as if they were

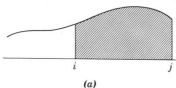

(a)

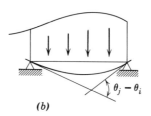

(b)

Figure 8.6

associated with a simply supported span. Furthermore, if the applied loading is divided into concentrated loads at the various stations, we will have no applied load between stations and can therefore write the end moments as functions of the end slopes as was done in Chapter 7. Thus

$$M_i^{ij} = \frac{2EI_{ij}}{L_{ij}} (2\theta_i^{ij} - \theta_j^{ij})$$

$$M_j^{ij} = \frac{2EI_{ij}}{L_{ij}} (-\theta_i^{ij} + 2\theta_j^{ij})$$

(18)

where the superscripts ij identify the span as that extending from station i to station j, and the subscripts identify the end of the span being considered. Thus θ_j^{ij} is the slope at end j of span ij. We solve 8.3.18 for the end slopes and find

$$\theta_i^{ij} = \frac{L_{ij}}{6EI_{ij}} (2M_i^{ij} - M_j^{ij})$$

$$\theta_j^{ij} = \frac{L_{ij}}{6EI_{ij}} (-M_i^{ij} + 2M_j^{ij})$$

(19)

In matrix form this becomes

$$\begin{Bmatrix} \theta_i^{ij} \\ \theta_j^{ij} \end{Bmatrix} = \begin{bmatrix} \dfrac{L_{ij}}{3EI_{ij}} & -\dfrac{L_{ij}}{6EI_{ij}} \\ -\dfrac{L_{ij}}{6EI_{ij}} & \dfrac{L_{ij}}{3EI_{ij}} \end{bmatrix} \begin{Bmatrix} M_i^{ij} \\ M_j^{ij} \end{Bmatrix}$$

(20)

or

$$\boldsymbol{\theta}^{ij} = \mathbf{a}^{ij}\mathbf{M}^{ij}$$

(21)

When all segments of the span are considered together, we get a matrix expression of the form

$$\begin{Bmatrix} \theta_1^{12} \\ \theta_2^{12} \\ \theta_2^{23} \\ \theta_3^{23} \\ \theta_3^{34} \\ \theta_4^{34} \end{Bmatrix} = \begin{bmatrix} x & x & 0 & 0 & 0 & 0 \\ x & x & 0 & 0 & 0 & 0 \\ 0 & 0 & x & x & 0 & 0 \\ 0 & 0 & x & x & 0 & 0 \\ 0 & 0 & 0 & 0 & x & x \\ 0 & 0 & 0 & 0 & x & x \end{bmatrix} \begin{Bmatrix} M_1^{12} \\ M_2^{12} \\ M_2^{23} \\ M_3^{23} \\ M_3^{34} \\ M_4^{34} \end{Bmatrix}$$

(22)

or

$$\boldsymbol{\theta} = \mathbf{a}\mathbf{M}$$

(23)

where the x marks indicate nonzero elements in the **a** matrix.

In a statically determinate structure, we can find the end moments associated with any station directly from the equations of static equilibrium. Expressing these as functions of the equivalent set of concentrated loads $\mathbf{R}$, we write in matrix form

$$\mathbf{M} = \boldsymbol{\alpha}\mathbf{R} \tag{24}$$

Now substituting 8.3.23 and 8.3.24 into 8.3.17 we obtain

$$U = \tfrac{1}{2}(\mathbf{R}^T\boldsymbol{\alpha}^T)(\mathbf{a})(\boldsymbol{\alpha}\mathbf{R}) \tag{25}$$

or

$$U = \tfrac{1}{2}\mathbf{R}^T(\boldsymbol{\alpha}^T\mathbf{a}\boldsymbol{\alpha})\mathbf{R} \tag{26}$$

The law of conservation of energy now requires that W in 8.3.9 equal U in 8.3.26. Equating these, premultiplying through by the inverse of $\mathbf{R}^T$, and postmultiplying through by the inverse of $\mathbf{R}$, we find

$$\boldsymbol{\delta} = \boldsymbol{\alpha}^T\mathbf{a}\boldsymbol{\alpha} \tag{27}$$

This elegant result indicates that the $\boldsymbol{\delta}$ matrix, sometimes called the *flexibility matrix*, can be found directly from the $\boldsymbol{\alpha}$ and $\mathbf{a}$ matrices. The work involved in finding $\boldsymbol{\delta}$ in this fashion is materially less than that involved using the direct approach illustrated in Example 8.3.1. This can be seen in the following example.

Example 8.3.2   Find the $\boldsymbol{\delta}$, $\mathbf{a}$, and $\boldsymbol{\alpha}$ matrices for the beam of Example 8.3.1 and compare $\boldsymbol{\delta}$ with that found in the example. Here we have the following bending moments:

$$
\begin{aligned}
M_1 &= (0.75R_1 + 0.50R_2 + 0.25R_3)\lambda \\
M_2 &= (0.75R_1 + 0.50R_2 + 0.25R_3)2\lambda - R_1\lambda \\
M_3 &= (0.75R_1 + 0.50R_2 + 0.25R_3)3\lambda - 2R_1\lambda - R_2\lambda
\end{aligned} \tag{28}
$$

or

$$
\begin{Bmatrix} M_1 \\ M_2 \\ M_3 \end{Bmatrix} = \lambda \begin{bmatrix} 0.75 & 0.50 & 0.25 \\ 0.50 & 1.00 & 0.50 \\ 0.25 & 0.50 & 0.75 \end{bmatrix} \begin{Bmatrix} R_1 \\ R_2 \\ R_3 \end{Bmatrix} \tag{29}
$$

The associated end moments will be

$$
\begin{Bmatrix} M_0{}^{01} \\ M_1{}^{01} \\ M_1{}^{12} \\ M_2{}^{12} \\ M_2{}^{23} \\ M_3{}^{23} \\ M_3{}^{34} \\ M_4{}^{34} \end{Bmatrix} = \lambda \begin{bmatrix} 0 & 0 & 0 \\ -0.75 & -0.50 & -0.25 \\ 0.75 & 0.50 & 0.25 \\ -0.50 & -1.00 & -0.50 \\ 0.50 & 1.00 & 0.50 \\ -0.25 & -0.50 & -0.75 \\ 0.25 & 0.50 & 0.75 \\ 0 & 0 & 0 \end{bmatrix} \begin{Bmatrix} R_1 \\ R_2 \\ R_3 \end{Bmatrix} = \boldsymbol{\alpha}\mathbf{R} \tag{30}
$$

Since all segments of the beam have the same length, λ, and the same flexural rigidity EI, we have the matrix $[a_{ij}]$ for any segment given by 8.3.20

$$[a_{ij}] = \frac{\lambda}{6EI}\begin{bmatrix} 2 & -1 \\ -1 & 2 \end{bmatrix} \tag{31}$$

and $\mathbf{a}$ for the entire span given by

$$\mathbf{a} = \frac{\lambda}{6EI}\begin{bmatrix}
2 & -1 & 0 & 0 & 0 & 0 & 0 & 0 \\
-1 & 2 & 0 & 0 & 0 & 0 & 0 & 0 \\
0 & 0 & 2 & -1 & 0 & 0 & 0 & 0 \\
0 & 0 & -1 & 2 & 0 & 0 & 0 & 0 \\
0 & 0 & 0 & 0 & 2 & -1 & 0 & 0 \\
0 & 0 & 0 & 0 & -1 & 2 & 0 & 0 \\
0 & 0 & 0 & 0 & 0 & 0 & 2 & -1 \\
0 & 0 & 0 & 0 & 0 & 0 & -1 & 2
\end{bmatrix} \tag{32}$$

The product $\mathbf{a}\alpha$ is found to be

$$\mathbf{a}\alpha = \frac{\lambda^2}{6EI}\begin{bmatrix}
2 & -1 & 0 & 0 & 0 & 0 & 0 & 0 \\
-1 & 2 & 0 & 0 & 0 & 0 & 0 & 0 \\
0 & 0 & 2 & -1 & 0 & 0 & 0 & 0 \\
0 & 0 & -1 & 2 & 0 & 0 & 0 & 0 \\
0 & 0 & 0 & 0 & 2 & -1 & 0 & 0 \\
0 & 0 & 0 & 0 & -1 & 2 & 0 & 0 \\
0 & 0 & 0 & 0 & 0 & 0 & 2 & -1 \\
0 & 0 & 0 & 0 & 0 & 0 & -1 & 2
\end{bmatrix}\begin{bmatrix}
0 & 0 & 0 \\
-0.75 & -0.50 & -0.25 \\
0.75 & 0.50 & 0.25 \\
-0.50 & -1.00 & -0.50 \\
0.50 & 1.00 & 0.50 \\
-0.25 & -0.50 & -0.75 \\
0.25 & 0.50 & 0.75 \\
0 & 0 & 0
\end{bmatrix}$$

$$= \frac{\lambda^2}{6EI}\begin{bmatrix}
0.75 & 0.50 & 0.25 \\
-1.50 & -1.00 & -0.50 \\
2.00 & 2.00 & 1.00 \\
-1.75 & -2.50 & -1.25 \\
1.25 & 2.50 & 1.75 \\
-1.00 & -2.00 & -2.00 \\
0.50 & 1.00 & 1.50 \\
-0.25 & -0.50 & -0.75
\end{bmatrix} \tag{33}$$

δ is now found to be

$$\delta = \alpha^T a \alpha = \begin{bmatrix} 0 & -0.75 & 0.75 & -0.50 & 0.50 & -0.25 & 0.25 & 0 \\ 0 & -0.50 & 0.50 & -1.00 & 1.00 & -0.50 & 0.50 & 0 \\ 0 & -0.25 & 0.25 & -0.50 & 0.50 & -0.75 & 0.75 & 0 \end{bmatrix}$$

$$\times \begin{bmatrix} 0.75 & 0.50 & 0.25 \\ -1.50 & -1.00 & -0.50 \\ 2.00 & 2.00 & 1.00 \\ -1.75 & -2.50 & -1.25 \\ 1.25 & 2.50 & 1.75 \\ -1.00 & -2.00 & -2.00 \\ 0.50 & 1.00 & 1.50 \\ -0.25 & -0.50 & -0.75 \end{bmatrix} \frac{\lambda^3}{6EI}$$

$$= \frac{L^3}{256EI} \begin{bmatrix} 3.00 & 3.67 & 2.33 \\ 3.67 & 5.33 & 3.67 \\ 2.33 & 3.67 & 3.00 \end{bmatrix} \tag{34}$$

This agrees exactly with the matrix found in Example 8.3.1.

We may note in the foregoing example that the **a** matrix of 8.3.30 could be reduced in this case to the form

$$\begin{Bmatrix} M_0{}^{01} \\ M_1{}^{12} \\ M_2{}^{23} \\ M_3{}^{34} \\ M_4{}^{34} \end{Bmatrix} = \lambda \begin{bmatrix} 0 & 0 & 0 \\ 0.75 & 0.50 & 0.25 \\ 0.50 & 1.00 & 0.50 \\ 0.25 & 0.50 & 0.75 \\ 0 & 0 & 0 \end{bmatrix} \begin{Bmatrix} R_1 \\ R_2 \\ R_3 \end{Bmatrix} \tag{35}$$

since $M_1{}^{01}$, $M_2{}^{12}$, and $M_3{}^{23}$ can be easily found when $M_1{}^{12}$, $M_2{}^{23}$, and $M_3{}^{34}$ are known, due to the relations

$$\begin{aligned} M_1{}^{01} &= -M_1{}^{12} \\ M_2{}^{12} &= -M_2{}^{23} \\ M_3{}^{23} &= -M_3{}^{34} \end{aligned} \tag{36}$$

Using the reduced matrix 8.3.35 for α requires reduction of the form of the **a** matrix of 8.3.32 also. This is done by observing that we eliminated the second, fourth, and sixth rows of the α matrix and must now combine rows (and columns) of the **a** matrix by subtracting the even numbered rows (and

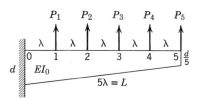

Figure 8.7

columns) from the next rows (and columns) in sequence; that is, the second from the third, etc. The **a** matrix in 8.3.32 becomes

$$\mathbf{a} = \frac{\lambda}{6EI} \begin{bmatrix} 2 & 1 & 0 & 0 & 0 \\ 1 & 4 & 1 & 0 & 0 \\ 0 & 1 & 4 & 1 & 0 \\ 0 & 0 & 1 & 4 & 1 \\ 0 & 0 & 0 & 1 & 2 \end{bmatrix} \tag{37}$$

We again find the value of δ to be as found in 8.3.34; however, the work involved is reduced considerably. In programing for electronic computers it will not normally be found advantageous to make this reduction.

For beams of variable rigidity EI, Clough* has given the following matrix to replace that of 8.3.20 and has used it in solving the problem given as Example 8.3.3 below.

$$[a_{ij}] = \frac{L_{ij}}{6EI_0} \begin{bmatrix} (0.9r_i + 1.2r_c - 0.1r_j)(0.1r_i + 0.8r_c + 0.1r_j) \\ (0.1r_i + 0.8r_c + 0.1r_j)(-0.1r_i + 1.2r_c + 0.9r_j) \end{bmatrix} \tag{38}$$

where EI_0 is some reference value of EI and r_i, r_c, and r_j are dimensionless numbers relating the values of EI at the i-end, center, and j-end, respectively, to the reference value. Thus

$$r_i = \frac{EI_0}{EI_i}, \qquad r_c = \frac{EI_0}{EI_c}, \qquad r_j = \frac{EI_0}{EI_j} \tag{39}$$

Example 8.3.3 Find the matrices **a**, $\boldsymbol{\alpha}$, and δ for the cantilever beam of Figure 8.7. First we calculate values of EI at each station and halfway between stations, and then substitute in equation 8.3.38 to find the reduced form

$$\mathbf{a} = \frac{\lambda}{6EI_0} \begin{bmatrix} 2.27 & 1.30 & 0 & 0 & 0 \\ 1.30 & 6.90 & 2.31 & 0 & 0 \\ 0 & 2.31 & 13.12 & 4.73 & 0 \\ 0 & 0 & 4.73 & 30.01 & 12.25 \\ 0 & 0 & 0 & 12.25 & 93.86 \end{bmatrix} \tag{40}$$

* See R. W. Clough, "Matrix Analysis of Beams," *Proceedings* ASCE, v. 84 EM-1, 1958, pp. 1–24. Also see earlier work by J. H. Argyris, "Energy Theorems and Structural Analysis," *Aircraft Engineering*, October 1954 (p. 343), November 1954 (p. 383), February 1955 (p. 42), March 1955 (p. 80), April 1955 (p. 125) and May 1955 (p. 145).

Also we have

$$
\begin{Bmatrix} M_0^{01} \\ M_1^{12} \\ M_2^{23} \\ M_3^{34} \\ M_4^{45} \end{Bmatrix} = \lambda \begin{bmatrix} 1 & 2 & 3 & 4 & 5 \\ 0 & 1 & 2 & 3 & 4 \\ 0 & 0 & 1 & 2 & 3 \\ 0 & 0 & 0 & 1 & 2 \\ 0 & 0 & 0 & 0 & 1 \end{bmatrix} \begin{Bmatrix} P_1 \\ P_1 \\ P_3 \\ P_4 \\ P_5 \end{Bmatrix} = \alpha R \tag{41}
$$

This yields

$$
\delta = \alpha^T a \alpha = \frac{\lambda^3}{6EI_0} \begin{bmatrix} 2.27 & 5.84 & 9.41 & 12.98 & 16.55 \\ 5.84 & 21.18 & 38.83 & 56.48 & 74.13 \\ 9.41 & 38.83 & 85.99 & 137.88 & 189.77 \\ 12.98 & 56.48 & 137.88 & 258.75 & 391.87 \\ 16.55 & 74.13 & 189.77 & 391.87 & 712.33 \end{bmatrix} \tag{42}
$$

Finally, we can find the deflections Δ at any station by assigning values to the forces P and then expanding

$$
\Delta = \delta R \tag{43}
$$

When the value of EI is assumed constant over any segment and is given the average value for that segment, the matrix δ becomes

$$
\delta = \frac{\lambda^3}{6EI_0} \begin{bmatrix} 2.6 & 6.5 & 10.4 & 14.4 & 18.3 \\ 6.5 & 22.9 & 41.7 & 60.5 & 79.1 \\ 10.4 & 41.7 & 91.9 & 146.8 & 201.8 \\ 14.4 & 60.5 & 146.8 & 277.6 & 421.0 \\ 18.3 & 79.1 & 201.8 & 421.0 & 799.9 \end{bmatrix} \tag{44}
$$

This is less exact than 8.3.42, which can be shown to agree very well with the exact solution.*

8.4 Indeterminate Stress Resultants—Force Method

Displacement

In solving a problem that is statically indeterminate, there are two possible methods of approach. In one, exemplified by the slope-deflection equations, we choose a number of joint displacements as redundants and calculate their values using the equilibrium conditions at the joints of the given structure. In the other method, exemplified by the conjugate beam and virtual work solutions of Chapter 5, we choose a number of stress resultants as redundants and calculate the values of these redundants, using the continuity conditions on slopes and/or deflections. The first of these is the basis for the matrix development of the present section.

* See R. W. Clough, op. cit.

The second is the basis of the development given in the following section.*
We begin by choosing as redundants as many joint displacements (rotations and/or translations) as would be necessary to prevent all joint movement if all redundants were set equal to zero. Setting the redundants equal to zero, we have what we shall call the *auxiliary structure*. It consists of members fixed against rotation and translation at their ends and loaded with the forces applied to the original structure. The moment at any section of the original structure is given by

$$M = M_A + M_r \tag{1}$$

where M_A is the moment at the section in question in the auxiliary structure (redundants set equal to zero) and M_r is the moment at the section in question due only to the redundants. Values of M_A may be found by the methods of Chapter 5, for they are the fixed end moments for the various members. The values of end moments and end shears due to the redundants are given by the slope-deflection equations of Chapter 7 as follows:

$$M_{ir}{}^{ij} = \frac{2EI_{ij}}{L_{ij}} (2\theta_{ir}{}^{ij} + \theta_{jr}{}^{ij}) + \frac{6EI_{ij}}{L_{ij}{}^2} (\Delta_{ir}{}^{ij} - \Delta_{jr}{}^{ij})$$

$$M_{jr}{}^{ij} = \frac{2EI_{ij}}{L_{ij}} (\theta_{ir}{}^{ij} + 2\theta_{jr}{}^{ij}) + \frac{6EI_{ij}}{L_{ij}{}^2} (\Delta_{ir}{}^{ij} - \Delta_{jr}{}^{ij}) \tag{2}$$

$$V_{ir}{}^{ij} = V_{jr}{}^{ij} = - \frac{6EI_{ij}}{L_{ij}{}^2} (\theta_{ir}{}^{ij} + \theta_{jr}{}^{ij}) - \frac{12EI_{ij}}{L_{ij}{}^3} (\Delta_{ir}{}^{ij} - \Delta_{jr}{}^{ij})$$

where the subscript r signifies "due to the redundant." We may write these in the matrix form

$$
\left\{
\begin{array}{c}
M_{ir}{}^{ij} \\
M_{jr}{}^{ij} \\
V_{ir}{}^{ij} \\
V_{jr}{}^{ij}
\end{array}
\right\}
= EI_{ij}
\left[
\begin{array}{cccc}
\dfrac{4}{L_{ij}} & \dfrac{2}{L_{ij}} & \dfrac{6}{L_{ij}{}^2} & \dfrac{-6}{L_{ij}{}^2} \\[2ex]
\dfrac{2}{L_{ij}} & \dfrac{4}{L_{ij}} & \dfrac{6}{L_{ij}{}^2} & \dfrac{-6}{L_{ij}{}^2} \\[2ex]
\dfrac{-6}{L_{ij}{}^2} & \dfrac{-6}{L_{ij}{}^2} & \dfrac{-12}{L_{ij}{}^3} & \dfrac{12}{L_{ij}{}^3} \\[2ex]
\dfrac{-6}{L_{ij}{}^2} & \dfrac{-6}{L_{ij}{}^2} & \dfrac{-12}{L_{ij}{}^3} & \dfrac{12}{L_{ij}{}^3}
\end{array}
\right]
\left\{
\begin{array}{c}
\theta_{ir}{}^{ij} \\
\theta_{jr}{}^{ij} \\
\Delta_{ir}{}^{ij} \\
\Delta_{jr}{}^{ij}
\end{array}
\right\}
\tag{3}
$$

or

$$\mathbf{M}_r{}^{ij} = \mathbf{a}^{ij}\boldsymbol{\theta}_r{}^{ij} \tag{4}$$

where $\mathbf{M}_r{}^{ij}$ represents the single column matrix of stress resultants and $\boldsymbol{\theta}_r{}^{ij}$ represents the single column matrix of end displacements. When

* In addition to references of previous sections, see F. V. Filho, "Matrix Analysis of Plane Rigid Frames," *Proceedings*, ASCE, v. 86, ST-7, 1960, p. 95–108.

several members are present in the structure, an equation such as 8.4.4 may be written for each. These can then be combined into a single matrix equation of the form

$$\mathbf{M}_r = \mathbf{a}\boldsymbol{\theta}_r \tag{5}$$

where, for example

$$\mathbf{a} = \begin{bmatrix} \mathbf{a}^{12} & 0 & 0 & 0 \\ 0 & \mathbf{a}^{23} & 0 & 0 \\ 0 & 0 & \mathbf{a}^{34} & 0 \\ 0 & 0 & 0 & \mathbf{a}^{45} \end{bmatrix} \tag{6}$$

The end moments for members of the auxiliary structure can be written as a single column matrix $\mathbf{M}_A$. The total end moment can then be written as

$$\mathbf{M} = \mathbf{M}_A + \mathbf{a}\boldsymbol{\theta}_r \tag{7}$$

In all these calculations, rotations and translations are measured relative to the undeformed positions of the joints.

The displacements $\boldsymbol{\theta}_r$ can be readily found in terms of the redundant displacements $\mathbf{X}$ and expressed in matrix form

$$\boldsymbol{\theta}_r = \alpha\mathbf{X} \tag{8}$$

Substitution in 8.4.7 gives

$$\mathbf{M} = \mathbf{M}_A + \mathbf{a}\alpha\mathbf{X} \tag{9}$$

Let us premultiply through by the transpose of $\boldsymbol{\theta}_r$, recalling that

$$\boldsymbol{\theta}_r{}^T = (\mathbf{a}\mathbf{X})^T = \mathbf{X}^T\alpha^T \tag{10}$$

to obtain

$$\mathbf{X}^T\alpha^T\mathbf{M} = \mathbf{X}^T\alpha^T\mathbf{M}_A + \mathbf{X}^T\alpha^T\mathbf{a}\alpha\mathbf{X} \tag{11}$$

This represents the work done by the end moments of the original structure on the joint displacements due only to the redundants. The left-hand side is identically zero for every joint as can be seen by expanding it for a typical joint having three members, say, framing into it. In the original structure, the end moments are of the type M_{21}, M_{23}, and M_{24} (the first subscript indicating the joint). Equilibrium requires

$$M_{21} + M_{23} + M_{24} = 0 \tag{12}$$

The end slopes due only to the redundants are θ_{21}, θ_{23}, and θ_{24}, say. These are known to be equal for rigid framed structures. Thus,

$$\theta_{21} = \theta_{23} = \theta_{24} = \theta_2 \tag{13}$$

Expanding $\boldsymbol{\theta}_r{}^T\mathbf{M}$ we find

$$\begin{aligned} \boldsymbol{\theta}_r{}^T\mathbf{M} &= M_{21}\theta_{21} + M_{23}\theta_{23} + M_{24}\theta_{24} \\ &= \theta_2\,(M_{21} + M_{23} + M_{24}) = 0 \end{aligned} \tag{14}$$

by 8.4.12. The matrix $\mathbf{M}$ contains end moments and also end shear forces. The matrix $\boldsymbol{\theta}_r$ contains end slopes as well as end deflections. We consider an end moment to be positive when it causes a positive end slope; that is, when it acts clockwise on the member. Similarly, an end shear force is positive when it causes a positive end deflection; that is, when it acts in a positive y direction. Denoting that portion of $\boldsymbol{\theta}_r$ that consists only of end deflections by $\boldsymbol{\Delta}_r$ we find

$$\boldsymbol{\Delta}_r{}^T\mathbf{V} = 0 \qquad (15)$$

This states that the work done by redundant shear forces on the original joint translations must equal zero. In the structure of Figure 8.7, for example, the only non-zero joint translations are the horizontal translations of joints 2 and 3. We expand 8.4.15 to get

$$(0)V_{1r}{}^{12} + \Delta_{2r}{}^{12}V_{2r}{}^{12} + (0)V_{2r}{}^{23} + (0)V_{3r}{}^{23} + (0)V_{4r}{}^{34} + \Delta_{3r}{}^{34}V_{3r}{}^{34} = 0 \qquad (16)$$

or

$$\Delta_{2r}{}^{12}V_{2r}{}^{12} + \Delta_{3r}{}^{34}V_{3r}{}^{34} = 0 \qquad (17)$$

But

$$\Delta_{2r}{}^{12} = \Delta_{3r}{}^{34} \qquad (18)$$

Thus

$$V_{2r}{}^{12} + V_{3r}{}^{34} = 0 \qquad (19)$$

This is nothing more than the horizontal force equilibrium equation of the girder. We may say that 8.4.15 is valid. We can now set the right-hand side of 8.4.11 equal to zero, premultiply through by the inverse of $\mathbf{X}^T$ and get

$$0 = \boldsymbol{\alpha}^T\mathbf{M}_A + (\boldsymbol{\alpha}^T\mathbf{a}\boldsymbol{\alpha})\mathbf{X} \qquad (20)$$

We solve for $\mathbf{X}$ to get

$$\mathbf{X} = -(\boldsymbol{\alpha}^T\mathbf{a}\boldsymbol{\alpha})^{-1}\,\boldsymbol{\alpha}^T\mathbf{M}_A \qquad (21)$$

Having $\mathbf{X}$ we now find $\boldsymbol{\theta}_r$ from 8.4.8, then find $\mathbf{M}_r$ from 8.4.5 and finally find $\mathbf{M}$ from 8.4.1. The following example worked in detail illustrates the method.

Example 8.4.1 Given the continuous beam shown in Figure 8.8, find the bending moments at the ends of all members. We begin by choosing the rotation at joint 2 as the only redundant. Since no work is done by the redundant shear forces acting on the deflections of the original structure, we need not consider V or Δ values in the various matrices. The slopes due to the redundant are

$$\begin{Bmatrix} \theta_{1r}{}^{12} \\ \theta_{2r}{}^{12} \\ \theta_{2r}{}^{23} \\ \theta_{3r}{}^{23} \end{Bmatrix} = \begin{Bmatrix} 0 \\ 1 \\ 1 \\ 0 \end{Bmatrix}\theta_2 \quad \text{or} \quad \boldsymbol{\theta}_r = \boldsymbol{\alpha}\mathbf{X} \qquad (22)$$

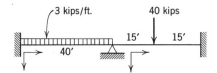

Figure 8.8

In this very elementary example α is a single column matrix rather than a multiple column matrix and X is a single number rather than a single column matrix. θ_r is a single column matrix as usual. Using 8.4.6 we find

$$\mathbf{M}_r = \mathbf{a}\theta_r = \begin{Bmatrix} M_{1r}{}^{12} \\ M_{2r}{}^{12} \\ M_{2r}{}^{23} \\ M_{3r}{}^{23} \end{Bmatrix} = EI_0 \begin{bmatrix} \frac{4}{40} & \frac{2}{40} & 0 & 0 \\ \frac{2}{40} & \frac{2}{40} & 0 & 0 \\ 0 & 0 & \frac{4}{30} & \frac{2}{30} \\ 0 & 0 & \frac{2}{30} & \frac{4}{30} \end{bmatrix} \begin{Bmatrix} \theta_{1r}{}^{12} \\ \theta_{2r}{}^{12} \\ \theta_{2r}{}^{23} \\ \theta_{3r}{}^{23} \end{Bmatrix} \tag{23}$$

where

$$\mathbf{a} = EI_0 \begin{bmatrix} 0.10 & 0.05 & 0 & 0 \\ 0.05 & 0.10 & 0 & 0 \\ 0 & 0 & 0.133 & 0.067 \\ 0 & 0 & 0.067 & 0.133 \end{bmatrix} \tag{24}$$

When θ_2 is set equal to zero we have the auxiliary structure. The end moments and shears have the values

$$\mathbf{M}_A = \begin{Bmatrix} M_{1A}{}^{12} \\ M_{2A}{}^{12} \\ M_{2A}{}^{23} \\ M_{3A}{}^{23} \end{Bmatrix} = \begin{Bmatrix} -400 \text{ ft-kips} \\ +400 \text{ ft-kips} \\ -150 \text{ ft-kips} \\ +150 \text{ ft-kips} \end{Bmatrix} \tag{25}$$

We now compute $\alpha^T\mathbf{M}_A$ and $\alpha^T\mathbf{a}\alpha$. Thus

$$\alpha^T\mathbf{M}_A = (400 - 150) = 250 \text{ ft-kips} \tag{26}$$

$$\mathbf{a}\alpha = EI_0 \begin{Bmatrix} 0.05 \\ 0.10 \\ 0.133 \\ 0.067 \end{Bmatrix} \quad \text{and} \quad \alpha^T\mathbf{a}\alpha = 0.233EI_0 \tag{27}$$

From 8.4.11,

$$250 + 0.233EI_0\theta_2 = 0$$
$$\theta_2 = -1072.96/EI_0 \tag{28}$$

From 8.4.8 and 8.4.5

$$\theta_r = \frac{1}{EI_0} \begin{Bmatrix} 0 \\ -1072.96 \\ -1072.96 \\ 0 \end{Bmatrix}, \quad \mathbf{M}_r = \begin{Bmatrix} -53.65 \text{ ft-kips} \\ -107.30 \text{ ft-kips} \\ -143.03 \text{ ft-kips} \\ -71.51 \text{ ft-kips} \end{Bmatrix} \tag{29}$$

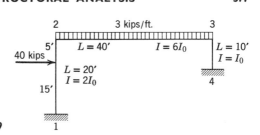

Figure 8.9

From 8.4.7

$$\mathbf{M} = \mathbf{M}_A + \mathbf{M}_r = \begin{Bmatrix} -453.65 \text{ ft-kips} \\ +292.70 \text{ ft-kips} \\ -293.03 \text{ ft-kips} \\ -78.49 \text{ ft-kips} \end{Bmatrix} \qquad (30)$$

The bending moments can be found from the end moments of 8.4.30 and are given signs consistent with the axes shown in Figure 8.8.

$$\begin{array}{ll} \text{Member 12:} & \begin{array}{l} M_1 = -453.65 \\ M_2 = -292.70 \end{array} \\ \text{Member 23:} & \begin{array}{l} M_2 = -293.03 \\ M_3 = +78.49 \end{array} \end{array} \qquad (31)$$

Example 8.4.2   Find the end shears and moments at the ends of all members of the frame shown in Figure 8.9, using the *force matrix* method. We begin by choosing the joint rotations θ_2 and θ_3 at joints 2 and 3 and the joint translation Δ_3 as the redundants. All other joint displacements can be expressed in terms of these three. We set these equal to zero to get the auxiliary structure. The end moments (positive when clockwise on the member) are as follows:

$$M_{1A}{}^{12} = -\frac{Pab^2}{L^2} = -\frac{(40)(15)(5)^2}{(20)^2} = -37.5 \text{ ft-kips}$$

$$M_{2A}{}^{12} = +\frac{(40)(15)^2(5)}{(20)^2} = +112.5 \text{ ft-kips}$$

$$V_{1A}{}^{12} = V_{2A}{}^{12} = -33.75 \text{ kips} \qquad (32)$$

$$M_{2A}{}^{23} = -\frac{(3)(40)^2}{12} = -400 \text{ ft-kips} = -M_{3A}{}^{23}$$

$$V_{2A}{}^{23} = V_{3A}{}^{23} = M_{3A}{}^{34} = M_{4A}{}^{34} = V_{3A}{}^{34} = V_{4A}{}^{34} = 0$$

Thus

$$\mathbf{M}_A = \begin{Bmatrix} 112.5 \text{ ft-kips} \\ -33.75 \text{ kips} \\ -400.0 \text{ ft-kips} \\ +400.0 \text{ ft-kips} \\ 0 \\ 0 \end{Bmatrix} \qquad (33)$$

Values of $V_{1A}{}^{12}$, $V_{2A}{}^{23}$, $V_{3A}{}^{23}$, $V_{4A}{}^{34}$, $M_{1r}{}^{12}$, and $M_{4r}{}^{34}$ have been omitted, since values of Δ or θ are zero at these points and hence do not contribute to 8.4.15.

We now find $\mathbf{a}$, by using 8.4.5, to be

$$
\begin{Bmatrix} M_{2r}{}^{12} \\ V_{2r}{}^{12} \\ M_{2r}{}^{23} \\ M_{3r}{}^{23} \\ M_{3r}{}^{34} \\ V_{3r}{}^{34} \end{Bmatrix} = EI_0 \begin{bmatrix} 0.4 & -0.03 & 0 & 0 & 0 & 0 \\ -0.03 & 0.003 & 0 & 0 & 0 & 0 \\ 0 & 0 & 0.6 & 0.3 & 0 & 0 \\ 0 & 0 & 0.3 & 0.6 & 0 & 0 \\ 0 & 0 & 0 & 0 & 0.4 & -0.06 \\ 0 & 0 & 0 & 0 & -0.06 & 0.012 \end{bmatrix} \begin{Bmatrix} \theta_{2r}{}^{12} \\ \Delta_{2r}{}^{12} \\ \theta_{2r}{}^{23} \\ \theta_{3r}{}^{23} \\ \theta_{3r}{}^{34} \\ \Delta_{3r}{}^{34} \end{Bmatrix} \tag{34}
$$

or

$$\mathbf{M}_r = \mathbf{a}\boldsymbol{\theta}_r \tag{35}$$

We express the $\boldsymbol{\theta}_r$ in terms of the redundant $\mathbf{X}$ as follows:

$$
\begin{Bmatrix} \theta_{2r}{}^{12} \\ \Delta_{2r}{}^{12} \\ \theta_{2r}{}^{23} \\ \theta_{3r}{}^{23} \\ \theta_{3r}{}^{34} \\ \Delta_{3r}{}^{34} \end{Bmatrix} = \begin{bmatrix} 1 & 0 & 0 \\ 0 & 0 & 1 \\ 1 & 0 & 0 \\ 0 & 1 & 0 \\ 0 & 1 & 0 \\ 0 & 0 & 1 \end{bmatrix} \begin{Bmatrix} \theta_2 \\ \theta_3 \\ \Delta_3 \end{Bmatrix} \qquad \text{or} \qquad \boldsymbol{\theta}_r = \boldsymbol{\alpha}\mathbf{X} \tag{36}
$$

We now find

$$
\mathbf{a}\boldsymbol{\alpha} = EI_0 \begin{bmatrix} 0.4 & 0 & -0.03 \\ -0.03 & 0 & 0.003 \\ 0.6 & 0.3 & 0 \\ 0.3 & 0.6 & 0 \\ 0 & 0.4 & -0.06 \\ 0 & -0.06 & 0.012 \end{bmatrix}
$$

$$
\boldsymbol{\alpha}^T\mathbf{a}\boldsymbol{\alpha} = EI_0 \begin{bmatrix} 1.0 & 0.3 & -0.03 \\ 0.3 & 1.0 & -0.06 \\ -0.03 & -0.06 & 0.015 \end{bmatrix} \tag{37}
$$

The matrix ($\boldsymbol{\alpha}^T\mathbf{a}\boldsymbol{\alpha}$) must now be inverted. We find its adjoint to be

$$
\text{Adj} (\boldsymbol{\alpha}^T\mathbf{a}\boldsymbol{\alpha}) = EI_0 \begin{bmatrix} 0.0114 & -0.0027 & 0.0120 \\ -0.0027 & 0.0141 & 0.0510 \\ 0.0120 & 0.0510 & 0.9100 \end{bmatrix} \tag{38}
$$

and its determinant to be

$$|\boldsymbol{\alpha}^T\mathbf{a}\boldsymbol{\alpha}| = 0.01023(EI_0)^3 \tag{39}$$

The inverse is now found to be

$$(\alpha^T a \alpha)^{-1} = \frac{1}{EI_0} \begin{bmatrix} 1.1144 & -0.2639 & 1.1730 \\ -0.2639 & 1.3783 & 4.9853 \\ 1.1730 & 4.9853 & 88.9541 \end{bmatrix} \tag{40}$$

We now find

$$\alpha^T M_A = \begin{Bmatrix} -287.5 \text{ ft-kips} \\ 400 \text{ ft-kips} \\ -33.75 \text{ kips} \end{Bmatrix} \tag{41}$$

Finally, we substitute into 8.4.21 to obtain

$$\begin{Bmatrix} \theta_2 \\ \theta_3 \\ \Delta_3 \end{Bmatrix} = -(\alpha^T a \alpha)^{-1} \alpha^T M = \frac{1}{EI_0} \begin{Bmatrix} 465.543 \\ -458.945 \\ 1345.307 \end{Bmatrix} \tag{42}$$

From 8.4.5 and 8.4.1, we then find

$$M_r = \begin{Bmatrix} 145.858 \text{ ft-kips} \\ -9.930 \text{ kips} \\ 141.642 \text{ ft-kips} \\ -135.704 \text{ ft-kips} \\ -264.296 \text{ ft-kips} \\ 43.680 \text{ kips} \end{Bmatrix} \quad \text{and} \quad M = \begin{Bmatrix} 258.358 \text{ ft-kips} \\ -43.680 \text{ kips} \\ -258.358 \text{ ft-kips} \\ 264.296 \text{ ft-kips} \\ -264.296 \text{ ft-kips} \\ 43.680 \text{ kips} \end{Bmatrix} \tag{43}$$

8.5 Indeterminate Stress Resultants—Displacement Method

In using the displacement method we choose as redundants those stress resultants which when set equal to zero leave a stable and statically determinate structure. The reduced structure is called the *auxiliary structure*. We let this set of redundants be denoted by the single column matrix **Y**. We begin by computing the end moments and end shears, M_r, in all members due only to these redundants and express our results in the form

$$M_r = \beta Y \tag{1}$$

This is merely a problem in statics.

We note that the displacements θ in the original structure equal the displacements θ_A in the auxiliary structure plus the displacements θ_r due to the redundants. Thus

$$\theta = \theta_A + \theta_r \tag{2}$$

The θ_r can be expressed in terms of the M_r by the relation

$$\theta_r = b M_r \tag{3}$$

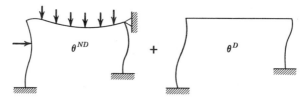

Figure 8.10

Using an argument similar to that in §8.4, we find that the work done by the $\mathbf{M}_r$ acting on the original displacements $\boldsymbol{\theta}$ must be zero. In matrix form this becomes

$$\mathbf{M}_r{}^T\boldsymbol{\theta} = \mathbf{0} \qquad (4)$$

Now the displacements $\boldsymbol{\theta}$ may be considered to be equal to the displacements $\boldsymbol{\theta}^{ND}$ that would be present if no joint translation were permitted plus

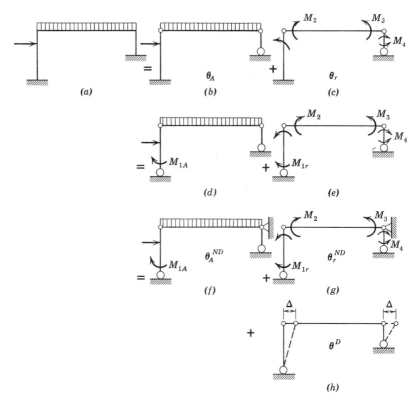

Figure 8.11

the displacements θ^D that would be due only to joint translations as illustrated in Figure 8.10 for the frame of Figure 8.9. This gives

$$\mathbf{M}_r{}^T\theta^{ND} + \mathbf{M}_r{}^T\theta^D = 0 \tag{5}$$

The term $\mathbf{M}_r{}^T\theta^D$ is, itself, identically equal to zero since it represents the work done by a set of forces in equilibrium, Figure 8.11c, on a virtual displacement θ^D, Figure 8.11h. When applied to 8.4.2, this leaves

$$\mathbf{M}_r{}^T\theta_A{}^{ND} + \mathbf{M}_r{}^T\theta_r{}^{ND} = 0 \tag{6}$$

We substitute 8.5.1 and 8.5.3 into 8.5.6 to obtain

$$\mathbf{Y}^T\boldsymbol{\beta}^T\theta_A{}^{ND} + \mathbf{Y}^T\boldsymbol{\beta}^T\mathbf{b}\boldsymbol{\beta}\mathbf{Y} = 0 \tag{7}$$

where the matrix $\mathbf{b}$ as well as the matrix $\theta_A{}^{ND}$ are computed for no joint translation as shown in Figures 8.11f and 8.11g. We premultiply through by the inverse of $\mathbf{Y}^T$ and solve for $\mathbf{Y}$ to get

$$\mathbf{Y} = -(\boldsymbol{\beta}^T\mathbf{b}\boldsymbol{\beta})\boldsymbol{\beta}^T\theta_A{}^{ND} \tag{8}$$

The following example illustrates the computations.

Example 8.5.1   Find the end moments at joints 2, 3, and 4 for the structure of Example 8.4.2, using the displacement matrix method. We begin by expressing the end stress resultants in terms of the redundants shown in Figure 8.11c.

$$\begin{Bmatrix} M_{1r}{}^{12} \\ M_{2r}{}^{12} \\ M_{2r}{}^{23} \\ M_{3r}{}^{23} \\ M_{3r}{}^{34} \\ M_{4r}{}^{34} \end{Bmatrix} = \begin{bmatrix} 1 & -2 & 2 \\ -1 & 0 & 0 \\ 1 & 0 & 0 \\ 0 & -1 & 0 \\ 0 & 1 & 0 \\ 0 & 0 & -1 \end{bmatrix} \begin{Bmatrix} M_2 \\ M_3 \\ M_4 \end{Bmatrix} = \boldsymbol{\beta}\mathbf{Y} \tag{9}$$

The slopes in the statically determinate structure with no sidesway are found to be

$$\begin{Bmatrix} \theta_{1A}{}^{12} \\ \theta_{2A}{}^{12} \\ \theta_{2A}{}^{23} \\ \theta_{3A}{}^{23} \\ \theta_{3A}{}^{34} \\ \theta_{4A}{}^{34} \end{Bmatrix} = \frac{1}{EI_0} \begin{Bmatrix} -1687.5 \\ 562.5 \\ 1333.3 \\ 1333.3 \\ 0 \\ 0 \end{Bmatrix} = \theta_A{}^{ND} \tag{10}$$

These matrices are especially easy to compute since all relate to slopes of simply supported beams carrying bending moments distributed as in the auxiliary structure. Similarly, we find

$$\boldsymbol{\theta}_r{}^{ND} = \frac{1}{EI_0}\begin{bmatrix} 3.33 & -1.67 & 0 & 0 & 0 & 0 \\ -1.67 & 3.33 & 0 & 0 & 0 & 0 \\ 0 & 0 & 2.22 & -1.11 & 0 & 0 \\ 0 & 0 & -1.11 & 2.22 & 0 & 0 \\ 0 & 0 & 0 & 0 & 3.33 & -1.67 \\ 0 & 0 & 0 & 0 & -1.67 & 3.33 \end{bmatrix} \quad \{M_r\} = \mathbf{bM}_r \tag{11}$$

We now find

$$\mathbf{b\beta} = \frac{1}{EI_0}\begin{bmatrix} 5.00 & -6.67 & 6.67 \\ -5.00 & 3.33 & -3.33 \\ 2.22 & 1.11 & 0 \\ -1.11 & -2.22 & 0 \\ 0 & 3.33 & 1.67 \\ 0 & -1.67 & -3.33 \end{bmatrix} \tag{12}$$

and

$$\mathbf{\beta}^T\mathbf{b\beta} = \frac{1}{EI_0}\begin{bmatrix} 12.22 & -8.89 & 10.00 \\ -8.89 & 18.88 & -11.67 \\ 10.00 & -11.67 & 16.67 \end{bmatrix} \tag{13}$$

and

$$|\mathbf{\beta}^T\mathbf{b\beta}| = 1050.78\left(\frac{1}{EI_0}\right)^3 \tag{14}$$

The inverse is

$$(\mathbf{\beta}^T\mathbf{b\beta})^{-1} = (EI_0)\begin{bmatrix} 0.1700 & 0.0300 & -0.0810 \\ 0.0300 & 0.0986 & 0.0510 \\ -0.0810 & 0.0510 & 0.1444 \end{bmatrix} \tag{15}$$

Furthermore, we obtain

$$\mathbf{\beta}^T\boldsymbol{\theta}_A{}^{ND} = \frac{1}{EI_0}\begin{Bmatrix} -916.7 \\ 4708.3 \\ -3375.0 \end{Bmatrix} \tag{16}$$

and finally

$$\mathbf{Y} = -(\mathbf{\beta}^T\mathbf{b\beta})^{-1}\mathbf{\beta}^T\boldsymbol{\theta}_A{}^{ND} = \begin{Bmatrix} -258.785 \text{ ft-kips} \\ -264.612 \text{ ft-kips} \\ 172.974 \text{ ft-kips} \end{Bmatrix} \tag{17}$$

When due regard is made for signs, these results will be seen to agree with end moments calculated in Example 8.4.2.

Problems

8.1.1 Spell out the relations (a) $c_2 = \sum\limits_{k=1}^{4} a_{2k}x_k$

(b) $c_{32} = \sum\limits_{k=1}^{4} a_{3k}b_{k2}$

8.1.2 Evaluate the following matrix products:

(a) $\begin{bmatrix} 7 & 0 \\ 0 & 6 \end{bmatrix}\begin{bmatrix} 4 & 5 \\ 3 & 2 \end{bmatrix} = ?$

(b) $\begin{bmatrix} 2 & 3 & 1 \\ 3 & 4 & 2 \end{bmatrix}\begin{bmatrix} 0 & 1 \\ 3 & 5 \\ 2 & 6 \end{bmatrix} = ?$

(c) $\begin{bmatrix} 7 & 3 & 4 \\ 3 & 7 & 3 \\ 1 & 6 & 9 \end{bmatrix}\begin{bmatrix} 1 & 0 & 0 \\ 0 & 1 & 0 \\ 0 & 0 & 1 \end{bmatrix} = ?$

8.1.3 Evaluate the following:

(a) $3\begin{bmatrix} 4 & 4 & 4 \\ 2 & 3 & 7 \end{bmatrix}\begin{bmatrix} 2 & 1 \\ 2 & 1 \\ 1 & 4 \end{bmatrix} + \begin{bmatrix} 1 & 9 \\ 0 & 7 \end{bmatrix} = ?$

(b) $\begin{bmatrix} 6 & 4 & 2 \\ 6 & 2 & 1 \\ 6 & 3 & 7 \end{bmatrix}\begin{bmatrix} 6 \\ 7 \\ 9 \end{bmatrix} - 10\begin{bmatrix} 1 \\ 2 \\ 6 \end{bmatrix} = ?$

8.1.4 For the matrix of Example 8.1.2, find the minors and cofactors of the elements in the third column and check the value of the determinant.

8.1.5 Use Cramer's rule to find the value of x_3 in the following:

$$2x_1 + x_3 = 6$$
$$x_2 + x_1 = 2$$
$$x_1 + x_2 + x_3 = 4$$

8.1.6 Find the transpose, adjoint, and inverse of the coefficient matrix in Problem 8.1.5. Use these to find the roots of the set of equations.

8.2.1 A beam of length L is loaded with a sinusoidal load $q(x) = A \sin(\pi x/L)$. Divide the beam into four equal lengths and find the matrix **R** using 8.2.2, 8.2.10, and 8.2.14 for **N**.

8.2.2 A beam is fixed at its left end, simply supported at its right end and hinged a distance $0.4L$ from the left where L is the span. Use the matrix approach to find the bending moment at every $0.2L$ points due to a triangular load varying from zero at the ends of the beam to a maximum value of $\bar{q}$ at the midspan.

8.2.3 Find the deflections for the beam of the previous example. Let EI be constant.

8.3.1 Write the δ matrix for the beam of Example 8.2.3 using the length $0.2L$ between stations.

8.3.2 Use the δ matrix in finding the deflections of the beam of Problem 8.2.3.

8.3.3 Find the δ matrix via the α and **a** matrices for Problem 8.3.1.

8.3.4 Repeat Problem 8.3.3 with EI to the left of the hinge equal to twice the value to the right of the hinge.

8.4.1 Use the force method to find the bending moments at the ends of the members in problem
         (a) 7.3.1(a)
         (b) 7.3.1(b)
         (c) 7.6.1(b)

8.5.1 Use the displacement method to find the bending moments at the ends of the members in problem
         (a) 7.3.1(a)
         (b) 7.3.1(b)
         (c) 7.6.1(b)

9 FREQUENCY ANALYSIS
OF STRUCTURES

9.1 Degrees of Freedom and Modes of Vibration

When a structure is acted on by an externally applied disturbance that is subsequently removed, the structure responds to the removal of the disturbance by oscillating to and fro. The displacement for an elastic structure varies periodically between specific limits, the maximum displacement in either direction being spoken of as the *amplitude* of the motion. Since no external forces are present during the oscillation, the motion is spoken of as a *free vibration*. If there is any frictional resistance encountered during the oscillation, the amplitude does not remain constant but steadily diminishes until all motion has been damped out. The agent causing such a resistance may be the internal frictional resistance of the molecules of the structure, the drag effects of the surrounding air or other medium in which the structure may be immersed, or the dry frictional resistance of adjacent structures that are in contact with the structure in question. When all motion has been damped out, the structure comes to rest in a position of static equilibrium. When frictional resistance is present, we have *damped free vibrations*. During the interval of time over which the externally applied disturbance is operative, we have a *forced motion* that may be an *undamped forced motion* or a *damped forced motion*, depending on the presence or absence of damping agents.

Many engineering problems may be considered as problems of a single concentrated mass. The vertical cantilever beam shown in Figure 9.1 falls into this class if the concentrated weight that it supports at its free end has associated with it a mass that is very large in proportion to the remaining mass of the structure. During a free vibration of such a structure, the forces that come into play are the inertia forces ($F = Ma$) due to the

Figure 9.1

accelerating of the mass, the restoring forces associated with the elasticity of the structure, and the frictional forces. For undamped free motion, the frictional forces are absent. For forced motion, the force (or its equivalent) arising from the disturbance must also be considered.

In many instances the exact position of the mass may be defined by the knowledge of a single coordinate of displacement (the amount of translation in a given direction or the amount of rotation about a given axis). With the position of the mass known, the position of any other portion of the structure can be determined. When a single coordinate or single variable is sufficient to define at any time the position of any section of the structure, the structure is said to have a single *degree of freedom*. If several coordinates or variables are necessary to define the position of the structure at any time, the structure is said to move with several degrees of freedom. The single mass structure, for example, may require as many as six variables to define its position (three components of translation and three components of rotation). A system of n concentrated masses may have as many as $6n$ degrees of freedom. Then again, a system of n concentrated masses may have but a single significant degree of freedom. An example of this is a system of n masses arranged along a single straight line, connected with straight ties, and acted on by a disturbing force that acts in a direction coincident with their line of centers.

A continuous elastic structure, such as a beam, may be considered as consisting of an infinitely large number of infinitesimally small concentrated masses joined together. In the light of such a point of view, we would speak of a system with an infinite number of degrees of freedom. The cantilever beam of Figure 9.1 is in reality a system that vibrates with an infinite number of degrees of freedom. The very large size of the concentrated mass is such that the inertia force associated with it when the structure moves is much greater than the inertia forces associated with the mass of the beam, and the structure may be considered as one that moves *as with* a single mass.

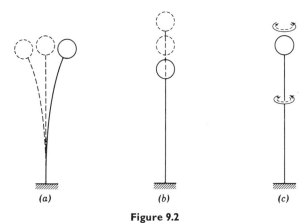

Figure 9.2

It can be shown that systems having a finite number of degrees of freedom may be approached mathematically if we consider a system of simultaneous ordinary differential equations, but that a system with an infinite number of degrees of freedom gives rise to a system of partial differential equations. The relative ease of solution of ordinary equations over partial differential equations leads us many times to approximate a distributed mass by a finite number of concentrated masses.

If the free end of the cantilever of Figure 9.1 is displaced a certain amount horizontally and then suddenly released, there ensues a time-dependent displacement from left to right as indicated in Figure 9.2a. Such a motion is associated with the bending of the cantilever, and the vibration is described as a vibration in a *flexural mode*. If the free end of the cantilever is displaced a certain amount vertically and then suddenly released, there ensues a vibratory motion up and down. Such a motion is associated with the lengthening and shortening of the stem and is described as a vibration in an *extensional mode*. If the free end is caused to rotate about a vertical axis through a certain angle and then suddenly released, there ensues a vibratory motion in the nature of a twisting of the stem. Such a motion is described as a vibration in a *torsional mode*. These last two structures are illustrated in Figures 9.2b and 9.2c. The motion of a given structure may be in any one or any combination of these three modes.

Another structure of importance in structural engineering that may be considered as a structure having a single mass is the simple bent of Figure 9.3. In this structure the mass of the columns is considered to be small in proportion to the mass of the girder. The girder is assumed to be infinitely rigid. The entire motion of this structure may be determined if we know the displacement of the mass center of the girder. When the girder is

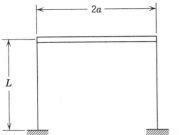

Figure 9.3

assumed to be flexible, a good approximation to the actual behavior may be found by assuming the mass of the girder to be concentrated at the tops of the columns, thus giving a two-mass system to study.

Let a force $F(t)$ act vertically downward at the mass center of the bent having a rigid girder as shown in Figure 9.4. If the bent is symmetrical with respect to the size, shape, and material composition of the columns and the girder, the mass center is on the axis of geometric symmetry for the structure, and the displacement of the girder at any time may be expressed in terms of the vertical translation of the mass center. The dead weight W of the structure will have caused the columns to shorten at their tops by an amount Δ, called the *static deflection*. The force $F(t)$ gives rise to an additional shortening (or lengthening) of amount x. For columns of combined area A, modulus of elasticity E, and length L, the force required to cause a unit shortening is AE/L. If we consider displacement downward as positive, it must follow that a shortening of amount $(\Delta + x)$ must give rise to a resisting (or restoring) elastic force of amount $(\Delta + x)AE/L$. By Newton's second law of motion, we have

$$\sum F = Ma \qquad (1)$$

where $\sum F$ is the sum of the forces acting on a concentrated mass M and a is the acceleration of the mass. In the present case, we have

$$W + F(t) - \frac{AE(\Delta + x)}{L} = M\ddot{x} \qquad (2)$$

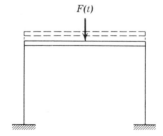

Figure 9.4

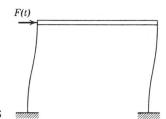

Figure 9.5

where $\ddot{x}$ is to be interpreted as the second derivative of x with respect to time, x being the displacement of the mass center of the girder. Since

$$\Delta = \frac{WL}{AE} \tag{3}$$

the equation of motion reduces to

$$M\ddot{x} + \frac{AE}{L}x = F(t) \tag{4}$$

If along with the force $F(t)$, there were a foundation disturbance such as to cause the bases of the columns to be displaced vertically by an amount x_0 at any time t, the amount of the shortening of the columns would no longer be x, but would be $x - x_0$, since x measures the absolute vertical displacement of the mass center of the girder. Introducing this into 9.1.2 and clearing, we would then have instead of 9.1.4,

$$M\ddot{x} + \frac{AE}{L}x = F(t) + \frac{AE}{L}x_0 \tag{5}$$

When x_0 is a function of time, it alone gives rise to a forced motion just as does $F(t)$. In the absence of all forcing functions, we have the equation for free undamped motion

$$M\ddot{x} + \frac{AE}{L}x = 0 \tag{6}$$

Let the force $F(t)$ act horizontally on the girder through its mass center as shown in Figure 9.5. Let the base of the columns be subjected to a time-dependent horizontal translation x_0. For columns of combined moment of inertia I, a force of magnitude $12EI/L^3$ is required to cause a horizontal displacement of unit amount. If the absolute horizontal displacement of the mass center is now denoted by x, we write as the equilibrium equation

$$F(t) - \frac{12EI(x - x_0)}{L^3} = M\ddot{x} \tag{7}$$

or

$$M\ddot{x} + \frac{12EI}{L^3}x = F(t) + \frac{12EI}{L^3}x_0 \tag{8}$$

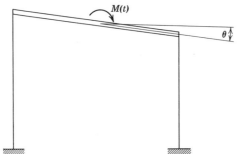

Figure 9.6

When all forcing functions are removed, we have the free flexural vibration governed by the equation

$$M\ddot{x} + \frac{12EI}{L^3}x = 0 \tag{9}$$

As a final variation on the problem, let the girder be acted on by a couple $M(t)$, which acts in a vertical plane as shown in Figure 9.6. The couple, when acting clockwise, produces a rotation of the girder that causes a shortening of the right column and a lengthening of the left column, each by an amount x. If the girder is of length $2a$, the rotation of the girder is given by

$$\tan \theta = \theta = x/a \tag{10}$$

where the tangent of the angle is approximately equal to the angle measured in radians only if the displacement is small. The restoring couple here is $(AEx/L)(2a)$ and the appropriate statement of Newton's second law is

$$\sum T = I\ddot{\theta} \tag{11}$$

where I is the mass moment of inertia of the structure about an axis that passes through the mass center and is perpendicular to the plane of the paper and θ is the angular acceleration. We may write

$$I\ddot{\theta} + \frac{2AEa^2}{L}\theta = M(t) \tag{12}$$

If the foundation of the structure were subjected to a time-dependent rotation as well, say θ_0, we would have

$$I\ddot{\theta} + \frac{2AEa^2}{L}\theta = M(t) + \frac{2AEa^2}{L}\theta_0 \tag{13}$$

For free vibrations this becomes

$$I\ddot{\theta} + \frac{2AEa^2}{L}\theta = 0 \tag{14}$$

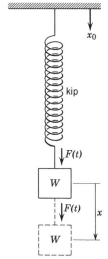

Figure 9.7

Equations 9.1.6, 9.1.9, and 9.1.14 are the governing differential equations for free extensional, flexural, and torsional (or rocking) vibrations of the simple bent. Note that all have the same mathematical form.

A convenient model for use in studying the response of a single degree of freedom structure to time-dependent disturbances is the simple spring-mass mechanical system of Figure 9.7. The spring is assumed to be massless and linearly elastic; that is, its elongation under load is directly proportional to the magnitude of the load, where the constant of proportionality is called the *spring constant* and is denoted by the letter k. The spring constant is measured in the units of force per unit of length. The force exerted on the mass by the spring is at any time equal to the product of the spring constant and the change in length of the spring at that time. If the support suffers a vertical displacement x_0, this is $k(x - x_0)$, where x is the absolute displacement of the mass. Newton's second law gives in this case

$$M\ddot{x} + k(x - x_0) = F(t) \tag{15}$$

or

$$M\ddot{x} + kx = F(t) + kx_0 \tag{16}$$

In the absence of all disturbing agents, we have the free vibrations governed by the equation

$$M\ddot{x} + kx = 0 \tag{17}$$

Equation 9.1.17 is of the same form as those governing the free vibrations of the bent in its three modes. Because of the mathematical similarity of the equations, we sometimes introduce the terms *extensional spring constant, flexural spring constant*, and *torsional spring constant*, which we denote by k_e, k_f, and k_t, and from a comparison of the equations give them the values

$$k_e = AE/L \qquad k_f = 12EI/L^3 \qquad k_t = 2AEa^2/L \qquad (18)$$

The spring constant is a property of the structure itself and as such is independent of the loading or disturbance that is brought to bear on it. It may be determined simply from considerations of static equilibrium and defined as the force (or couple) required to cause a unit translation (or rotation) of the structure at the point of attachment of the concentrated mass.

Note further that the equation of forced vibrations for the spring-mass system as given by 9.1.16 is also identical in form to equations 9.1.5 for extensional vibrations, 9.1.8 for flexural vibrations, and 9.1.13 for torsional vibrations.

9.2 Undamped Free Vibrations

As pointed out in the previous section, the governing differential equation for the undamped free vibrations of a single degree of freedom structure is

$$M\ddot{x} + kx = 0 \qquad (1)$$

If we introduce the symbol

$$p^2 = k/M \qquad (2)$$

it becomes

$$\ddot{x} + p^2 x = 0 \qquad (3)$$

The static deflection Δ associated with a weight W is

$$\Delta = W/k \qquad (4)$$

and with the mass expressed as

$$M = W/g \qquad (5)$$

we may write

$$p^2 = g/\Delta \qquad (6)$$

Equation 9.2.3 is a second-order, linear, homogeneous, ordinary differential equation with constant coefficients, and as such should be investigated for solutions of the form

$$x = Ce^{mt} \qquad (7)$$

By substituting 9.2.7 into 9.2.3 and clearing, we obtain the auxiliary equation

$$m^2 + p^2 = 0 \qquad (8)$$

having the two roots

$$m = \pm ip \qquad (9)$$

where i is the square root of negative one. The solution of 9.2.3 may now be written as

$$x = C_1 e^{ipt} + C_2 e^{-ipt} \tag{10}$$

Making use of Euler's formula

$$e^{i\theta} = \cos\theta + i\sin\theta \tag{11}$$

we write

$$e^{ipt} = \cos pt + i\sin pt \tag{12}$$

$$e^{-ipt} = \cos pt - i\sin pt \tag{13}$$

and finally

$$x = (C_1 + C_2)\cos pt + (C_1 i - C_2 i)\sin pt \tag{14}$$

Since C_1 and C_2 are arbitrary constants to be evaluated by applying the appropriate time conditions to the equations, we may introduce the new arbitrary constants A and B and write

$$x = A\sin pt + B\cos pt \tag{15}$$

The velocity of the moving mass at any time is given by the first time derivative of 9.2.15 to be

$$\dot{x} = Ap\cos pt - Bp\sin pt \tag{16}$$

That the displacement and velocity both vary periodically with time may be verified with the following demonstration. At any time $t = t_1$, we have

$$x_1 = A\sin pt_1 + B\cos pt_1 \tag{17}$$

$$\dot{x}_1 = Ap\cos pt_1 - Bp\sin pt_1 \tag{18}$$

At some later time $t_2 = t_1 + T$, we have

$$x_2 = A\sin p(t_1 + T) + B\cos p(t_1 + T) \tag{19}$$

$$\dot{x}_2 = Ap\cos p(t_1 + T) - Bp\sin p(t_1 + T) \tag{20}$$

Because of the periodicity of the sine and cosine functions, it is evident that by choosing T equal to $2\pi/p$, the expressions for displacement and velocity at t_2 are equal to the values at t_1. The displacement and velocity are said to be periodic with the period

$$T = \frac{2\pi}{p} \tag{21}$$

where the *period T* is measured in seconds per cycle and is usually given simply as seconds. Its reciprocal, the *natural frequency*, is measured in cycles per second and equals

$$f = \frac{p}{2\pi} \tag{22}$$

The quantity p, is called the *circular frequency*, and is expressed in radians per second. These three quantities depend on the values of k, g, and W. They are characteristics of the structure and do not depend on the agent causing the motion.

A convenient alternate mode of expressing 9.2.15 is

$$x = C \cos (pt - \alpha) \tag{23}$$

where C and α are now the two arbitrary constants. Expanding this we have

$$x = C(\cos \alpha \cos pt + \sin \alpha \sin pt) \tag{24}$$

which, when compared with 9.2.15, leads to the identities

$$A = C \sin \alpha \qquad B = C \cos \alpha \tag{25}$$

Squaring both sides of 9.2.25 and adding, we find

$$C^2 = A^2 + B^2 \tag{26}$$

Dividing the first of 9.2.25 by the second we obtain

$$\tan \alpha = \frac{A}{B} \tag{27}$$

The angle α is called the *phase angle* of the motion and C is called the *amplitude* of the motion.

The evaluation of the constants A and B of 9.2.15 and C and α of 9.2.23 requires the knowledge of two bits of independent information about the displacement and/or velocity of the motion. The displacement at two different times, the velocity at two different times, the displacement at one time and the velocity at another time, or the displacement and velocity at the same time, will suffice to determine the constants. If, for example, the displacement and velocity are both known at some time $t = \tau$, we may write

$$x(\tau) = x_\tau \qquad \dot{x}(\tau) = \dot{x}_\tau \tag{28}$$

and using 9.2.15 and 9.2.16, write

$$x_\tau = A \sin p\tau + B \cos p\tau \tag{29}$$

$$\dot{x}_\tau = Ap \cos p\tau - Bp \sin p\tau \tag{30}$$

Multiplying 9.2.29 through by $\sin p\tau$ and 9.2.30 through by $(\cos p\tau)/p$, and adding we obtain

$$A = x_\tau \sin p\tau + \frac{\dot{x}_\tau}{p} \cos p\tau \tag{31}$$

Similarly, we can find

$$B = x_\tau \cos p\tau - \frac{\dot{x}_\tau}{p} \sin p\tau \tag{32}$$

Substituting these into 9.2.15, we have

$$x = \left(x_\tau \sin p\tau + \frac{\dot{x}_\tau}{p} \cos p\tau\right) \sin pt + \left(x_\tau \cos p\tau - \frac{\dot{x}_\tau}{p} \sin p\tau\right) \cos pt \quad (33)$$

This may be written in the more compact form

$$x = x_\tau \cos p(t - \tau) + \frac{\dot{x}_\tau}{p} \sin p(t - \tau) \quad (34)$$

with

$$\dot{x} = -x_\tau p \sin p(t - \tau) + \dot{x}_\tau \cos p(t - \tau) \quad (35)$$

Note that at $t = \tau$, $x(\tau) = x_\tau$ and $\dot{x}(\tau) = \dot{x}_\tau$ as required. For the special case of $\tau = 0$, we obtain the familiar forms

$$x = x_0 \cos pt + \frac{\dot{x}_0}{p} \sin pt \quad (36)$$

$$\dot{x} = -x_0 p \sin pt + \dot{x}_0 \cos pt \quad (37)$$

For given values of p, t, x_τ, and $\dot{x}_\tau$, we may find x and $\dot{x}$ for any value of t. Applying the same procedure to the alternate form 9.2.34, we find

$$x = \sqrt{x_\tau^2 + (\dot{x}_\tau^2/p)} \cos(pt - p\tau - \alpha) \quad (38)$$

$$\frac{\dot{x}}{p} = -\sqrt{x_\tau^2 + (\dot{x}_\tau^2/p)} \sin(pt - p\tau - \alpha) \quad (39)$$

where

$$\tan \alpha = \frac{\dot{x}_\tau/p}{x_\tau} \quad (40)$$

Again, when $\tau = 0$, these become

$$x = \sqrt{x_0^2 + (\dot{x}_0^2/p)} \cos(pt - \alpha) \quad (41)$$

$$\frac{\dot{x}}{p} = -\sqrt{x_0^2 + (\dot{x}_0^2/p)} \sin(pt - \alpha) \quad (42)$$

where

$$\tan \alpha = \frac{\dot{x}_0/p}{x_0} \quad (43)$$

Several examples of free undamped motion of structures follow.

Example 9.2.1 Determine the period of free flexural vibrations of the multibay bent shown in Figure 9.8a. The girder is to be assumed as infinitely stiff, and the columns are assumed to have negligible mass in proportion to the mass M of the girder.

The problem involved here is basically that of determining the spring constant for the structure, since the period of vibration may be found readily once it is

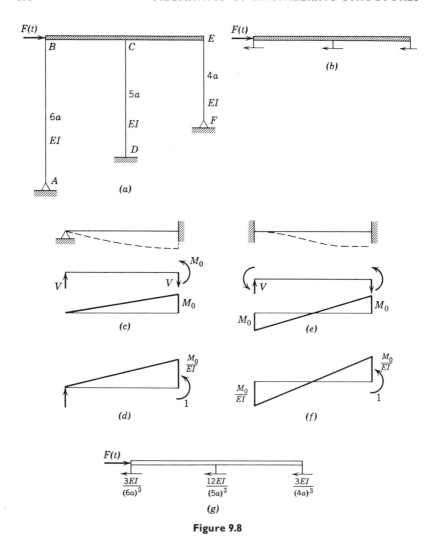

Figure 9.8

known. We seek first, therefore, the magnitude of the static load that is required to displace the girder through a unit horizontal distance. This, in turn, means that we must determine the force required to translate the tops of the various columns through a unit horizontal distance, since the sum of the three forces acting on the column tops equals the force required for the structure as a whole. This is shown on the partial free-body diagram in Figure 9.8b.

As an aid in determining these forces, consider the related problem of a uniform beam hinged at one end and fixed at the other, subjected to a unit translation of the fixed support. The free-body diagram and the bending-moment diagram for such a beam are shown in Figure 9.8c. We shall seek the relationship between the fixed end moment M_0 and the translation by use of the conjugate beam method of analysis. In this method we select a conjugate beam that has the length of the real beam and a load distribution equal to the M/EI distribution for the real beam. In selecting the supports of the conjugate beam, we recall that a deflection in the real beam is analogous to a bending moment in the conjugate beam and that a slope in the real beam is analogous to a shear force in the conjugate beam. The real beam simple support (deflection equal to zero but slope not equal to zero) remains a simple support in the conjugate beam (bending moment equal to zero but shear force not equal to zero). At the other end of the real beam we have a unit deflection and a zero slope. At the corresponding end of the conjugate beam we have a unit bending moment and a zero shear force. The free-body diagram of the conjugate beam must look, therefore, like that shown in Figure 9.8d. By taking the sum of the moments about the left end of the conjugate beam, we write

$$1 = \frac{M_0}{EI} \frac{L}{2} \frac{2L}{3} = \frac{M_0 L^2}{3EI} \tag{44}$$

or

$$M_0 = \frac{3EI}{L^2} \tag{45}$$

Similarly, the shear force at the right end of the real beam may now be found by summing moments about the left end to give

$$VL = M_0 \tag{46}$$

or

$$V = \frac{3EI}{L^3} \tag{47}$$

For a beam that is also fixed at the left end, we have the free-body diagram and bending-moment diagram, as shown in Figure 9.8e, with the conjugate beam loaded and supported as in Figure 9.8 f. Here the conjugate beam yields for a unit translation of the right support

$$M_0 = \frac{6EI}{L^2} \tag{48}$$

The shear force at the right end of the real beam is found to be

$$V = \frac{12EI}{L^3} \tag{49}$$

A unit horizontal displacement of the girder calls into play the shear forces at the tops of the columns, as shown in Figure 9.8g. The spring constant is then read off to be

$$k = \frac{EI}{a^3} (\tfrac{1}{72} + \tfrac{12}{125} + \tfrac{3}{64}) = 0.157 \frac{EI}{a^3} \tag{50}$$

The period of free vibrations in a flexural mode will then be

$$T = 2\pi \sqrt{M/k} = 15.8 \sqrt{Ma^3/EI} \tag{51}$$

where EI is the rigidity of a single column (all columns have the same EI in this example) and M is the total mass of the girder.

Example 9.2.2   A simply supported beam of length L and rigidity EI supports a weight of $3W_0$ acting at midspan. At $t = 0$, one-third of the weight is suddenly removed. What is the equation for the displacement at midspan at any time thereafter?

For this problem, we need to know first the spring constant. It is well known that the deflection Δ at the center of a simply supported beam when a load of P is applied at midspan is given by

$$\Delta = \frac{PL^3}{48EI} \tag{52}$$

The spring constant in flexure is thus

$$k = \frac{P}{\Delta} = \frac{48EI}{L^3} \tag{53}$$

The circular frequency is given by

$$p = \sqrt{k/M} \tag{54}$$

where M is the mass present *during the motion*; in this case, $2W_0/g$. Thus

$$p = \sqrt{24EIg/W_0L^3} \tag{55}$$

At $t = 0$, the structure is at rest under the load of $3W_0$. Therefore the initial conditions are

$$x(0) = x_0 = \frac{W_0L^3}{16EI} \tag{56}$$

$$\dot{x}(0) = \dot{x}_0 = 0 \tag{57}$$

Applying these two conditions to the displacement equation 9.2.36 for free vibrations, we obtain

$$x = \frac{W_0L^3}{16EI} \cos pt \tag{58}$$

where p is as given by 9.2.55.

Example 9.2.3   A cable is suspended from a rigid structure and supports a mass M_0 at its end, which is very large in proportion to the mass of the cable. The cable is of length L, cross sectional area A, and has a modulus of elasticity E. If the cable and mass are caused to vibrate vertically, what is the natural frequency of the free vibration?

If the cable is elastic, Hooke's Law applies and we may write $s = E\epsilon$, where s is the normal stress and ϵ is the longitudinal strain. For a load of P applied along the axis of the cable, s is P/A. If the extension associated with the load P is Δ, we shall have a strain of $\epsilon = \Delta/L$. Combining these relations, we obtain $\Delta = PL/AE$. From this the spring constant is found to be $k = EA/L$, and the natural frequency of the free vibration becomes

$$f = \frac{p}{2\pi} = \sqrt{k/4\pi^2M_0} = \sqrt{EA/4\pi^2M_0L} \tag{59}$$

9.3 Damped Free Vibrations

In § 9.2 the vibrations discussed were assumed to continue indefinitely without diminution of amplitude or change in frequency. Observations of any actual vibrating system disclose, however, that such a situation can never be realized, for in every instance there will be enough resistance to the motion supplied by frictional forces to eventually dampen out all the motion. These damping agents may be of many different forms. They may be (1) the frictional forces associated with the rubbing of surfaces in contact, such as might be associated with the end bearings of a beam or the semirigid riveted connections of a frame, (2) the resistance to motion supplied by the enclosing air or fluid within which the structure is located, or (3) the internal frictional resistance associated with the molecular structure of the material of which the structure is made. Regardless of the exact form of the resistance, the end result is a dampening of all free motion.

The mathematical formulation of the resisting forces causing damping is difficult, if not impossible, to derive for actual physical systems. Our attempts will give us, at best, only approximations which will guide our thinking with respect to these forces. Most of the formulations suggested in the past have been special cases of the general resisting force

$$D(t) = c\dot{x}^n \tag{1}$$

where $D(t)$ is some function of time, c is a constant of proportionality, $\dot{x}$ is the velocity of the moving mass, and n is an integer. For $n = 0$, we have the formulation associated with *dry frictional resistance* and accredited to Coulomb. Here, the total resistance is constant

$$D(t) = c \tag{2}$$

The direction of the resisting force will be opposite to that of the velocity vector for the motion. For $n = 1$, we have a damping force that is proportional to the velocity of the motion. Thus,

$$D(t) = c\dot{x} \tag{3}$$

This damping is referred to as *velocity* or *viscous damping*, since it is of the type associated with the resistance to motion of a body in a viscous fluid. This expression is considered to be very good for representing the resistance to motion of air surrounding a body that moves at a low speed, or the internal frictional resistance of most solid materials. It has the important attribute that it is easily handled mathematically. For $n = 2$, we have *velocity squared damping*, given by

$$D(t) = c\dot{x}^2 \tag{4}$$

This formulation is sometimes used for the resistance of air to bodies moving through it at high velocities or to hydraulic resistance.

A final formulation sometimes used in aircraft work is the force that varies with the displacement and always has the same phase as the velocity.*

* R. H. Scanlan and R. Rosenbaum, *Aircraft Vibration and Flutter*, Macmillan Co., New York, 1951.

In terms of the imaginary quantity i, it is written

$$D(t) = cix \tag{5}$$

Jacobsen* has shown that most of the damping forces mentioned previously may be replaced, for practical purposes, by equivalent viscous damping forces that cause the same amount of energy dissipation per cycle of vibration. In the light of this finding, it is the practice of structural engineers to introduce such an equivalent viscous force into their calculations, which is assumed to represent all the energy dissipated in the system. Such a procedure is defensible physically and mathematically and may be handled with relative ease.

The governing differential equation for free vibrations with damping is

$$M\ddot{x} + D(t) + kx = 0 \tag{6}$$

We shall consider here the value of $D(t)$ given for viscous damping, which yields the equation

$$M\ddot{x} + c\dot{x} + kx = 0 \tag{7}$$

where c is referred to as the *damping coefficient*. Solutions to this equation will be investigated that have the form

$$x = Ae^{mt} \tag{8}$$

By substituting 9.3.8 into 9.3.7 and clearing, we obtain the auxiliary equation

$$Mm^2 + cm + k = 0 \tag{9}$$

or

$$m^2 + 2nm + p^2 = 0 \tag{10}$$

where

$$p^2 = \frac{k}{M} \tag{11}$$

$$2n = \frac{c}{M} \tag{12}$$

The two solutions of the auxiliary equation may be found, through the use of the quadratic formula, to be

$$m = -n \pm \sqrt{n^2 - p^2} \tag{13}$$

Several special cases of this solution will now be considered.

Critical damping. Critical damping shows values of $p^2 = n^2$. Here we see from 9.3.13 that the roots of the auxiliary equation are repeated roots

---

* L. S. Jacobsen, "Steady Forced Vibration as Influenced by Damping," *Transactions*, ASME, v. 52, pp. APM 168–181, 1930.

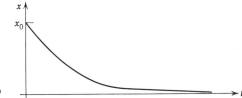

Figure 9.9

of $m = -n$. The solution of the differential equation must assume the form

$$x = A_1 e^{-nt} + A_2 t e^{-nt} = e^{-nt}(A_1 + A_2 t) \qquad (14)$$

In order to illustrate the displacement-time relationship, consider the special set of initial conditions $x(0) = x_0$, $\dot{x}(0) = 0$. This yields values of $A_1 = x_0$ and $A_2 = n x_0$. Or,

$$x = e^{-nt}(x_0 + n x_0 t) = e^{-nt} x_0 (1 + nt) \qquad (15)$$

A plot of this expression is shown in Figure 9.9, where no vibratory motion is indicated. Although critical damping is of little practical importance in itself, it assumes great significance as a measure of the damping capacity of a structure. At critical damping, the damping coefficient c, from 9.3.12, is given as

$$c = 2Mp \qquad (16)$$

The damping coefficient for other cases may be conveniently expressed in the form of some percentage of critical damping. For example, a structure with 20% critical damping has a damping coefficient of $c = 0.20(2Mp) = 0.4Mp$.

Overdamping. For values of $p^2 < n^2$, the damping coefficient c is greater than that for critical damping as given by 9.3.16. A structure having such a damping coefficient is said to be overdamped. In such a structure, the roots of the auxiliary equation are

$$m_1 = -n + \sqrt{n^2 - p^2} \qquad (17)$$

$$m_2 = -n - \sqrt{n^2 - p^2} \qquad (18)$$

Since $n^2 - p^2$ is always positive and less than n^2, the two roots will be always real and negative. The solution to the differential equation of motion will be

$$x = e^{-nt}(A_1 e^{n^2 - p^2 t} + A_2 e^{-n^2 - p^2 t}) \qquad (19)$$

This will be illustrated for the special case of $x(0) = x_0$, $\dot{x}(0) = 0$ and for a damping equal to 200% critical. Thus $c = 4Mp$ or $n = 2p$ and $\sqrt{n^2 - p^2} = \sqrt{3}p$. Equation 9.3.19 is rewritten as

$$x = e^{-2pt}(A_1 e^{\sqrt{3}pt} + A_2 e^{-\sqrt{3}pt})$$

The initial conditions yield

$$A_1 + A_2 = x_0 \qquad 0.268A_1 + 3.7324A_2 = 0 \qquad (21)$$

$$x = e^{-2pt}x_0(1.077e^{\sqrt{3}pt} - 0.077e^{-\sqrt{3}pt}) \qquad (22)$$

A plot of the displacement-time relationship for this case is shown in Figure 9.10. There is no vibratory motion. When the mass is released at $t = 0$, it slowly moves back to a position of static equilibrium.

Underdamping. For values of $p^2 > n^2$, the damping coefficient c will be less than for critical damping, and a structure having such a coefficient is said to be underdamped. In such structures the roots of the auxiliary equation are

$$m = -n \pm ip^* \qquad (23)$$

where

$$p^{*2} = p^2 - n^2 \qquad (24)$$

and i is the square root of negative one. The solution of the equation of motion becomes

$$x = e^{-nt}(A_1e^{ip^*t} + A_2e^{-ip^*t}) \qquad (25)$$

Referring to § 9.2, we may write this in the form

$$x = e^{-nt}(A \sin p^*t + B \cos p^*t) \qquad (26)$$

where the expression in parentheses is identical in form to the equation of undamped free vibrations. As in that case we may adopt an alternate form

$$x = e^{-nt}C \cos (p^*t - \psi) \qquad (27)$$

where C and ψ are the new arbitrary constants. The motion of a one degree of freedom structure that is freely vibrating and is underdamped has an amplitude that diminishes in time with an exponential decay. The period of the motion is constant, however, but somewhat greater than the period of free undamped vibrations, being equal to

$$T^* = \frac{2\pi}{p^*} = \frac{2\pi}{p} \frac{1}{\sqrt{1 - (n/p)^2}} \qquad (28)$$

Figure 9.10

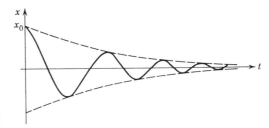

Figure 9.11

Consider again the prescribed conditions $x(0) = x_0$ and $\dot{x}(0) = 0$. Using 9.3.26, we have

$$x_0 = B \tag{29}$$

$$0 = Ap^* - nB \qquad A = \frac{nx_0}{p^*} \tag{30}$$

Thus

$$x = e^{-nt}\left(\frac{nx_0}{p^*}\sin p^*t + x_0 \cos p^*t\right) \tag{31}$$

A plot of the displacement-time relationship for this case is shown in Figure 9.11.

If we measure the amplitude of the displacement at any time t and a later time $t + T^*$, we shall find that their ratio is a constant quantity. Thus

$$\frac{x_t}{x_{t+T^*}} = \frac{e^{-nt}}{e^{-nt-nT^*}} = e^{-nT^*} \tag{32}$$

The natural logarithm of this quantity will be denoted by β and called the *logarithmic decrement*.

$$\beta = nT^* \tag{33}$$

The logarithmic decrement is a measure of the damping capacity of the structure and is particularly useful in experiments designed for measuring the damping coefficient c. The relationship that exists between the logarithmic decrement and ρ, the decimal equivalent of the percentage of critical damping, is easily found.

$$c = \rho 2Mp = 2nM = 2M\frac{\beta}{T^*} \tag{34}$$

or

$$\rho = \frac{\beta}{pT^*} \tag{35}$$

The damping capacity of structures has been studied by many investigators and values have been quoted in terms of the logarithmic decrement as well as a percentage of critical damping. By and large, the greatest amount of work has been devoted to determining such values for a given material as a measure of the internal frictional resistance of that material. Although this is important in itself, the structural engineer has a far greater interest in the damping capacity of a structure taken as a whole. Bleich and Teller* conducted experiments on solid rolled steel members alongside of built-up (bolted) trusses that were of the same length, approximately the same weight per foot, moment of inertia, and natural period. The character of the amplitude decay for the solid elements was essentially logarithmic as predicted, assuming a viscous type damping. The decay of the amplitude for the bolted truss was much more complex. The supports closely resembled the conditions of a smooth roller at one end and a rocker bearing at the other. Under these conditions the logarithmic decrement varied between the values of 0.0036 and 0.0070 for the solid sections and from 0.0060 to 0.0300 for the bolted sections—the stress level being between 1000 psi and 10,000 psi. The difference can be attributed to the friction losses at the joints primarily. This is verified by additional tests that show that the degree of tension in a bolt, the looseness of a joint, contributes greatly to increased values of the decrement.

When supporting conditions were used that more nearly resembled actual conditions (considerable dry frictional resistance) the values of the decrement increased appreciably, reaching as high as 0.291 in some instances. To convert this latter figure into an equivalent percentage of critical damping, we assume that the value of p is approximately equal to the value of p^* and use 9.3.35 to give a value of 4.6% critical damping. Selberg† conducted tests on existing suspension bridges with various combinations of floor and girder systems and found decremental values from 0.07 to 0.185 which are equivalent to values of 1.1 to 2.95% critical. Hudson and Housner‡ obtained a value of 3.4% critical damping for a steel frame building and Alford and Housner§ obtained a value of 7% for a concrete building. Values for buildings as high as 15% might be expected, depending on the nature of the material used and the degree of looseness in the connections.

Negative Damping. It is interesting to point out that for any of the foregoing cases an unstable motion is indicated for negative values of n.

* F. Bleich and L. W. Teller, "Structural Damping in Suspension Bridges," *Transactions*, ASCE, v. 117, pp. 165–203, 1952.

† A. Selberg, "Dampening Effect in Suspension Bridges," *Publications*, International Association of Bridge and Structural Engineers, v. 10, pp. 183–198, 1950.

‡ D. E. Hudson and G. W. Housner, "Structural Vibrations Produced by Ground Motion," *Transactions*, ASCE, v. 122, pp. 705–721, 1957.

§ J. L. Alford and G. W. Housner, "A Dynamic Test of a Four-Story Reinforced Concrete Building," *Bulletin*, Seismological Society of America, v. 43, no. 1, pp. 7–16, 1953.

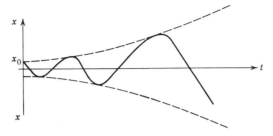

Figure 9.12

The coefficient e^{-nt} for negative values of n assumes an ever increasing magnitude as t increases. When a structure is acted on by a disturbance that varies as the velocity, the effect is that of a free vibration with negative damping. This is an example of the *self-excited vibration* commonly referred to as *flutter*.* See Figure 9.12 for the displacement-time curve.

Coulomb (dry friction) damping is of interest to structural engineers, but the mathematical treatment of it will not be given here. Timoshenko,† for example, presents a discussion that indicates that whereas viscous damping leads to an exponentially decaying amplitude, the Coulomb damping leads to a linear decay as shown in Figure 9.13.

9.4 Forced Motion due to Pulsating Load

A structure may be acted on by externally applied disturbances such as forces or displacements that give rise to time-dependent motions. During the time interval when the disturbance is active, we have a forced motion.

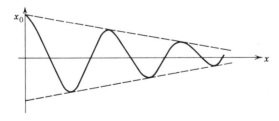

Figure 9.13

* R. H. Scanlan and R. Rosenbaum, *Aircraft Vibration and Flutter*, Macmillan Co., New York, 1951.

† S. P. Timoshenko, *Vibration Problems in Engineering*, D. Van Nostrand Co., Princeton, N. J., Third edition, 1955.

Upon the removal of the disturbance we have a free motion. The general case of a forced motion when no damping is present is governed by equation 9.1.16. The presence of a damping force $D(t)$ changes that equation to

$$M\ddot{x} + D(t) + kx = F(t) + kx_0 \tag{1}$$

For viscous damping, this becomes

$$M\ddot{x} + c\dot{x} + kx = f(t) \tag{2}$$

where $f(t)$ is intended to represent the entire right-hand side of 9.4.1. Equation 9.4.2 is a nonhomogeneous equation and as such has a general solution consisting of the homogeneous solution (right-hand side of the differential equation equal to zero) plus the particular solution. Thus

$$x = x_h + x_p \tag{3}$$

For the underdamped vibrations (which is the only case of real concern to structural engineers) we find

$$x_h = e^{-nt}(A \sin p^*t + B \cos p^*t) \tag{4}$$

where n and p^* are as defined in § 9.3. The particular solution x_p is any solution that will satisfy 9.4.2 in its entirety. The particular solution is unique; therefore, if we can find a particular solution, then we shall have found *the* particular solution. We write the general solution in the form

$$x = e^{-nt}(A \sin p^*t + B \cos p^*t) + x_p \tag{5}$$

Regardless of the exact nature of x_p, certain general conclusions may be drawn from observations of 9.4.5. For example, as time increases, it is evident that the contribution of the homogeneous solution to the general solution becomes steadily less. Since the homogeneous portion makes a significant contribution to the displacement for a relatively short length of time, it is known as a *transient*. Recognizing this, it is the practice with many people to concern themselves totally with the particular solution in discussing a given problem.

As an important illustration of the effect of damping on a forced motion, we consider the classical problem of a pulsating load $F_0 \sin \omega t$ acting as the disturbing agent and write the governing differential equation as

$$M\ddot{x} + c\dot{x} + kx = F_0 \sin \omega t \tag{6}$$

Using the abbreviations of the previous section, we rewrite 9.4.6 as

$$\ddot{x} + 2n\dot{x} + p^2x = \frac{F_0 \sin \omega t}{M} \tag{7}$$

We shall employ the method of undetermined coefficients in finding the particular solution for this equation. The method is very useful when the right sides of the differential equations are simple in form. Most reference works on ordinary differential equations, for example Rainville,* discuss the method in detail. We shall assume a particular solution of the type

$$x = D \sin \omega t + G \cos \omega t \tag{8}$$

substitute it into 9.4.7, and determine D and G so as to satisfy the equation. The successive derivatives of 9.4.8 are

$$\dot{x} = D\omega \cos \omega t - G\omega \sin \omega t \tag{9}$$

$$\ddot{x} = -D\omega^2 \sin \omega t - G\omega^2 \cos \omega t \tag{10}$$

We substitute these into 9.4.7 and collect terms involving the $\sin \omega t$ and $\cos \omega t$ as follows:

$$\sin \omega t(-D\omega^2 - 2nG\omega + p^2 D - F_0/M)$$
$$+ \cos \omega t(-G\omega^2 + 2nD\omega + p^2 G) = 0 \tag{11}$$

So that this equation be satisfied for all values of t we must ask that the terms in parentheses be individually equal to zero. This gives a set of two algebraic equations in the two unknowns D and G.

$$D(p^2 - \omega^2) + G(-2n\omega) = \frac{F_0}{M} \tag{12}$$

$$D(2n\omega) + G(p^2 - \omega^2) = 0 \tag{13}$$

From 9.4.13,

$$D = -G\frac{p^2 - \omega^2}{2n\omega} \tag{14}$$

Substitution of this equation into 9.4.12 yields

$$G = -\frac{2n\omega F_0}{M[(p^2 - \omega^2)^2 + (2n\omega)^2]} \tag{15}$$

and 9.4.14 gives

$$D = \frac{F_0(p^2 - \omega^2)}{M[(p^2 - \omega^2)^2 + (2n\omega)^2]} \tag{16}$$

Using the p^* notation, the general solution becomes

$$x = e^{-nt}(A \sin p^*t + B \cos p^*t) + \frac{F_0(p^2 - \omega^2) \sin \omega t - 2n\omega \cos \omega t}{M(p^2 - \omega^2)^2 + (2n\omega)^2} \tag{17}$$

* E. D. Rainville, *Differential Equations*, Macmillan Co., New York, 1949.

The static deflection of a force F_0 applied to the structure is

$$\Delta = \frac{F_0}{k} = \frac{F_0}{Mp^2} \tag{18}$$

In terms of Δ, we may write the particular solution as

$$x_p = \Delta H\left[\left(1 - \left(\frac{\omega}{p}\right)^2\right)\sin \omega t - \frac{2n\omega}{p^2}\cos \omega t\right] \tag{19}$$

where H is defined by

$$H = \frac{1}{\left[1 - \left(\frac{\omega}{p}\right)^2\right]^2 + \frac{4n^2\omega^2}{p^4}} \tag{20}$$

and is called a *magnification factor*. The product $H\Delta$ is a measure of the amplitude of the forced motion. Curves relating H to ω/p are given in Figure 9.14.

For the case of no damping, the general solution assumes the simpler form

$$x = A \sin pt + B \cos pt + \frac{F_0 \sin \omega t}{Mp^2[1 - (\omega/p)^2]} \tag{21}$$

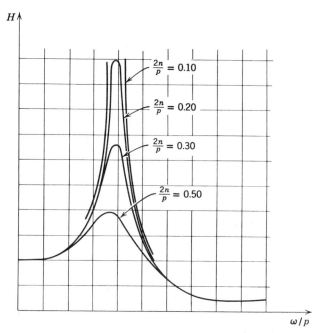

Figure 9.14 (after Timoshenko)

From the appearance of 9.4.21 we might conclude that for values of the force frequency ω equal to the structural frequency p, the contribution of the right term would be infinitely large, and as a consequence infinitely large displacement would occur. Such a condition, known as *mathematical resonance*, can easily be shown not to exist under normal circumstances by actually evaluating the constants A and B and then studying the equation. Consider, for example, $x(0) = x_0$ and $\dot{x}(0) = \dot{x}_0$. We evaluate the constants to be

$$B = x_0 \tag{22}$$

$$A = \frac{\dot{x}_0}{p} - \frac{F_0}{Mp^2}\left[\frac{(\omega/p)}{1 - (\omega/p)^2}\right] \tag{23}$$

yielding finally

$$x = \frac{\dot{x}_0}{p} \sin pt + x_0 \cos pt - \frac{F_0[(\omega/p) \sin pt - \sin \omega t]}{Mp^2[1 - (\omega/p)^2]} \tag{24}$$

The particular part of this solution, being periodic in nature and enduring as long as the force remains on the structure, is called the *steady-state* portion of the motion. Now, let us examine the equation for values of ω equal to p. It appears that rather than getting an infinitely large value from the right-hand term, we get instead, the indeterminate form $0/0$. The exact limit for this term may be found using l'Hospital's rule: take the derivative of numerator and denominator with respect to ω and then let ω approach p as a limit. Here the differentiation yields

$$\frac{F_0[(1/p) \sin pt - t \cos \omega t]}{2Mp^2(-\omega/p^2)}$$

which for $\omega = p$ gives the limiting value. The expression for x at the limit may now be written as

$$x = \frac{\dot{x}_0}{p} \sin pt + x_0 \cos pt - \frac{F_0}{2Mp}\left[t \cos pt - \frac{\sin pt}{p}\right] \tag{25}$$

It is clear from 9.4.25 that infinitely large values of x cannot be obtained unless the load is applied for an indefinitely long period of time. If the load is removed at a time t_1, the displacement at that time is still finite and the displacement in the free vibration which follows is finite thereafter. The lesson to be learned from this demonstration is that mathematical resonance can never be realized in an undamped structure so long as the forcing function is applied for only a finite length of time. Practically, however, the structural engineer is not interested in displacements that are infinite but rather in displacements that are large enough to cause excessive stresses and strains to be set up in the system. It might be well, therefore, to think rather in terms of an *engineering resonance* and define it as the condition in which the displacements are large enough to be objectionable from the point of view of deflections, stresses, or strains.

9.5 The Multistory Shear Building

One of the most instructive examples of a structure that moves as with many degrees of freedom is the multistory shear building. Briefly, a shear building may be defined as a structure in which there is no rotation of a horizontal section at the level of the floors. In this respect, the deflected building will have many of the features of a cantilever beam that is deflected by the shear forces only; hence the name *shear building*. To accomplish such a deflection in a building we must make the following assumptions: (1) that the total mass of the structure is concentrated at the levels of the floors, (2) that the girders of the structure are infinitely rigid as compared to the columns, and (3) that the deformation of the structure does not depend on the axial forces present in the columns. The first assumption makes possible the reduction of the problem from one of a structure with an infinite number of degrees of freedom (due to the distributed mass of the columns and girders) to a structure that has as many degrees of freedom as it has lumped masses at the story levels. A four story structure, for example, will have associated with it four lumped masses that will move as with four degrees of freedom. Additional degrees of freedom will be introduced if the structure is caused to rock as well as translate laterally. The second assumption leads to the requirement that members framing into a single joint suffer no relative rotation. The third assumption fixes the deformation in such a way that the rigid girders remain horizontal when there is no rocking of the structure. This implies, using assumption 2, that the columns retain vertical slopes at their ends and thus act as fixed-end beams that are subject to settlement of the supports in a direction perpendicular to the beam axes. A differential settlement is equivalent to a differential horizontal displacement of the ends of a given column.

If we desire to consider the effects of the axial forces on the deformed structure, assumption 3 must be omitted. Here the rigid girder would be free to rotate and the resulting deformation would be akin to a beam in shear bending. Results found using the concept of a shear building would have to be corrected, in this case, to account for the rotation of the girders.

It should be noted that it is not necesary to think of a shear building solely in terms of a single bay structure as long as the above stated assumptions are made. It is merely for convenience that we represent such a building as a single bay structure.

In Figure 9.15, the floors are numbered from bottom to top. At the jth floor we find the mass M_j connected to the columns of the jth story

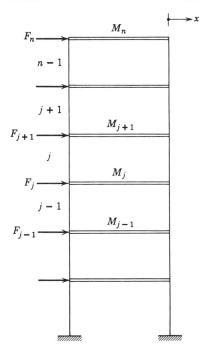

Figure 9.15

above and the $(j-1)$th story below. The lateral displacement of the mass is denoted by x_j. Figure 9.16 shows a partially completed free-body diagram indicating the shear forces V_j and V_{j-1}, which act on the mass through the columns of the adjacent stories. The shear force necessary in a given story to cause a unit relative horizontal displacement of adjacent floor levels is denoted by the symbol K_j and called the spring constant for the story. The shear force associated with any other magnitude of relative displacement is given by

$$V_j = K_j(x_{j+1} - x_j) \qquad (1)$$

where x_{j+1} and x_j are the displacements of the masses M_{j+1} and M_j which lie at the top and bottom of the jth story.

Let the displacements and forces be measured positive to the right. Force equilibrium for the jth girder requires

$$M_j\ddot{x}_j = V_j - V_{j-1} + F_j \qquad (2)$$

where F_j is any applied force on the girder. Using 9.5.1, this becomes

$$M_j\ddot{x}_j + K_{j-1}(x_j - x_{j-1}) - K_j(x_{j+1} - x_j) = F_j \qquad (3)$$

An equation of this type may be written for each moving mass, except the mass at the top of the structure where the equation becomes $(j = n)$

$$M_n\ddot{x}_n + K_{n-1}(x_n - x_{n-1}) = F_n \qquad (4)$$

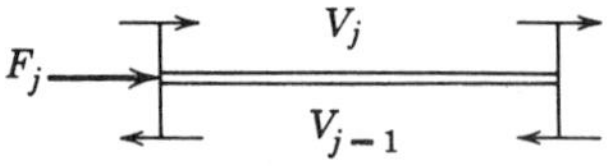

Figure 9.16

If the story mass is subjected to an imposed time-dependent displacement x_0, this fact may be incorporated into the equations by modifying the right-hand sides. If damping is to be considered, additional terms must be added to the left-hand sides to account for it.

When free vibrations are under consideration, the right-hand sides are all zero since F_j equals zero. For this case we divide each equation through by the mass of the story to obtain the set of equations

$$\ddot{x}_2 + \frac{K_2 + K_1}{M_2} x_2 - \frac{K_2}{M_2} x_3 = 0$$

$$\ddot{x}_3 + \frac{K_3 + K_2}{M_3} x_3 - \frac{K_3}{M_3} x_4 - \frac{K_2}{M_3} x_2 = 0$$

$$\ddot{x}_4 + \frac{K_4 + K_3}{M_4} x_4 - \frac{K_4}{M_4} x_5 - \frac{K_3}{M_4} x_3 = 0 \tag{5}$$

$$\cdots\cdots\cdots\cdots\cdots\cdots\cdots = 0$$

$$\ddot{x}_n + \frac{K_{n-1}}{M_n} x_n - \frac{K_{n-1}}{M_n} x_{n-1} = 0$$

For free vibrations of the undamped structure, we investigate solutions of the form

$$x_j = X_j \sin pt \tag{6}$$

where X_j is the amplitude of the motion. Substitute 9.5.6 into 9.5.5 to obtain

$$(k_2'' - p^2)X_2 - k_2 X_3 = 0$$

$$-k_3' X_2 + (k_3'' - p^2)X_3 - k_3 X_4 = 0 \tag{7}$$

$$-k_4' X_3 + (k_4'' - p^2)X_4 - k_4 X_5 = 0$$

$$\cdots\cdots\cdots\cdots\cdots\cdots = 0$$

where

$$k_j = \frac{K_j}{M_j} \tag{8}$$

$$k_j' = \frac{K_{j-1}}{M_j} \tag{9}$$

$$k_j'' = \frac{K_j + K_{j-1}}{M_j} \tag{10}$$

The set of equations 9.5.7 is a homogeneous algebraic set containing $n - 1$ unknown X and an unknown p^2. There are, consequently, $n - 1$ equations in n unknowns. We can solve for the p^2 explicitly and then for the X

quantities to within an arbitrary constant. Since the set of equations is homogeneous and algebraic, we know that the determinant of the coefficients must be equal to zero. The general theory is closely associated with the theory of matrix algebra.

9.6 Frequency Analysis of Multidegree of Freedom Structures

The shear building of § 9.5 is but a single example of a multidegree of freedom structure. Most generally, the free vibrations of an undamped elastic structure that moves with many degrees of freedom may be described in terms of a set of algebraic equations of the form

$$
\begin{aligned}
a_{11}X_1 + a_{12}X_2 + a_{13}X_3 + \cdots + a_{1n}X_n &= p^2 M_1 X_1 \\
a_{21}X_1 + a_{22}X_2 + a_{23}X_3 + \cdots + a_{2n}X_n &= p^2 M_2 X_2 \\
a_{31}X_1 + a_{32}X_2 + a_{33}X_3 + \cdots + a_{3n}X_n &= p^2 M_3 X_3 \\
& \quad \cdots \cdots \cdots \cdots \cdots \\
a_{n1}X_1 + a_{n2}X_2 + a_{n3}X_3 + \cdots + a_{nn}X_n &= p^2 M_n X_n
\end{aligned} \tag{1}
$$

where the a_{ji}'s represent constant coefficients depending on the elasticity of the structure and the M_j's represent magnitudes of lumped masses. The unknowns are the displacement amplitudes X_j and the frequency p. The quantity p may take on as many values as there are equations in the system and for every value of p there will correspond a set of values of the X_j. Problems of this type are known as *characteristic value problems* and the constant p is known as a *characteristic number*. The set of values of X_i corresponding to a particular value of p_i is known as the *i*th *characteristic vector*. The set of equations 9.6.1 may be expressed in the matrix form

$$
\mathbf{a}X_i = p_i^2 \mathbf{M}X_i \tag{2}
$$

where $\mathbf{M}$ is a diagonal matrix. The product of the diagonal matrix $\mathbf{M}$ and the column matrix $\mathbf{X}_i$ is itself a column matrix. A more convenient form of 9.6.2 for many problems is

$$
(\mathbf{a} - p_i^2 \mathbf{M})\mathbf{X}_i = 0 \tag{3}
$$

The set of equations described by 9.6.3 is a set of algebraic, linear, homogeneous equations. By Cramer's rule, it follows that there can be other than trivial values of the $\mathbf{X}_i$ only if the determinant of the coefficients of $\mathbf{X}_i$ vanishes. This implies the necessity of

$$
|\mathbf{a} - p_i^2 \mathbf{M}| = \begin{vmatrix}
a_{11} - p_i^2 M_1 & a_{12} & a_{13} & \cdots & a_{1n} \\
a_{21} & a_{22} - p_i^2 M_2 & a_{23} & \cdots & a_{2n} \\
a_{31} & a_{32} & a_{33} - p_i^2 M_3 & \cdots & a_{3n} \\
\cdots & \cdots & \cdots & \cdots & \cdots \\
a_{n1} & a_{n2} & a_{n3} & \cdots & a_{nn} - p_i^2 M_n
\end{vmatrix} = 0 \tag{4}
$$

Upon expanding this determinant we get an nth order equation in $p_i{}^2$. For each value of $p_i{}^2$ there is a corresponding X_i.

Example 9.6.1   Given: the three-story single bay bent of Figure 9.17a. The masses are lumped at the story levels and have the magnitudes indicated. The spring constants for the various stories are also noted. Determine the periods of the three modes of flexural vibration.

j	M_j	K_j
1	—	10 kpi
2	15 lb. sec.^{2}/in.	9 kpi
3	15 lb. sec.^{2}/in.	8 kpi
4	15 lb. sec.^{2}/in.	—

Here the **M** matrix is a scalar matrix, since all the masses are equal in magnitude.

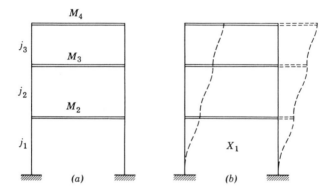

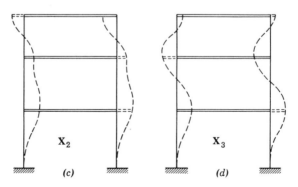

Figure 9.17

The governing equations of motion for the structure are

$$M_4\ddot{x}_4 = -K_3(x_4 - x_3) \tag{1}$$

$$M_3\ddot{x}_3 = -K_2(x_3 - x_2) + K_3(x_4 - x_3) \tag{2}$$

$$M_2\ddot{x}_2 = -K_1(x_2) + K_2(x_3 - x_2) \tag{3}$$

For free vibrations we assume the solution

$$x_j = X_j \cos(pt + \alpha) \tag{4}$$

and obtain the following set of algebraic equations (using the numerical values from the foregoing table.)

$$19{,}000X_2 - 9{,}000X_3 = 15p^2X_2$$

$$-9{,}000X_2 + 17{,}000X_3 - 8{,}000X_4 = 15p^2X_3 \tag{5}$$

$$- 8{,}000X_3 + 8{,}000X_4 = 15p^2X_4$$

This·is of the form

$$\mathbf{aX} = \mathbf{M}p^2\mathbf{X} \tag{6}$$

where

$$\mathbf{a} = \begin{bmatrix} 19{,}000 & -9{,}000 & 0 \\ -9{,}000 & 17{,}000 & -8{,}000 \\ 0 & -8{,}000 & 8{,}000 \end{bmatrix}; \quad \mathbf{M} = \begin{bmatrix} 15 & 0 & 0 \\ 0 & 15 & 0 \\ 0 & 0 & 15 \end{bmatrix} \tag{7}$$

We now collect terms and set the determinant associated with the form

$$(\mathbf{a} - \mathbf{M}p^2)\mathbf{X} = 0 \tag{8}$$

equal to zero. After dividing through by 15, this yields

$$\begin{vmatrix} 1267 - p^2 & -600 & 0 \\ -600 & 1133 - p^2 & -533 \\ 0 & -533 & 533 - p^2 \end{vmatrix} = 0 \tag{9}$$

Expanding the determinant, we obtain the cubic equation in p^2

$$p^6 - 2933p^4 + 2{,}070{,}622p^2 - 213{,}306{,}600 = 0 \tag{10}$$

which has the roots

$$p_1 = 11.14 \text{ rdn./sec}; \quad p_2 = 30.07 \text{ rdn./sec}; \quad p_3 = 43.64 \text{ rdn./sec}. \tag{11}$$

The corresponding natural frequencies and periods are

$$\begin{aligned} f_1 &= 1.77 \text{ cps.} & T_1 &= 0.56 \text{ sec.} \\ f_2 &= 4.79 \text{ cps.} & T_2 &= 0.21 \text{ sec.} \\ f_3 &= 6.95 \text{ cps.} & T_3 &= 0.14 \text{ sec.} \end{aligned} \tag{12}$$

Associated mode shapes are also suggested in Figure 9.17.

9.7 Influence Coefficients

The concept of influence coefficients is of great importance in the study of multidegree of freedom structures. The formulation for the shear building of § 9.5 is a single example of their use as will be seen. The ideas involved in the study of influence coefficients are exactly the same as those involved in the study of influence lines for beams and influence surfaces for slabs, all being problems in "cause and effect." The formulation of dynamic problems involving beams and framed structures may be based on either (1) displacement influence coefficients or (2) force influence coefficients. Which to use depends on the particular problem under consideration.

Force influence coefficients will be denoted by the symbol ρ_{ij}, which is defined as the force required at mass M_i when the structure is loaded in a manner such that all masses are restrained against translating, except the mass M_j, which is caused to move a unit horizontal distance. The finding of the ρ_{ij} is basically a problem in statics. For a three-story single bay bent they are as depicted in Figures 9.18a, b, and c. If the mass M_j is caused to move a horizontal distance x_j and all other masses are held against translation, the force required at a mass M_i will be $\rho_{ij}x_j$. Similarly, a unit translation of the mass M_k when all other masses are restrained will require a force at mass M_i equal to ρ_{ik}. If instead of a unit displacement we had the translation x_k, the force at M_i would be $\rho_{ik}x_k$. By superposition, we may further state that when a given set of mass displacements are considered, the force F_i at mass M_i which is consistent with these displacements is

$$F_i = \sum_j \rho_{ij}x_j \tag{1}$$

For a particular structure the force F_i may be due to the inertia force associated with an accelerating mass and in addition externally applied

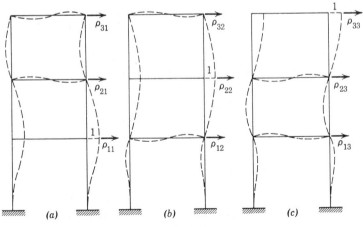

Figure 9.18

forces $F_i(t)$. For undamped forced motion the equilibrium equation associated with the mass M_i assumes the form

$$M_i \ddot{x}_i + \sum_j \rho_{ij} x_j = F_i(t) \tag{2}$$

For free undamped vibrations this becomes

$$M_i \ddot{x}_i + \sum_j \rho_{ij} x_j = 0 \tag{3}$$

We investigate solutions of the form

$$x_i = X_i \cos (pt + \alpha) \tag{4}$$

to obtain the reduced algebraic equation

$$-M_i X_i p^2 + \sum_j \rho_{ij} X_j = 0 \tag{5}$$

For the three-story frame of Figure 9.16, we obtain

$$
\begin{aligned}
\rho_{11} X_1 + \rho_{12} X_2 + \rho_{13} X_3 &= p^2 M_1 X_1 \\
\rho_{21} X_1 + \rho_{22} X_2 + \rho_{23} X_3 &= p^2 M_2 X_2 \\
\rho_{31} X_1 + \rho_{32} X_2 + \rho_{33} X_3 &= p^2 M_3 X_3
\end{aligned}
\tag{6}
$$

The set of equations for any multimass structure may be expressed in the matrix form

$$\boldsymbol{\rho} \mathbf{X} = p^2 \mathbf{M} \mathbf{X} \tag{7}$$

where $\mathbf{M}$ is a diagonal matrix of the masses and $\boldsymbol{\rho}$ is the square matrix of the force influence coefficients. We shall speak of $\boldsymbol{\rho}$ as the "rho" matrix. An alternate form of 9.7.7 is

$$(\boldsymbol{\rho} - p^2 \mathbf{M}) \mathbf{X} = 0 \tag{8}$$

Displacement influence coefficients will be denoted by δ_{ij} and are defined as the displacement of a mass M_i due to a unit force acting at mass M_j when no other forces act on the structure. When a force F_j is applied at mass M_j and no other forces act, the displacement at mass M_i becomes $\delta_{ij} F_j$. More generally, the displacement at mass M_i due to any set of forces at the other masses is given by

$$x_i = \sum_j \delta_{ij} F_j \tag{9}$$

The force F_j may be an inertia force

$$F_j = -M_j \ddot{x}_j \tag{10}$$

or an externally applied force $F(t)$. In such cases, we write

$$x_i + \sum_j \delta_{ij} M_j \ddot{x}_j = \sum_j \delta_{ij} F_j(t) \tag{11}$$

For free undamped motion we have

$$x_i + \sum_j \delta_{ij} M_j \ddot{x}_j = 0 \tag{12}$$

Again, we investigate a solution of the form

$$x_j = X_j \cos (pt + \alpha) \tag{13}$$

to obtain

$$X_i - \sum_j p^2 \delta_{ij} M_j X_j = 0 \tag{14}$$

For the three-story structure we obtain

$$X_1 = p^2(\delta_{11} M_1 X_1 + \delta_{12} M_2 X_2 + \delta_{13} M_3 X_3)$$

$$X_2 = p^2(\delta_{21} M_1 X_1 + \delta_{22} M_2 X_2 + \delta_{23} M_3 X_3) \tag{15}$$

$$X_3 = p^2(\delta_{31} M_1 X_1 + \delta_{32} M_2 X_2 + \delta_{33} M_3 X_3)$$

For the general structure, we express the set of equations in matrix form as follows.

$$\mathbf{X} = p^2 \, \boldsymbol{\delta} \mathbf{M} \mathbf{X} \tag{16}$$

where $\boldsymbol{\delta}$ is the square matrix of the displacement influence coefficients. We shall speak of $\boldsymbol{\delta}$ as the "delta" matrix.

It is interesting to note that upon premultiplication of 9.7.7 by the inverse of the rho matrix, $\boldsymbol{\rho}^{-1}$, we obtain

$$\mathbf{X} = p^2 \boldsymbol{\rho}^{-1} \mathbf{M} \mathbf{X} \tag{17}$$

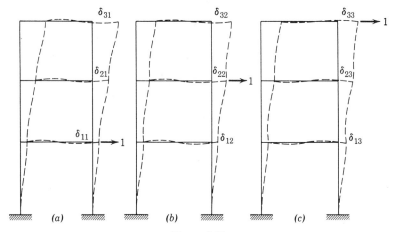

Figure 9.19

Equations 9.7.17 and 9.7.16 both describe the free vibrations of an un-damped structure and must be identical. This means that the relation

$$\delta = \rho^{-1} \tag{18}$$

must be satisfied. Thus, the delta matrix is mathematically equivalent to the inverse of the rho matrix and vice versa.

The formulation of the problem of the shear building given in § 9.5 can be observed to be equivalent to the rho matrix formulation. For a delta matrix formulation, we have the physical interpretation of the meanings of the elements δ_{ij} given in Figures 9.19(a, b, and c). The use of the second method of attack is illustrated in the following numerical example of a freely vibrating beam of uniform section throughout.

Example 9.7.1 Given a simply supported beam of uniform section and mass distribution throughout its length, find the frequency of the first mode of free vibration by assuming that the mass of the beam is lumped at the ends, quarter points, and midpoint as shown in Figure 9.20a.

If the mass is given as m per unit of length, the concentrations at the quarter points and midpoint will be equal to

$$M_1 = M_2 = M_3 = \frac{mL}{4} = \frac{M}{4}$$

$$M_0 = M_4 = \frac{mL}{8} = \frac{M}{8} \tag{1}$$

where M is the total mass of the beam. The most convenient approach to this problem is through the use of displacement influence coefficients and the delta matrix. Figures 9.20b, c, and d show the proper interpretation of the elements of the matrix. We may find these values by any of the classical methods, such as the conjugate beam method. They are

$$\delta_{11} = \delta_{33} = \frac{3L^3}{256EI}$$

$$\delta_{21} = \delta_{12} = \delta_{32} = \delta_{23} = \frac{3.67L^3}{256EI}$$

$$\delta_{13} = \delta_{31} = \frac{2.33L^3}{256EI} \tag{2}$$

$$\delta_{22} = \frac{5.33L^3}{256EI}$$

The delta matrix becomes

$$\delta = \frac{L^3}{256EI} \begin{bmatrix} 3.00 & 3.67 & 2.33 \\ 3.67 & 5.33 & 3.67 \\ 2.33 & 3.67 & 3.00 \end{bmatrix} \tag{3}$$

We now write 9.7.16 as follows:

$$X \left(\frac{1}{p^2} I - \delta M \right) = 0 \tag{4}$$

Solutions for **X** are nontrivial only if the determinant of coefficients vanishes. This means for the present problem, where $B = L^3/256\,EI$,

$$\begin{bmatrix} 3.00 - (1/Bp^2) & 3.67 & 2.33 \\ 3.67 & 5.33 - (1/Bp^2) & 3.67 \\ 2.33 & 3.67 & 3.00 - (1/Bp^2) \end{bmatrix} = 0 \qquad (5)$$

Expanding and solving for p^2, we find the fundamental mode frequency to be

$$p^2 = 97.32 \frac{EI}{mL^4} \qquad (6)$$

This compares very well with the exact value as given in more advanced books when the coefficient is found to be 97.41.

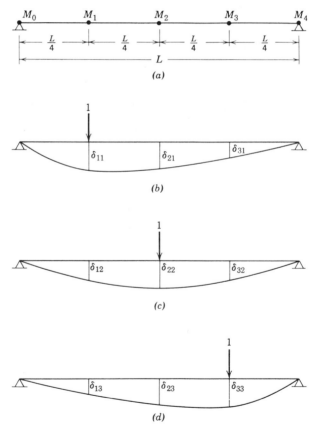

(a)

(b)

(c)

(d)

Figure 9.20

Problems

9.1.1 Determine the spring constants for translatory and rotatory motion of the following system.

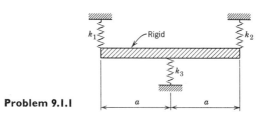

Problem 9.1.1

9.1.2 Determine the flexural spring constant for the following systems. EI = constant.

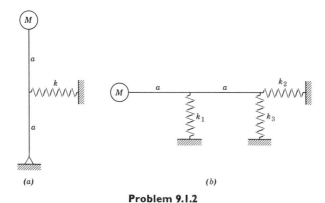

(a)   (b)

Problem 9.1.2

9.2.1 Express C and α in terms of A and B if $x = C \cos(pt + \alpha)$ is used instead of equation 9.2.15.

9.2.2 The concrete umbrella structure shown in the figure has a column that is 10 in. in diameter and 10 ft. high and a top slab that is 8 ft. in diameter and 3 in. thick. The unit weight of concrete is to be taken as 150 pcf, E as 4000 ksi, and G as

Problem 9.2.2

1800 ksi. Approximate the behavior of this structure by using a one-degree-of-freedom structure with a single concentrated mass lumped at the top of the column. Let the lumped mass be equal to the total mass of the slab plus half the mass of the column. Determine the period, circular frequency, and natural frequency of this structure when freely vibrating in (a) an extensional mode, (b) a flexural mode, and (c) in a torsional mode.

9.2.3 A simply supported $30\text{W}^{\!F}210(I = 9872.4 \text{ in.}^4)$ steel beam supports a rigidly attached vertical load of 10 kips at its mid-span. The beam is 10 ft. long. Lump one-half the mass of the beam at mid-span and one-quarter the mass at each support. Find the displacement and velocity of the mid-span at $t = 12$ seconds if the 10-kip load is (a) suddenly removed at $t = 2$ seconds, (b) suddenly applied at $t = 2$ sec. In each case assume that the beam is at rest just prior to removal or application of the load.

9.2.4 What is the period of free vibration of a propped cantilever beam (one end fixed and the other simply supported) based on a lumping of the total mass at mid-span? Express your result in terms of m, the mass per unit of length; L, the length of the beam; and EI, the flexural rigidity of the beam cross section.

9.2.5 Find the period of free flexural vibrations for the frame shown in the figure. Consider that the horizontal girder is rigid ($I_g = \infty$). Let $E = 30{,}000$ ksi and $I_0 = 1000 \text{ in.}^4$

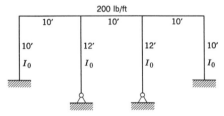

Problem 9.2.5

9.2.6 Find the period of free flexural vibrations for the frame of Problem 9.2.5 assuming a flexible girder with $I_g = 10I_0$. Lump the girder mass at the column tops in equal amounts. *Suggestion:* use moment distribution to find the spring constant in this case.

9.3.1 Let the frame of Problem 9.2.5 be acted on by a horizontal impulsive force at the level of the girder such that the initial conditions on the horizontal motion of the girder are $x(0) = 0$, $\dot{x}(0) = 10$ ft./sec. Find the displacement and velocity at $t = 3$ seconds if the damping is 10% of critical.

9.3.2 The displacement-time record of a structure which is freely vibrating has the form of an exponentially decaying sine wave. An accurate measurement indicates that the amplitude decreases 10% in 50 cycles. Estimate values for the logarithmic decrement and the percent of critical damping.

9.4.1 The circular frequency of a given structure is known to be π radians per second. There is no damping. An external force defined by $F(t) = 100 \sin \pi t$ is applied at $t = 0$ to the structure at rest. F is measured in pounds when t is measured in seconds. The mass of the structure is 25 lb. sec.²/ft. Find the maximum value of the displacement during the interval $t > 0$ if the force is applied for a period of (a)1 sec., (b) 2 sec., (c) 3 sec., (d)4 sec., (e) 5 sec., (f) 6 sec., and (g) 7 sec. Plot your results on the following set of axes: maximum displacement versus time duration of application of load. *Suggestion:* do not forget to check for maximum displacement during application of load as well as after removal of load.

9.4.2 A simple rectangular frame of period equal to 0.7 sec. is subjected to a ground acceleration of $a(t) = 10 \sin \pi t$, where $a(t)$ is measured in in./sec.^{2} when t is measured in seconds. This acceleration lasts for 1 sec. What will be the maximum absolute acceleration of the girder?

9.4.3 A structure having the period $T = 0.3$ sec., is subjected to a ground acceleration as indicated in the figure. Find the displacement and velocity of the girder at $t = 3$ sec., if at $t = 0$, both the displacement and velocity are zero. Use the step-by-step procedure.

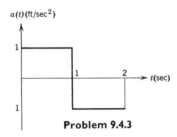

Problem 9.4.3

9.5. No problems for this section.

9.6.1 Find the periods of free vibration and the mode shapes for the following structure.

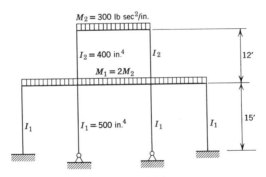

Problem 9.6.1

9.7.1 Find the force influence coefficients and the displacement influence coefficients for the shear building shown in Problem 9:6.1. Show that the corresponding δ matrix is the inverse of the ρ matrix.

9.7.2 Repeat Problem 9.7.1 assuming that the girders are flexible with $I_g = 1200$ in.^{4} Recompute the coefficients taking into account the rotation of the joints.

INDEX